FIELD

Aus

WILDFL⏝WERS

Over 1000 Common Australian Wildflowers

FIELD GUIDE TO
Australian
WILDFLOWERS
Over 1000 Common Australian Wildflowers

Denise Greig

Published in Australia by
New Holland Publishers (Australia) Pty Ltd
Sydney • Auckland • London • Cape Town

14 Aquatic Drive Frenchs Forest NSW 2086 Australia
218 Lake Road Northcote Auckland New Zealand
86 Edgware Road London W2 2EA United Kingdom
80 McKenzie Street Cape Town 8001 South Africa

First published in 1999 and reprinted in 2001.

National Library of Australia
  Cataloguing-in-Publication Data:

  Greig, Denise, 1945-.
  Field guide to Australian wildflowers.

  Includes index.
  ISBN 1 86436 334 7.

  1. Wildflowers - Australia - Identification. I Title.

582.130994

Project Editors: Fiona Doig, Kathy Metcalfe
Editor: Lynn Cole
Designer: Peta Nugent
Layout by: Clive Collins
Reproduction by : DNL Resources
Printed by: Kyodo Printers, Singapore

COVER PHOTOGRAPHS: (TL) *Eucalyptus pyriformis*; (TR) *Grevillea juncifolia*; *Verticordia
picta*; (BR) *Thelymitra nuda* (c) NHIL Jaime Plaza Van Roon.

CONTENTS

Dedicated to my children, Katie and Alex, with love.

PREFACE

Much has been said and written about the beautiful wildflowers of Australia, but at whatever time in life we are personally captured by their charm, we find them remarkable for their secret intricate allure or bold outstanding formations. Their leaves, buds and fruits also fascinate with their bewildering diversity. I do not know of anyone who at some time has not been enchanted. This book is written for Australians of all ages and stages of plant discovery to help stimulate their interest, reinforce their understanding and satisfy the inevitable need to identify and call a plant by its name. Hopefully visitors to this country will find it a helpful one-book introduction to our magnificent plant life.

The book is intended as a field guide rather than a definitive reference work. It covers some 1000 common species of the wildflowers most likely to be encountered growing naturally in accessible or regularly visited places. As there are some 18,000 species of flowering plants throughout Australia, grouped in about 200 families of widely varying size, there are many that are not referred to. Some species are widespread and common in all States while others may be an important component of a small geographical area. Species covered range in size from tiny annuals and terrestrial orchids to large perennials and shrubs. Only a few trees are listed and these are mostly colourful rainforest species of eastern Australia or large-flowered mallees seen mostly in the southwest. Only some of the more common and conspicuous introduced plants are mentioned. Ferns, fungi, sedges and grasses are not included.

Many people want to know more about the exceptional plant life of this continent and being able to identify wildflowers helps us to appreciate and gain knowledge of one of Earth's most fascinating and beautiful floras. Fortunately, much of the bushland is accessible for recreation and enjoyment. In the interests of conservation, flowers should not be picked. It is illegal to pick or dig up any plants in a national park or nature reserve.

The photographs in this book have been taken over a period of 20 years and during this time my photographic collection has swollen to tens of thousands. Although I have been assisted by many people in various herbaria and professional positions, my thanks go especially to people who have shown kindness and assistance in unasked-for ways: the friend who in the early days enthusiastically trundled us around in his old 4-wheel-drive across the baked land around Kalgoorlie, Western Australia, in search of eremophilas; the rangers who came looking for us on the Freycinet Peninsula, Tasmania, at dusk, when my children's then small legs slowed us down on a particularly long and difficult walk; the friendly woman and her adult son who chatted and lifted my spirits on a long and lonely summertime trek across the main range of Kosciusko, where the wildflowers were sensational but the heat unbearable, the March flies biting, the bottled water low and I had left my cigarettes at the lodge.

Occasionally I have needed to use the services of local people to find elusive species. On a very wet and misty morning at Barrington Tops, New South Wales, when the ancient

Antarctic Beech (*Nothofagus moorei*) trees were at their almost spiritually photographic best, the tour operator gave us makeshift plastic raincoats and made cups of tea to delay the other people, while I juggled with the tripod (and persistent leeches) in the mud and took some of the most beautiful photographs I've taken in my life.

I have a cousin in Coonamble who lives on a farming property on the Pilliga Road, New South Wales. Until I visited with cameras, film and detailed maps in tow, she had not ventured into the Pilliga Scrub, because of the intricacies of the tracks, but mainly because of the well-entrenched town stories about the Yowie. At first we explored the Pilliga with a carload of people, but over the ensuing years Diane and I have made numerous trips together and now know many of the tracks and the plant life along them by heart. Although parts of the Pilliga Scrub are logged and managed by State Forests, the shrubby understorey is rich and varied and from late winter to mid spring the wildflowers are stunning and abundant. The pub at Gwabegar is a national treasure.

One of the kindest and most approachable professional people I have met, and one whom I hope always to have contact with, is Jan Wilson, curator of the National Plant Photographic Index of the Australian National Botanic Gardens.

When I first began photographing Australian flora, I had a beginner's fantasy of recording all the flowering species photographically. I soon realised that this was not only very silly, but humanly impossible. I soon learned also that it was no use whatsoever having boxes of images of plants without names. This rapidly led to a 20-year intensive study of almost every flora written on Australian plants. It is unwieldy to acknowledge all of these books and hard-working authors, but a comprehensive list is included at the back of the book for Further Reading.

If I have achieved anything at all, it is my hope that this field guide might stimulate the interest and become a useful working tool for new people starting out on the job. New and better photographs of Australian plant life will always be needed, if only to excite, educate or remind people of our beautiful floral heritage.

On many of my trips I have been accompanied by my mother, who usually insisted on driving, mainly because she was a nervous passenger, but also so that I could more readily get in and out of the car with photographic equipment. Her plant-spotting eye is remarkable, matched only by her patience and tolerance. She is now 80 years old.

Last year on a particularly exhausting trip to the Top End, when temperatures were around 35°C, I kept asking her to stop the car every few kilometres while I got in and out, letting in blasting heat and unidentifiable insects, as well as flinging empty film packaging over my shoulder into the back of the car and, at the same time, making her write down difficult plant names quickly in sequence of frame and film. I said to her that I was glad she was my mother. In her characteristic unassuming manner she asked why. I replied, because no one else would put up with this nonsense. Although I have dedicated this book to my two children, who hopefully are plant and planet appreciators of the future, this and every other book I have written on Australian plants are really hers.

Denise Greig

INTRODUCTION

TERMINOLOGY AND NOMENCLATURE

Flowering plants are seed plants (angiosperms) and are distinguished from the cone-bearing plants (gymnosperms) in that their ovules are enclosed in a usually roundish vessel known as an ovary. The ovary is part of the flower, which includes the often showy petals and sepals as well as the sexual reproductive structures.

Flowering plants, which are generally the most conspicuous and most abundant elements in the Australian landscape, are customarily divided into two main groups: the mono-cotyledons, which have a single embryo leaf (cotyledon) on the seed, and the dicotyledons (comprising most of the species), characterised by seeds with two embryo leaves.

Scientific names are given to plants so that they may be distinguished from each other and to allow for the effective communication, storage and retrieval of all information about a particular plant or group of plants. Scientific names consist of a genus and species name. Genera (plural of genus) are placed into families, families into orders, orders into classes, classes into division and divisions into kingdoms – the highest taxonomic rank. Each of these categories is referred to as a taxon (plural taxa).

Eucalyptus costata, Ridge-fruited Mallee (Myrtaceae family)

3

Most of the taxa in this book are described species and have a standard two-word name (the genus named followed by the species name). A few are regarded as subspecies, which differ in minor characters (such as the size and shape of parts) from other members of the species, but not enough to rank them as species in their own right.

Reclassification of a plant may be required in the light of further knowledge, or else when the principle of priority laid down in the International Code of Botanical Nomenclature necessitates the displacement of a well-known specific epithet, if an older published name is found. An attempt has been made to use the most recent botanical name based on current scientific work. Further name changes will occur, however, as research continues. Common names have been given when such names have established usage.

In 1995, 'A revision of the bloodwoods, genus *Corymbia* (Myrtaceae)' was published in *Telopea*, Volume 6 (2-3), the journal of plant systemics published by the National Herbarium of New South Wales, Royal Botanic Gardens, Sydney. This major work by K. D. Hill and L. A. S. Johnson described 113 species in the genus *Corymbia*, of which 33 were described for the first time, with the remainder being reclassified from *Eucalyptus*. The new genus comprises those eucalypts traditionally known as bloodwoods and ghost gums. I do not wish to express an opinion about this change, but in this field guide I have retained the relevant species as *Eucalyptus* so as not to split the genus and confuse the reader.

Where possible, obscure botanical terminology has been avoided, but commonly used terms such as 'sessile' (without a stalk) and 'terminal' (at the end of the branches) are used throughout. To avoid repeating unnecessary phrases and to keep the text concise, but comprehensible, I have used a mixture of everyday and technical language. A glossary is provided at the back of the book to assist the reader in understanding some of these terms. In some cases the meaning of certain terms may be clarified by referring to the line drawing of a particular plant.

HOW TO USE THE GUIDE

In this book the plant families are arranged in alphabetical order. Family descriptions highlight easily observed characters between genera in a family and the probable relationship to closely related families. The family may be represented here by one or a number of genera. Within each family, the genera and species within each genus, are arranged in alphabetical order. Exceptions to this arrangement are *Acacia (Mimosaceae)*, which is arranged in three groups according to flower shape and leaf/phyllode structure; and the orchids, which are grouped under either epiphytic or terrestrial orchids.

HEADINGS

In the species identification section of the book the most recent botanical name based on current scientific work is followed by the most widely used common name. Where there has been a recent name change, the synonym, under which a particular plant was formerly known, precedes the species description.

Eucalyptus leucoxylon, Yellow Gum
(Myrtaceae family)

Caladenia flava, Cowslip Orchid
(Orchidaceae family)

THE SPECIES DESCRIPTIONS

Each flowering plant included in the guide is described in the text, including reference to all aspects that might be useful in the identification of the species in question, namely height, stems, leaves, inflorescences and flowers, and fruits. If necessary, refer back to the family description for further characteristics that may not be repeated in the species description. Brief reference is made to habitat and geographical distribution (which may help to confirm the identification), followed by the main flowering period of the species. Flowering often varies from year to year and bushfires and rainfall patterns can often influence the flowering period.

THE PHOTOGRAPHS

All species entries are illustrated with a photograph. In almost all cases, the plant is shown in flower, since this is the stage at which it is most obvious and when you are most likely to want to identify it. Every attempt has been made to select photographs that show diagnostic features or that convey the overall character of the plant. Most of the plants were photographed in their natural habitats, but in quite a few cases cultivated plants had to be used. Photographs are often the easiest tool for identifying a species. When a photograph that appears to represent the plant has been found, it is a good idea to check whether any of the other photos in that genus provide a better match. Finally, read the text on the species. It provides an abbreviated description of features deemed necessary for correct identification. A good quality hand-lens for observing the fine details of the plant will sometimes be useful.

LINE DRAWINGS

Ground-covering *Anthotroche pannosa*
(Solonaceae family)

Most plants listed in this book are illustrated by a line drawing of a mature leaf. Leaf shape can be extremely variable, and the leaf drawings supplied for many of the dicotyledons are no more than a rough guide. Most of the monocotyledons (lily-like plants and orchids) have similar grass-like leaves within a genus, and identification by leaf shape is usually of very little help, therefore leaf drawings are omitted. Line drawings of the capsules of the eucalypts are provided instead of adult leaves, which in many species do not differ greatly. The shape and size of the capsules and the outline of the valves are often important aids to identification in *Eucalyptus*. Usually the capsules or 'gumnuts' are retained somewhere on the tree and often can easily be found scattered on the ground below. Saltbushes and bluebushes (*Chenopodiaceae*) have distinctive and typical fruiting bodies and these are illustrated in preference to the leaves.

PLANT IDENTIFICATION MADE EASIER

Wildflowers show considerable variation in the structure of the different parts – leaves, flowers and fruits – when the whole range of Australian species is taken into consideration. At the same time, closely related species may be very similar, differing only in small details; accurate identification then becomes quite a challenge. Even individuals of the same species growing close to each other may show considerable variation in leaf size, shape and hairiness, as well as in the number of branchlets, leaves, flowers and fruits. It is usually necessary to identify plants through a combination of features.

HABIT

The form, whether herb, shrub or tree, and the general appearance of a plant, including shape, size, type of growth and the arrangement of various parts. The height is the range of the upper limits the plant normally attains. Growth rate and final size vary considerably with age and environmental factors, such as soil type and the degree of exposure. For prostrate species, which always grow along the ground, length may be given instead of height.

LEAVES

A leaf is usually green and typically consists of a leaf stalk (petiole) and a flattened leaf blade (lamina). It is the principal food-manufacturing organ of a green plant. Leaves are sometimes distinctive enough to permit identification and subsequent recognition of the species.

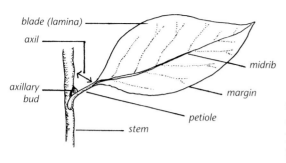

blade (lamina)
axil
axillary bud
midrib
margin
petiole
stem

Parts of a simple leaf

As well as the obvious points of leaf size, shape and arrangement on stem, there are several finer distinguishing features, such as colour variation of upper and lower surfaces, prominence of veins, presence of oil glands, hairs, scales, stipules, prickles or thorns, that can be checked. Use a hand lens to help you check small strutures. In this book, leaf measurements refer to the average mature size of the blade (not including the stalk). Remember, almost all plants have both large and some very small leaves.

FLOWERS AND THEIR FUNCTION

The flowers of each species are adapted in shape, structure, colour, the availability of pollen and nectar, and sometimes odour, to help attract their particular pollinating agents, such as birds, mammals and insects, as well as wind and water. The overall shape of the flower is largely determined by the petals, collectively known as the corolla. Within the petals are stamens, the male reproductive organs that consist of a sac-like anther containing the pollen. The anther is supported on a slender stalk. In the centre of the flower is the female reproductive organ, comprising the stigma, style and ovary; together they are called the carpel or pistil. The stigma acts as the receptive surface for pollen grains. The ovary contains varying numbers of ovules, which after fertilisation develop into seeds. The ovary wall develops into the fruit.

The flower provides the most constant and convenient features for identification. These include sepals and petals, the number of stamens, the type of pistil, the position of the ovary, the number of carpels and ovules, the type of fruit and the symmetry of the flower. Petals and

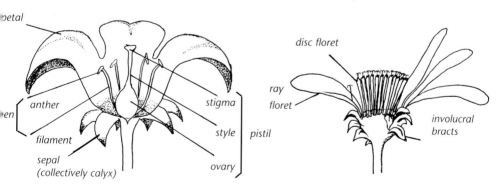

petal
anther
en
filament
sepal
(collectively calyx)
stigma
style
ovary
pistil
disc floret
ray floret
involucral bracts

The parts of a flower

Daisy flower head

sepals may be present or absent or joined in many ways. In many Australian wildflower species, the flowers themselves are small, but are aggregated into large showy heads (inflorescences). In this book, the arrangement of the inflorescence and dimensions are given, where applicable.

FRUIT
The term fruit refers to all seed-dispersing structures and is briefly described within the species identifications. Appearance and structure of fruit vary, ranging from small, single-seeded nutlets to many-seeded berries and large woody capsules. Fruits can be classified in a number of ways.

A simple, practical classification is to divide the fruits into two categories: dry fruits, such as pods and nuts, and fleshy succulent fruits, such as drupes and berries. If the fruit opens at maturity it is called dehiscent, otherwise it is indehiscent.

AREA COVERED BY THE FIELD GUIDE
The geographical range covered by this book includes the Australian mainland and Tasmania. The States of Australia are abbreviated by conventional standards. As plants are not constrained by political boundaries, the plant distribution in this book does not differentiate between NSW and the ACT.

THE VEGETATION OF AUSTRALIA
Every plant community is the result of a unique combination of certain environmental conditions and emanates from the interactions of species populations through time. All the plant communities together constitute the vegetation of a region. Rainfall, temperature, altitude and latitude are among factors that contribute to the characteristics of flora and vegetation.

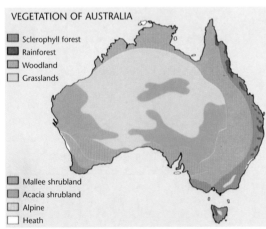

VEGETATION OF AUSTRALIA

- Sclerophyll forest
- Rainforest
- Woodland
- Grasslands
- Mallee shrubland
- Acacia shrubland
- Alpine
- Heath

This map shows the range of different types of vegetation zones throughout Australia.

In Australia, summer rainfall predominates in the north, winter rainfall in the south, while the eastern coast shows a more general distribution of rainfall throughout the year.

Many ecologists differ in their descriptions of vegetation zones or plant communities and the outline presented here is a framework only and should be regarded simply as a general guide to Australian vegetation.

Castanospermum australe, Black Bean
(Fabaceae family)

Calanthe triplicata, Christmas Orchid
(Orchidaceae family)

RAINFOREST

A rainforest is dominated by closely spaced trees with dense crowns, forming an unbroken canopy of one or more layers of foliage. The closed canopy produces a perpetually shaded and humid interior capable of supporting a variety of epiphytes, orchids, treeferns and climbing plants. As the light on the forest floor is usually insufficient for many sun-loving plants, there is an absence of grasses and annuals. Wildflowers are rarely seen, except those on trees high in the canopy and some epiphytic orchids, which attach themselves to the lower trunks and branches of a wide variety of trees. Sometimes the only evidence of flowers is found among the rich leaf litter on the forest floor. Some tree species in tropical rainforests have the interesting habit of producing flowers directly from the trunk and lower branches (cauliflory). In disturbed sunlit areas of rainforest quick-growing woody plants such as *Acacia*, *Omalanthus* and *Commersonia* might be present. Also some colourful rainforest species that might be forest giants in an undisturbed habitat, might take on smaller proportions on the edges of certain sections of rainforest.

In mainland Australia, rainforests are confined to the coastal strips and highlands of eastern Australia. They rarely occur more than 160km inland. Their total area is relatively small and their distribution is discontinuous, with pockets extending across northern Australia and far north Queensland to southern Victoria. They also occur in large areas of southwestern Tasmania.

Australia's rainforests show a great degree of structural diversity related to rainfall, soil type, drainage, altitude and evolutionary history. In this book, the term rainforest has been used in the broad sense. See the Further Reading section at the back for a structural classification of rainforest vegetation in Australia by Dr Len Webb.

OPEN FORESTS

Also called sclerophyll forests. This type of forest is dominated by trees with sclerophyll leaves, mainly the eucalypts. The trees are usually of forest form with tall, straight trunks equal to, or greater in height than the depth of the canopy. The trees usually have flattish crowns and an open canopy of between 30 and 70 percent. Sclerophyll forests are common along the east coast of Australia, much of Tasmania and in the wetter parts of southwestern Australia. The structure and composition of the understorey of open forest changes with rainfall, latitude and other environmental conditions. Two major types of open forests occur in Australia: dry sclerophyll and wet sclerophyll.

DRY SCLEROPHYLL FORESTS

These are composed of medium-sized trees that are usually less than 30m tall forming an open-canopy forest on poor soils in moderately low or irregular rainfall areas. Usually there are two or more species of eucalypts dominating the tree layer. The distinguishing characteristic of dry sclerophyll forest, however, is its undergrowth, which consists of large numbers of beautiful flowering shrubs, usually with hard, often small and spiny leaves. These include many different varieties of *Acacia*, *Grevillea*, *Hakea*, *Boronia* and pea-flowers (family Fabaceae).

Boronia barkeriana, Barker's Boronia (Rutaceae family)   *Hakea ulicina*, Gorse Hakea (Proteaceae family)

This type of forest can survive a fire; although the crowns of the trees may be burnt, they will regenerate from epicormic buds buried within the bark. Species of the understorey may recover from fire by shooting from underground rootstocks. In some species, such as *Hakea*, seeds are protected inside woody fruits that open after burning.

WET SCLEROPHYLL FORESTS

These are tall open forests consisting of stands of eucalypts, often more than 60m in height. They usually occur in higher rainfall areas (more than 100cm annually). The broken canopy does not completely shut out the light and the understorey may consist of small trees, shrubs and climbers, or grass species. There is no extensive layer of hard-leaved shrubs as found in dry sclerophyll forest. The dominant eucalypts vary from place to place and include the giant Karri, *Eucalyptus diversicolor*, in southwestern Western Australia and the towering Mountain Ash, *E. regnans*, of Victoria and Tasmania. In sheltered gullies of warmer parts of eastern Australia, the Blue Gum, *E. saligna*, and Flooded Gum, *E. grandis*, may dominate. Wet sclerophyll may occupy an immediate habitat between dry sclerophyll forest and rainforest, where eucalypts are absent.

Anigozanthos flavidus, Tall Kangaroo Paw (Haemodoraceae family)

WOODLAND

This vegetation type has a more open formation than sclerophyll forest. The trees are numerous but their trunks are shorter and the canopy cover is less than 30 percent. The dominant trees are chiefly *Eucalyptus* species and occasionally species of *Casuarina*, *Callitris*, *Melaleuca* and *Acacia*. There are three main types of woodland in Australia: tropical woodland, which extends across northern

Patersonia sericea, Silky Purple Flap (Iridaceae family)

Australia; temperate eucalypt woodland in the southwest and southeast; and semi-arid and arid woodland farther inland.

Occasionally, mention is made of the Western Australian goldfields around the Kalgoorlie–Norseman area, where annual rainfall is about 250mm. Nowhere else in the world do woodlands exist in such low-rainfall areas, yet this place is particularly rich in eucalypts of which 65 species are endemic. Many have large colourful flowers and have become valued as ornamental plants in dry inland towns as well as overseas.

The understorey in woodland varies according to region, rainfall, soil nutrient and available sunlight. In the better-watered parts of eastern Australia and the southwest of Western Australia, there may be a colourful mixture of attractive flowering shrubs and creepers. Small-growing herbaceous plants, such as terrestrial orchids, lilies and members of *Iridaceae* (Iris family), may be found close to the ground. In drier areas the understorey is often dominated by saltbushes and bluebushes, with interest and colour provided by species of *Acacia* and *Eremophila*.

Open woodlands, where grasses are continuous and well developed, are known as savannah woodlands. Trees may be continuous or in small stands and the grasses might include species of *Themeda*, *Stipa*, *Aristida* and other genera. A variety of annual and perennial herbs, vines and subshrubs competes with this grassy layer.

Swainsonia formosa, Sturt's Desert Pea (Fabaceae family)

SHRUBLANDS

These are dominated by multi-stemmed shrubs or low trees, usually less than 8m tall. They occur in semi-arid regions where the annual rainfall is usually less than 300mm. Low shrubland is dominated by saltbush and bluebush shrubs up to 2m tall. There are two widely recognised major shrubland types, based on the dominant low tree species.

MALLEE SHRUBLAND

This covers vast semi-arid areas of southern Australia extending from western Victoria and southwestern New South Wales across South Australia to Western Australia. Trees are replaced by several species of shrubby eucalypts with multiple stems arising from an underground rootstock known as a lignotuber. Small patches of mallee communities are retained in the intensively farmed wheatbelt region in Western Australia, where several spectacular flowering species of eucalypt are found in northern areas. These include the Pear-fruited Mallee, *Eucalyptus pyriformis*, Mottlecah, *E. macrocarpa*, the Rose Mallee, *E. rhodantha*, and the small Coarse-leaved Mallee, *E. grossa*. The understorey is sometimes dominated by one or more species of *Melaleuca*.

ACACIA SHRUBLAND

This type of shrubland comprises a widespread plant community of arid and semi-arid parts of inland Australia, in which small trees or shrubs of the genus *Acacia* are dominant rather than *Eucalyptus*. The plants range in height from 2 to 10m and by far the most common is the mulga, *Acacia aneura*, but other wattles of similar habit may be associated with it. The understorey consists of species of *Eremophila*, *Senna*, *Dodonaea* and *Maireana*.

Senna artemisioides subsp. *artemisioides*, Silver Cassia (Caesalpiniaceae family)

GRASSLANDS

Grasslands occur mostly in arid and semi-arid zones. Trees may be sparse or absent. Tussock grassland, which covers vast areas of Northern Australia from the Kimberley to the Barkly Tableland, is characterised by clumps of *Astrebla*, or Mitchell Grass. Another distinctive grassland formation in the central and arid half of Australia is hummock grassland, commonly referred to as spinifex. It is dominated by large,

perennial tussocks of spiky-leaved grasses *Trioda* and *Plectrachne*, which form a low, scattered cover with bare patches between, except after favourable rains when short-lived annuals germinate and transform the otherwise stark landscape into floral carpets.

ALPINE VEGETATION

The alpine region is defined as an area above the tree line, characterised by low-growing shrubs, herbs and grasses forming a variety of communities, such as herbfields, heath, feldmark, fens and bogs. The tree line is somewhat variable and usually occurs at around 1800 to 1830m elevation. The region is confined to the high mountain peaks of the Australian Alps in southeastern Australia.

Tasmania has many mountainous areas that are rich in alpine flora. The alpine areas support a rich and distinctive vegetation and

Leucochrysum albicano subsp. *alpinum*, Alpine Sunray (Asteraceae family)

Velleia montana (Goodeniaceae family)

contain some species that are found nowhere else in Australia. Many of these plants are shared by alpine areas in New South Wales, Victoria and Tasmania with a number of close relatives occurring in New Zealand. During mid-summer, these high peaks are covered in spectacular wildflower displays.

Within this region numerous plant communities exist according to combinations of environmental conditions. The greater part of the area is occupied by the short and tall herb-fields, where snow grasses are dominant and the vegetation consists almost entirely of herbs and other small plants. The more favourable, protected areas that are relatively rich in nutrients support the tall alpine herbfields and exhibit beautiful carpets of snow daisy, clumps of species of *Euphrasia* and the yellow, billy-button flowers of *Craspedia*.

HEATH

Heathland in general is dominated by hard-leaved shrubs less than 2m in height. Trees forming a mallee-like habit are sometimes present. Heaths are most common in patchy distribution along the southeast and western coastal strips. Small pockets of specialised heaths are also found in alpine areas, tablelands and in semi-arid regions. Often heath plants have to contend with salt-laden winds, extremely poor soils, drought or water-logged conditions.

Despite these harsh conditions many interesting and colourful flower plants are to be found. Beautiful flowering shrubs might include banksias, grevilleas, bottlebrushes, pea flowers, boronias, wattles and, in Western Australia, dryandras and feather flowers (*Verticordia*

Astroloma conostephioides, Flame Heath (Epacrideae family)

species), as well as many species of the Australian heath family Epacridaceae. In some areas where drainage may be impeded, unusual insectivorous plants, *Drosera* species, may be found. Heath plants are hardy, beautiful and diverse in form and are among the best known and most established native species in suburban gardens.

FLOWER FAMILIES

Plant families are part of the higher classification for plants and are the framework for a group of genera with definite features in common. Within this book the families are arranged in alphabetical order. This is a simplified arrangement and not an indication of plant relationships, which in a specific flora of a region would be listed in scientific order. Below is a guide to the families in this book, which is based on easily observed characteristics, helping to narrow down, by a process of elimination, the family of an unidentified plant.

AIZOACEAE (PAGE 26) PIGFACE FAMILY
Fleshy-leaved succulent herb family, usually with brightly coloured petal-like staminodes forming the showy part of the flower. The group known as subfamily Mesembryanthemoideae is represented here by the genera *Carpobrotus* and *Disphyma*. This family includes the ornamental succulents known as pigfaces.

AMARANTHACEAE (PAGE 28) AMARANTH FAMILY
Mainly annual or perennial herbs with very small flowers arranged in brightly coloured cylindrical or fluffy globular heads, usually surrounded by dry chaffy bracts. This family includes the showy mulla mullas or pussytails (*Ptilotus* spp.) of the dry inland.

AMARYLLIDACEAE (PAGE 32) AMARYLLIS FAMILY
Bulbous plants with lily-like flowers that are arranged mostly in umbels, but differ from Liliaceae in having an inferior ovary (below the flower parts).

ANTHERICACEAE (PAGE 34)
Perennial herbs, usually with a rhizome. Leaves often in a basal cluster or rosette. The small flowers have 6 soft segments arranged in 2 whorls. In areas with low rainfall, many Australia species die back in summer and reshoot annually after autumn or winter rains. Common in Australia and Africa. This family was previously included in the large lily family Liliaceae.

APIACEAE (UMBELLIFERAE) (PAGE 36) CARROT FAMILY
Large family of mostly annual, biennial or perennial herbs that includes food plants such as carrots, parsley, coriander and fennel. The stems and the deeply divided leaves are often aromatic when crushed. Small flowers are arranged in a simple or compound, flat-topped umbel. In *Actinotus* spp. (flannel flowers), the umbels are surrounded by woolly, petal-like bracts that give the inflorescence a daisy-like appearance.

ASTERACEAE (COMPOSITAE) (PAGE 38) DAISY FAMILY

One of the largest in the plant kingdom and characterised by its small flowers (ray and disc florets) that combine in the typical daisy-like head. The family contains many ornamentals, including *Aster, Calendula, Chrysanthemum, Dahlia* and *Zinnia*. About 1000 species are widely distributed throughout Australia and include well-known genera such as *Brachycome, Olearia* and *Senecio*. Botanical revision of Australian Asteraceae (used in this book) has placed species of *Helichrysum* and *Helipterum* in various other genera. Below is a list for easy cross-reference.

Old Names	New Names
Helichrysum apiculatum	***Chrysocephalum apiculatum***
Helichrysum baxteri	***Chrysocephalum baxteri***
Helichrysum bracteatum	***Bracteantha bracteata***
Helichrysum cassinianum	***Schoenia cassiniana***
Helichrysum diosmifolium	***Ozothamnus diosmifolius***
Helichrysum hookeri	***Ozothamnus hookeri***
Helichrysum obcordatum	***Ozothamnus obcordatus***
Helichrysum papillosum	***Bracteantha papillosum***
Helichrysum purpurascens	***Ozothamnus purpurascens***
Helichrysum rosmarinifolium	***Ozothamnus rosmarinifolius***
Helichrysum secundiflorum	***Ozothamnus secundiflorus***
Helichrysum semipapposum	***Chrysocephalum semipapposum***
Helichrysum thyrsoideum	***Ozothamnus thyrsoideus***
Helichrysum viscosum	***Bracteantha viscosa***
Helipterum albicans subsp. albicans	***Leucochrysum albicans subsp. albicans***
Helipterum albicans subsp. alpinum	***Leucochrysum albicans subsp. alpinum***
Helipterum anthemoides	***Rhodanthe anthemoides***
Helipterum roseum	***Rhodanthe chlorocephala subsp. rosea***
Helipterum manglesii	***Rhodanthe manglesii***
Helipterum tiekensii	***Rhodanthe tiekensii***

BAUERACEAE (PAGE 60)

Named after the 19th-century botanical artists Franz and Ferdinand Bauer, this small Australian family of only 1 genus, *Bauera*, consists of 3 shrub species with opposite trifoliate leaves appearing in whorls of 6. The regular, small pink or white cup-shaped flowers have 4–10 petals and are borne singly in the leaf axils.

BIGNONIACEAE (PAGE 62)

This large family of mostly woody climbers and shrubs occurs mainly in tropical climates with about 10 genera and 17 species represented in Australia. The leaves are simple or compound and the showy flowers are tubular or trumpet-shaped with 5 irregular lobes. Capsules are oblong and pointed.

BLANDFORDIACEAE (PAGE 62) CHRISTMAS BELL FAMILY
Confined to eastern Australia, this small family of 1 genus, *Blandfordia*, comprises 4 species commonly known as Christmas bells. They are tufted, perennial herbs with showy red bell-shaped flowers with yellow lobes, borne in large terminal racemes. The dry 3-sided capsules contain numerous brown furry seeds.

BORAGINACEAE (PAGE 64) FORGET-ME-NOT FAMILY
Large family of mostly perennial herbs or shrubs with rough stiff hairs and round stems. The white or blue flowers are tubular with 5 spreading lobes and 5 stamens arising from the corolla tube. The fruit splits into 4 nutlets. The family is poorly represented in Australia, where there are 19 genera and about 63 species. The family contains the widely naturalised Paterson's Curse or Salvation Jane, *Echium plantagineum*.

CAESALPINIACEAE (PAGE 66) SENNA FAMILY
A large family of mostly shrubs and trees widely distributed in tropical and subtropical regions of the world. The leaves are mostly pinnate with 1 to many pairs of leaflets. Flowers are usually slightly irregular with 5 spreading cupped petals and 10 stamens, often of unequal size. Fruit is a legume. About 20 genera and 85 species occur in Australia, the most common and widespread is the genera *Senna* (formerly known as *Cassia*). This family is often treated as the subfamily Caesalpinioideae of the family Fabaceae.

CAMPANULACEAE (PAGE 72) BLUEBELL FAMILY
Annual or perennial herbs, usually with a milky latex. Most of the 600 species are centred mainly in northern temperate regions of the world. Australia is represented by the widespread bluebell genus *Wahlenbergia*. Leaves are alternate, opposite or in whorls. The bell-shaped flowers with 5 spreading lobes are often blue or bluish. The capsule is surmounted by persistent calyx lobes. The Lobeliaceae, which is sometimes included in this family, is treated in this book as a separate family.

CHENOPODIACEAE (PAGE 74) SALTBUSH FAMILY
Large family of mostly herbs and shrubs, sometimes succulent, often inhabiting saline soils around the world. Australia has 29 genera and about 300 species commonly known as saltbushes, bluebushes or samphires. Leaves usually alternate, frequently covered with scales, fine hairs or mealy bloom. Some species appear leafless with very reduced leaves and fleshy, jointed stems. Flowers small, white or greenish, with 1–5 segments arranged in a single whorl. The fruits are often conspicuous and may be dry, berry-like, winged or spined.

CHLOANTHACEAE (PAGE 78)
Endemic Australian family of hairy shrubs or subshrubs found mainly in semi-arid and arid areas. The leaves are opposite or whorled, often wrinkled with entire margins. Flowers regular or irregular with densely hairy calyx lobes and tubular flowers with 4–8 lobes and 4–8

stamens, mostly inserted in the corolla tube. This family has previously been treated as a tribe of Verbenaceae, but differs in having 2 bracteoles at the base of each flower, and dry fruit.

CONVOLVULACEAE (PAGE 80) MORNING GLORY FAMILY

A large cosmopolitan family of mostly twining or prostrate plants with alternate, often lobed or heart-shaped leaves. Colourful funnel-shaped flowers have 5 fused petals and 5 stamens inserted toward the base of the corolla and alternating with the lobes. Australia has 20 genera and about 130 species with many in dry inland regions and rainforests.

DASYPOGONACEAE (PAGE 82)

This family is often included in Lomandraceae or in the grass tree family Xanthorrhoeaceae. There are 8 genera and 64 species found in Australia, New Guinea and New Caledonia, with the greatest concentration in southwest Western Australia. They are mostly perennial herbs or woody tree-like shrubs with tough grass-like leaves along the stem or in a terminal rosette. The usually small flowers, of 6 segments, are arranged in large compound spikes or heads or singly. The capsule contains 1 to several orange, red or brown seeds.

DILLENIACEAE (PAGE 84) GUINEA FLOWER FAMILY

Family of shrubs, climbers and sometimes trees mostly with entire leaves. The circular flowers are usually yellow with 5 petals, often notched, and a prominent clusters of stamens. Australia has 5 genera and 110 species, mostly centred in the temperate zones; the most widespread genus is *Hibbertia*, commonly known as guinea flowers.

DORYANTHACEAE (PAGE 92) SPEAR LILY FAMILY

This family consists of the single endemic genus *Doryanthes*, comprising 2 species of large tussock-forming plants found in eastern Australia and noted for their very tall, stout flowering stems bearing large blood-red flowers arranged in terminal globular heads or oblong racemes.

DROSERACEAE (PAGE 94) SUNDEW FAMILY

A family of insectivorous herbs widespread in temperate and tropical parts of the world, usually growing in moist places, often in very infertile soils. About 70 species are found in Australia, mostly belonging to the genus *Drosera*. The leaves in a basal rosette and/or along the stems are covered with sticky glandular hairs that trap insects and smother them in digestive fluid. The regular circular flowers have 4 or 5 cupped petals and 4 or 5 free stamens.

EPACRIDACEAE (PAGE 96) HEATH FAMILY

This family of mostly small shrubs and a few small trees is well developed in Australia with 29 genera and about 355 species frequently found in coastal heaths and sandplain communities. The leaves are alternate or in spirals, narrow, rigid and often pungent-pointed with several longitudinal veins. Flowers regular, forming bell-shaped or tubular flowers with 4 or 5 lobes. Stamens 4 or 5 alternating with corolla lobes and often projecting beyond the tube.

FABACEAE (PAGE 106) PEA FAMILY

A very large family of herbs, shrubs, trees and climbers of about 490 genera and more than 12,000 species found throughout the world. About 143 genera and 1115 species are widely distributed throughout Australia. The leaves are usually variously compound. The pea-shaped flowers are strongly irregular and consist of 5 petals – 1 large standard petal usually at the back of the flower, 2 lateral wing petals and 2 basal petals joined to form a keel. Stamens 10. Fruit a pod. In some classifications, other pod-bearing plants Mimosaceae (wattles) and Caesalpiniaceae (cassias) are included in this family as subfamilies.

GERANIACEAE (PAGE 128) PELARGONIUM FAMILY

This family contains many exotic species and hybrids of *Pelargonium* and *Geranium* cultivated as ornamental plants. They are perennial herbs and shrubs globally distributed, mostly in temperate zones. Three genera and about 36 species occur in Australia. The leaves are often pinnately or palmately lobed or dissected. The regular or irregular flowers have 5 petals and 10 stamens in 2 whorls. Fruit a dry slender capsule, which splits on maturity into 5 separate curled segments.

GOODENIACEAE (PAGE 130)

The majority of the 13 genera and about 390 species of this family are confined to Australia. They are mostly herbs with alternate or radical leaves. The irregular flowers are shortly tubular with 5 united petals that split almost to the base on one side. The petals (often winged) may spread evenly, as in *Scaevola*, but mostly are 2-lipped with the upper lip lobed and the lower one 3-lobed as in *Dampiera*, *Goodenia* and *Velleia*.

HAEMODORACEAE (PAGE 144) KANGAROO PAW FAMILY

Small family of perennial herbs with rhizomes, best known for the long-lasting kangaroo paws *Anigozanthos* species grown for the nursery and florist trade. Australia has about 7 genera and 85 species with many confined to the southwestern botanical province of Western Australia. The long grass-like leaves are mainly basal and may be flat, triangular in cross-section or terete; stem leaves smaller or absent. The woolly flowers consist of 6 segments, which are free or partly fused into a short or long tube. Stamens 3 or 6. Fruit a capsule.

IRIDACEAE (PAGE 152) IRIS FAMILY

Large family of erect perennial herbs with rhizomes or corms. About 85 genera and 1500 species are widely distributed throughout the world and include well-known ornamental plants, such as *Iris* and *Freesia* species and hybrids. Australian Iridaceae consists of 6 genera. Leaves are sword-shaped, basal or along stems arranged in 2 ranks. Flowers have 6 segments, 3 petals and 3 sepals, often united below to form a tube. Differs from closely related families in having only 3 stamens.

LAMIACEAE (PAGE 154) MINT FAMILY

This large cosmopolitan family of aromatic plants is especially noted for its Mediterranean culinary herbs, such as basil, mint, rosemary and thyme. Australian Lamiaceae consist of 39 genera and about 250 species, the main representative being the mint bushes *Prostanthera* (about 100 species). Most are shrubs or herbs; stems usually 4-angled. Leaves mostly opposite, each pair at right angles to the next (rarely whorled). Flowers irregular, usually 2-lipped or 5-lobed, often in dense clusters encircling the stem. Stamens 4, attached to the corolla tube.

LOBELIACEAE (PAGE 166) LOBELIA FAMILY

A family of mostly annual or perennial herbs centred in the tropical Americas and temperate regions in the Southern Hemisphere. Australia has 6 genera and about 50 species. A milky sap may be present. Flowers usually irregular with 5 petals united at the base of the corolla tube, which may be entire or slit to the base on the upper side. Stamens 5; anthers fused into a tube around the style. Fruit a capsule. This family is often considered to be a subfamily of Campanulaceae, but differs in its irregular flowers and fused anthers.

LORANTHACEAE (PAGE 168) MISTLETOE FAMILY

Partly parasitic shrubs or trees growing either on the stems or roots of host plants. Australia has 10 genera and 65 species, most of which are endemic. Entire leaves are usually opposite. Some host-specific species have leaves that mimic those of the host. The tubular flowers are usually large and brightly coloured with 4–6 strap-like petals; stamens mostly 4–6 opposite to and attached to the petals. Fruit a glutinous, 1-seeded berry.

MALVACEAE (PAGE 170) HIBISCUS FAMILY

Widely cultivated for its brightly coloured flowers, *Hibiscus* is the best known genus of this large cosmopolitan family of herbs, shrubs and small trees found mostly in warm-tropical and tropical regions of the world. Australia has 24 genera and about 160 species. Flowers are regular with 5 colourful free, overlapping petals. Characteristically, the numerous stamens are united into a tube and the style is branched.

MIMOSACEAE (PAGE 174) WATTLE FAMILY

This large, widespread and common family is often treated as the subfamily Mimosoideae of the family Fabaceae. About 17 genera and more than 750 species are widely distributed throughout Australia, with the wattles, *Acacia* (about 750 species), being the most widespread and best known. They are mainly trees and shrubs or rarely climbers and herbs. Leaves usually bipinnate, especially in seedling stage, but in mature plants of many species the leaves are reduced to phyllodes. The small flowers in tight clusters are arranged in fluffy spikes or globular heads. Fruit a pea-like pod.

MYOPORACEAE (PAGE 204) BOOBIALLA FAMILY

A small family of shrubs or trees with 5 genera and about 230 species occurring in Australia. Leaves, stems and floral parts are often sticky or resinous. Flowers irregular or almost regular (*Myoporum*), tubular, usually 5-lobed or sometimes 2-lipped (*Eremophila*). Stamens usually 5 (sometimes 4) enclosed or exserted. Fruit drupe-like or dry in some *Myoporum* species.

MYRTACEAE (PAGE 218) MYRTLE FAMILY
Distributed worldwide, this large family of about 70 genera and 1400 species comprises mostly shrubs and trees occurring in all States of Australia. The entire leaves are usually aromatic and show oil dots when held against the light. Flowers usually have showy stamens, which may be free or fused into groups or bundles, often forming brushes or balls, as in *Callistemon* and *Melaleuca*. Petals 4 or 5 free, or united with calyx to form a lid (operculum) covering the flower in bud (*Eucalyptus*). In some genera, such as *Thryptomene*, *Micromyrtus* and *Leptospermum*, the stamens are few and the 5 petals are prominent. The fruit is usually a capsule with numerous small seeds or a fleshy berry.

ORCHIDACEAE (PAGE 290) ORCHID FAMILY
A very large cosmopolitan family comprising about 730 genera and more than 30,000 species. Australia has about 100 genera and more than 1200 species. The orchid flower is irregular with a complex structure. There are 3 sepals and 3 petals; the front petal usually differs considerably from the others and is known as the labellum. The highly modified stamens are fused with the style into a single central structure (column). In some species, 1 or more segments form a hood over the column. The pollen is united into waxy masses (pollinia) concealed by an anther cap.

PHORMIACEAE (PAGE 304)
In some classifications this family is included with the broadly defined Liliaceae. There are about 4 genera and 20 species found in Australia. The majority are rhizomatous perennial herbs with fibrous roots and linear flax-like leaves. The star-like flowers, with 6 spreading segments, are borne in panicles. The fruit is a berry with numerous black seeds.

PITTOSPORACEAE (PAGE 306) PITTOSPORUM FAMILY
This family of resinous shrubs, trees and twining plants occurs in tropical and warm temperate areas in Africa, Asia, Australia and the Pacific Island. Most are endemic to Australia with 9 genera and about 42 species. The regular flowers form a bell-shaped tube with 5 spreading petals and are often perfumed. Fruit a berry or splitting capsule, sometimes brightly coloured.

PROTEACEAE (PAGE 310) BANKSIA FAMILY
Large family of mostly woody shrubs and trees with its main development in the Southern Hemisphere. Australia has about 50 genera and 900 species occurring in all States. The flowers are borne singly or in heads, spikes or racemes, sometimes surrounded by showy bracts. They have no separate petals and sepals but usually 4 spreading perianth segments united into a cylindrical or swollen tube. Stamens 4. The often long style is released as the flower splits open. Fruit a nut, drupe or follicle.

RANUNCULACEAE (PAGE 364) BUTTERCUP FAMILY
Large family of mostly herbs or woody climbers with a worldwide distribution. Australia has about 5 genera and 50 species, the best known being species of *Ranunculus* and *Clematis*. The

leaves are often lobed or dissected in a basal rosette or with bases forming a sheath. The white or yellow regular flowers are typically arranged in spirals along a rather elongated receptacle. Stamens numerous and spirally arranged. Fruit a cluster of small dry fruitlets (achenes), sometimes with plumed styles.

RHAMNACEAE (PAGE 368) BUCKTHORN FAMILY

Cosmopolitan family of shrubs and trees found mainly in tropical and subtropical regions. About 18 genera and 150 species are widely distributed throughout Australia, the largest and best known being *Pomaderris* (53 species). The small star-shaped or heath-like flowers have 5 free petals, often small and reduced. Stamens 5 opposite to and often embraced by the petals. Fruit a drupe.

RUTACEAE (PAGE 372) CITRUS FAMILY

This large family of woody plants is widespread in tropical and temperate regions and includes the important *Citrus* and a large number of ornamental plants. About 40 genera and 320 species occur in Australia, the largest and best known being *Boronia* (about 100 species). The aromatic leaves are simple or compound and usually gland-dotted. The star-shaped or bell-shaped flowers have 4 or 5 sepals forming a cup and 4 or 5 petals with 4 to 10 stamens. Fruit a berry, drupe or capsule.

SAPINDACEAE (PAGE 392) HOP BUSH FAMILY

Large family of trees, shrubs and climbers, with a worldwide distribution. Australia has 30 genera and about 190 species, the largest and best known being *Dodonaea* (about 60 species) found often in arid and semi-arid areas. The leaves are often divided and the small inconspicuous flowers are sometimes separately male and female (also bisexual), usually with a disc outside the stamens. Stamens usually 8. The fruit is usually more conspicuous than the flowers and is often papery with wing-like or lobed outgrowths.

SCROPHULARIACEAE (PAGE 398) SPEEDWELL FAMILY

Large cosmopolitan herbaceous family found mainly in temperate regions. Australia has 49 genera and about 200 species. The stems are round and leaves alternate, opposite or whorled. The irregular flowers are tubular often 2-lipped or 3-lobed to 5-lobed. Stamens 4, 2 of which are usually longer than the others.

SOLANACEAE (PAGE 400) POTATO FAMILY

This large cosmopolitan family is noted for its important food plants, such as potato, tomato, eggplants, chilli and capsicum. Australia has 23 genera and about 200 species, the largest and best-known genus being *Solanum* (about 100 species). They are mostly herbs, shrubs or small trees, with or without prickles. Leaves simple to pinnate, often strongly scented when crushed. Flowers bell-shaped, tubular or funnel-shaped usually with 5 united petals. Stamens usually 5, arising from the corolla tube and alternate with the lobes. Fruit a many-seeded berry or spiny capsule.

STACKHOUSIACEAE (PAGE 406)

Small family of annual or perennial herbs with slender ribbed stems. Three genera and 24 species occur in Australia. The simple, entire leaves are sometimes fleshy or rather leathery. Flowers are mostly regular and have 5 petals usually united into a tube with spreading lobes. The 5 stamens alternate with the petals. Fruit a schizocarp, separating into up to 5 nutlets.

STERCULIACEAE (PAGE 406) KURRAJONG FAMILY

Mostly tropical and subtropical trees and shrubs often covered with star-shaped hairs. Australia has 21 genera and about 160 species. The leaves are simple or palmately lobed. The often velvety flowers usually have 5 conspicuous sepals united in a bell-shaped manner and 5 petals that are often minute or absent. Stamens 5–30, either free or united into a short tube; when 5 they are opposite the petals and sometimes alternate with 5 staminodes. Fruit a capsule.

THYMELAEACEAE (PAGE 412) RICE FLOWER FAMILY

Mostly tropical and subtropical herbs, shrubs or small trees with tough bark and undivided leaves. About 9 or 10 genera and 95 species occur in Australia; *Pimelea*, commonly known as rice flowers (about 90 species), accounts for the majority of species. The small tubular flowers are often in dense heads. The 4 or 5 sepals are petal-like and usually with spreading lobes at the top of the floral-tube. Stamens 8–10 inserted in the tube, or 2 in *Pimelea*.

TREMANDRACEAE (PAGE 416)

Small endemic Australian family of 3 genera and 26 species, the largest being *Tetratheca* (20 species). They are small heath-like undershrubs usually with whorled leaves. Flowers bell-like with 3–5 petals and numerous dark stamens. Fruit a flattened capsule.

VIOLACEAE (PAGE 418) VIOLET FAMILY

This large family of herbs and shrubs includes the well-known cultivated exotic violets and pansies (*Viola* species). There are 3 Australian genera and about 26 species. The irregular flowers have 5 sepals and 5 petals, the lowest often the largest. Stamens 5, partly fused and alternating with the petals. Fruit a capsule or berry containing many fine seeds.

XANTHORRHOEACEAE (PAGE 420) GRASSTREE FAMILY

The distinctive and well-known grasstrees or blackboys belong to this small endemic Australian family of a single genus *Xanthorrhoea*. They are stout perennials with either a woody underground or above-ground trunk, often impregnated with resin. The grass-like leaves often angular in cross-section, arise from the tip of the trunk. The small creamy-white flowers, surrounded by floral bracts, are embedded in a tall spike-like inflorescence.

SPECIES IDENTIFICATION

AIZOACEAE | Pigface family

A very large family of annual or perennial succulent herbs or shrubs of about 150 genera and 2300 species, globally distributed, with many native to South Africa. About 19 genera and 60 species are widely distributed throughout Australia; 18 species of South African representatives are naturalised. Leaves alternate, opposite or whorled, usually succulent. Flowers small, regular, bisexual. Sepals 4 or 5. Petals small or absent. Stamens 4 to many. The family contains 2 distinct groups, which can be separated by the presence or absence of petal-like staminodes (large sterile stamens). The group with daisy-like flowers comprising numerous brightly coloured staminodes forming the showy part of the flower is known as subfamily Mesembryanthemoideae and is represented here by the genera *Carpobrotus* and *Disphyma*. The other group, without staminodes, has relatively small flowers with 4 or 5 small perianth segments, brightly coloured on the inside. The fruit is a dry capsule or is berry-like. The family contains the ornamental succulents known as pigfaces.

Carpobrotus glaucescens | Coastal Noonflower

Fleshy prostrate perennial herb to 2m across; stems take root at leaf nodes. **Leaves** 3-sided, 4–10cm long and up to 1.5cm wide, are thick and glaucous. **Flowers** purple with white at base, to 6cm across; 5 or 6 rows of 300–400 yellow stamens. **Fruit** berry-like, oblong, 2–3cm long and 1.5cm across, red to purple when ripe. Common along the east coast in sand dunes and headlands, close to the sea. Qld, NSW, Vic. Most of year.

Carpobrotus modestus | Inland Pigface

Fleshy prostrate perennial herb, 1–3m across. **Leaves** triangular in section, 3.5–7cm long to 7mm wide, straight or slightly incurved, dull green or glaucous with reddish tinges. **Flowers** light purple, white at the base, 1-2cm across. **Fruit** berry-like, oblong, 2cm long and to 1.5cm across, purple when ripe. Mostly inland. Vic, SA, WA. Spring, summer.

Carpobrotus rossii | Karkalla

Fleshy prostrate, perennial herb with slender stems to 1m long. **Leaves** triangular in section, 3.5–10cm long and about 1cm wide, bases stem-clasping, slightly incurved and tapering to the tip. **Flowers** light purple, shading to white at the base, 4–6cm across, with 100–250 stamens. **Fruit** berry-like, globular, about 2cm across, purplish-red when ripe. Widespread in coastal areas on rocky headlands and sand dunes. Vic, Tas, SA, WA. Spring, summer.

Disphyma crassifolium | Round-leaved Pigface

Formerly *D. australe* and *D. clavellatum*. Fleshy prostrate, perennial herb with stems to 1.5m long, rooting at nodes. **Leaves** opposite, club-shaped and almost cylindrical, 2-5cm long and 1cm wide, fused toward the base, tip rounded and often reddish. **Flowers** light magenta above and paler below, to 2.5cm across, on erect stalks to 10cm long. **Fruit** a 5-valve capsule. Widespread, samphire flats and sand dunes in coastal areas; salt pans inland. Qld, NSW, Vic, Tas, SA, WA. Spring, summer.

Carpobrotus glaucescens

Carpobrotus modestus

Carpobrotus rossii

Disphyma crassifolium

AMARANTHACEAE | Amaranth family

Large family of mainly annual or perennial herbs and shrubs with a few climbers. About 65 genera and 900 species globally distributed, with 15 genera and about 150 species native to Australia. Flowers very small, regular in cylindrical or globular heads, usually surrounded by dry, chaffy, often spinescent bracts. Perianth segments 3–5 or fused in a cup around the ovary. Fruit succulent or dry, opening by means of a lid.

Gomphrena canescens | Batchelor's Buttons

Erect branching annual to 75cm high; stems covered with long soft hairs. **Leaves**, linear to linear–lanceolate, 4–6cm long and about 5mm wide, opposite, sessile, hairy above, scaly below, tip pointed. **Flowerheads** globular, papery, to 4cm across, terminal, vary in colour from dark red to pale pink to grey-pink as they age. Individual flowers about 1.5cm long, woolly outside. Common among grasses and along roadsides in tropical woodlands across northern Australia. Qld, WA, NT. Autumn, winter.

Ptilotus atriplicifolius | Crimson Foxtail

Perennial subshrub to 1m high; stems covered with short dense white hairs. **Leaves** obovate, 1–5cm long to 4cm wide, grey-green and somewhat wavy. **Flowerheads** globular or cylindrical, 5cm long and about 3cm in diameter. Individual flowers pinkish-red covered with long grey and white hairs. Stamens crimson. Widespread in woodland communities. Qld, NSW, SA, WA, NT. Most of year.

Ptilotus calostachyus | Weeping Mulla Mulla

Short-lived perennial herb to 2m high; stems smooth. **Leaves** linear to thread-like, 2–6cm long, less than 1mm wide, alternate, sessile. **Flowerheads** cone-shaped to cylindrical, 2–8cm long and about 1.5cm in diameter, on long slender peduncles, sometimes arranged in panicles. Individual flowers pink with dense covering of long hairs. Northern tropical regions, often in open plains and woodlands. Qld, WA, NT. Winter, spring.

Ptilotus exaltatus | Tall Mulla Mulla

Erect perennial herb to 1.5m high; stems smooth. **Leaves** obovate or oblong–lanceolate, up to 20cm long and 5cm wide, rather thick, tip with fine point; upper leaves smaller, elliptic. **Flowerheads** cone-shaped, lengthening to cylindrical, 3–20cm long to 4.5cm in diameter. Individual flowers deep pink, densely clothed with silky hairs, except on the tips. Widespread in arid and semi-arid regions in a variety of habitats. All mainland States. Winter, spring.

Gomphrena canescens

Ptilotus atriplicifolius

Ptilotus calostachyus

Ptilotus exaltatus

Ptilotus macrocephalus | Green Pussytails

Erect perennial herb to 50cm high; stems smooth or sparsely hairy, usually unbranched. **Leaves** linear to narrow–lanceolate, to 5cm long and 3mm wide, shortly stalked margins wavy, tip pointed. **Flowerheads** oblong to cylindrical, 5–12cm long and to 6cm in diameter, terminal. Individual flowers yellowish-green covered with long hairs, except on the tips. Widespread in arid and semi-arid regions, in a variety of habitats. All mainland States Winter, spring.

Ptilotus nobilis | Yellowtails

Erect perennial herb to 1m high; stems smooth. **Leaves** spoon-shaped to oblong–lanceolate, up to 13cm long and 6cm wide, rather fleshy, often tipped with a short stiff point. **Flowerheads** oblong to cylindrical, to 22cm long and 4–5cm in diameter. Individual flowers yellowish-green covered with woolly hairs mixed with longer straight hairs, except on the tips. Widely distributed in drier regions in a wide range of habitats. Qld, NSW, SA, NT. Winter, spring.

Ptilotus obovatus | Silvertails

Shrubby perennial to 1m high; stems and leaves densely covered with white star-shaped and simple hairs. **Leaves** obovate to lanceolate, 1–4cm long and to 2cm wide, tip either blunt or mucronate. **Flowerheads** globular to short cylindrical, 1–3cm long and less than 1.5cm in diameter, single or in groups. Individual flowers pink covered with long white hairs, except on the tips. Widespread in inland districts in a wide range of habitats. Qld, NSW, SA, WA, NT. Most of year.

Ptilotus polystachyus | Longtails

Erect perennial herb to 1m high; stems at first hairy, later becoming smooth. **Leaves** linear or lanceolate, to 10cm long and about 0.5cm wide, margins wavy. **Flowerheads** cylindrical, 4–15cm long and to 3cm diameter, terminal on long stalks. Individual flowers yellowish-green, occasionally reddish-brown, covered with hairs, except on tips. Widespread in drier inland areas in a variety of habitats. Qld, NSW, SA, WA, NT. Winter, spring.

Ptilotus macrocephalus

Ptilotus nobilis

Ptilotus obovatus

Ptilotus polystachyus

AMARYLLIDACEAE | Amaryllis family

Family of lily-like, bulbous, perennial herbs. Different botanists characterise the family in different ways and there is no general agreement as to the size and composition of the family. It is closely allied to Liliaceae and genera are sometimes included in that family. Amaryllidaceae is commonly characterised by the arrangement of flowers in an umbel at the top of a leafless stalk, subtended by two fused bracts when in bud. Perianth segments 6; stamens 6. Ovary inferior, often visible as a swelling at the base of a long perianth tube. Fruit usually a capsule. The family contains many exotic ornamental plants, including *Amaryllis*, *Hippeastrum* and *Narcissus*. Leaves are not illustrated in this family as they are too similar for identification purposes.

Calostemma luteum | Yellow Garland Lily

Perennial bulbous herb to 50cm high. **Leaves** linear, bright green, flaccid, about 50cm long to 1cm wide. Leaves die down each year. **Flowers** funnel-shaped, bright yellow, to 3cm long, in terminal umbels of 20–30 flowers, on stalk to 50cm long. **Capsule** globular, to 12mm across, containing a single fleshy seed, which may germinate while still attached to the parent. Sometimes treated as a colour variety of *C. purpureum*. Mainly inland, in woodland and shrubland, on flats subjected to periodic flooding. Qld, NSW, Vic, SA. Summer, autumn.

Calostemma purpureum | Garland Lily

Perennial bulbous herb to 60cm high. **Leaves** linear, bright green, erect or slightly arching about 60cm long. Leaves die down each year. **Flowers** 2cm long, reddish-purple or pink, in terminal umbels of 12–25 flowers on stalk to 45cm long. **Capsule** globular, to 1cm across containing a single fleshy seed, which may germinate while still attached to the parent. Mainly inland, in woodland, often along watercourses and in rocky places. NSW, Vic, SA. Summer, autumn.

Crinum pedunculatum | Swamp Lily

Robust bulbous perennial herb 1–2m tall. **Leaves** broad–linear, up to 1m or more long and 15cm wide, arising from the base of the plant and forming a large tussock. **Flowers** white, in terminal umbels of 10–40 flowers, on stout leafless stalk to 1.5m long, perfumed. Each flower to 10cm across, has 6 slender segments and 6 stamens. **Capsule** globular, about 5cm across. Coastal swamps; along streams and tidal areas. Qld, NSW. Summer.

Calostemma luteum

Calostemma purpureum

Crinum pedunculatum

ANTHERICACEAE

Family of perennial herbs, usually with a rhizome. About 35 genera and 700 species with a wide distribution, but most common in Africa and Australia. Leaves often in basal cluster or rosette, usually sheathing at base. Flowers regular, bisexual. Perianth segments 6, in 2 whorls. Stamens usually 6, in 2 whorls, sometimes 3. Ovary superior. Fruit a capsule with black seeds. Leaves are not illustrated in this family as they are too similar for identification purposes.

Arthropodium fimbriatus | Nodding Chocolate Lily

Formerly *Dichopogon fimbriatus*. Erect perennial herb to 1m high. **Leaves** grass-like to 40cm long and 12mm wide in tufts of 2-12 leaves. **Flowers** blue to violet with darker anthers, to 3cm diameter, in groups of 2-3 along unbranched flowering stems, becoming nodding, usually chocolate-scented. **Capsule** globular, to 8mm across. Widespread in grassland, woodland and open forest, on a variety of soils. Qld, NSW, Vic, SA, WA. Spring, summer.

Laxmannia gracilis | Slender Wire Lily

Erect wiry herb to 40cm high. **Leaves** grass-like, narrow–linear, to 7.5cm long, in basal tufts or scattered, margins fringed, tip finely pointed. **Flowers** small, pink (rarely white) in terminal compact head, about 1.5cm across, on slender leafless stalks to 30cm long. Flowers open at night. **Capsule** ovoid, to 3mm diameter. Widespread from the coast to farther inland, often in woodland in sand or on sandstone. Qld, NSW, Vic. Winter, spring.

Sowerbaea laxiflora | Purple Tassels

Perennial tufted herb about 45cm high. **Leaves** basal, linear, 10–30cm long to 12mm wide, tip mucronate. **Flowers** purple, occasionally pink (rarely white), in terminal umbels comprising more than 30 flowers, to 3cm across, on stalks to 45cm long. **Capsule** globular, 3-lobed. Widespread in southwest, in near-coastal heath and woodland. WA. Spring.

Sowerbaea juncea | Vanilla Lily

Perennial tufted herb about 45cm high. **Leaves** basal, cylindrical, 20–40cm long to 2mm wide. Flowering stems about 45cm long. **Flowers** lilac-pink in terminal umbels of more than 20, to 3cm across. Stamens golden-yellow. **Capsule** globular, 3-lobed. Widespread from coast to the mou ntains, mainly in heath. Qld, NSW, Vic, Tas. Spring.

Thysanotus tuberosus | Common Fringe Lily

Erect perennial herb to 60cm high. **Leaves** linear to terete, 10–20cm long, shooting from the base of the plant annually (usually in spring) and withering at flowering time. **Flowers** mauve with 3 broad finely fringed petals, in groups of 1–8 at ends of branched stems to 80cm long. **Capsule** globular, to 7mm diameter. Widespread in heath, woodland and open forest. Qld, NSW, Vic, SA, WA. Spring, summer.

Arthropodium fimbriatus

Laxmannia gracilis

Sowerbaea laxiflora

Sowerbaea juncea

Thysanotus tuberosus

APIACEAE | Carrot family

A very large family of annual, biennial or perennial herbs and shrubs. It comprises about 250 genera and 3000 species, globally distributed, mainly in temperate regions. Australia has 42 genera and about 200 species. Leaves mostly alternate and usually divided into segments, forming a sheath at the base, without stipules. Inflorescence a simple or compound umbel. Flowers regular, bisexual. Calyx greatly reduced. Petals 5 free; stamens 5. Ovary inferior with 2 separate styles. Fruit a dry schizocarp that splits into 2 mericarps. The family includes food plants such as carrots, parsnips, celery, coriander and fennel.

Aciphylla glacialis | Mountain Celery

Robust perennial herb to 70cm high. **Leaves** dark green, leathery, 10–25cm long, sheathing at the base and divided 2–3 times into linear stiff segments with pointed tips. **Flowers** small, creamy-white, in large compound umbels, at the end of thick fleshy stalks. Common in alpine herbfields and swampy areas at high elevations. NSW, Vic. Summer.

Actinotus helianthi | Flannel Flower

Annual or short-lived perennial herb, 30–90cm high. The whole plant is covered in soft woolly hairs. **Leaves** about 5cm long and wide, deeply divided into linear lobes, grey-green and tomentose. **Flowers** tiny, closely packed in head-like umbel, to 8cm diameter, surrounded by cream downy petal-like bracts, sometimes green-tipped. Common along the coast, in heath and open forest. Qld, NSW. Mainly spring, also other times.

Platysace lanceolata | Shrubby Platysace

Small erect shrub to 1.5cm high; stems finely hairy. **Leaves** variable, linear to narrow-lanceolate or sometimes nearly circular, usually 1–5cm long and to 1.5cm wide, tip usually pointed. **Flowers** small, white, cream or pinkish, in compound umbels to 5cm diameter. Widespread from coast to farther inland in heath, woodland and dry open forest, often on sandy soil. Qld, NSW, Vic. Spring, autumn.

Trachymene caerulea | Blue Lace Flower

Erect annual or biennial herb to 1m or more high; stems sparsely to densely hairy. **Leaves** 2–6cm long, hairy, divided into 3 lobes, which are again divided or 3-lobed. **Flowers** deep blue to pale blue in compact rounded umbel, to 6cm across. Widespread in southwest on coastal plain and nearby ranges, on sand and limestone. WA. Winter, spring.

Aciphylla glacialis

Actinotus helianthi

Platysace lanceolata

Trachymene caerulea

ASTERACEAE | Daisy family

Very large family of herbs, shrubs and rarely trees or climbers of about 1100 genera and 25,000 species globally distributed. About 205 genera and 1000 species are widely distributed throughout Australia. Leaves usually alternate, rarely opposite, often in a basal rosette, without stipules. Flowers crowded into dense heads subtended by an involucre of bracts arranged in 1 or more whorls, the whole resembling a single flower. The calyx is modified as a ring of hairs, bristles, scales or barbs forming what is known as a pappus, but this is sometimes absent. Individual flowers are usually of 2 types: tubular disc florets, which have a narrow corolla with 5 lobes; and the outer strap-like ray florets, each with a flat, fused corolla, resembling a petal and which usually radiate outwards. Flowerheads may contain tubular disc florets only; tubular disc florets in the centre surrounded by ray florets; or outer ray florets only. Stamens 5. Ovary inferior. Fruit an achene, often with a persistent pappus. The family contains many ornamental plants, including aster, chrysanthemum and zinnia. Food plants include lettuce, globe artichoke and the sunflower.

Ammobium alatum

Erect perennial herb to 1m high; stems woolly silvery-white with distinct wings. **Leaves** ovate to obovate, 4-6cm long to 1.5cm wide, silvery, mostly in a basal rosette on stems to 10cm long; stem leaves smaller, lanceolate, stem-clasping and forming wings along the stems. **Flowerheads** 2cm across, are composed of bright yellow tubular flowers only, surrounded by several rows of white papery bracts. Occurs mainly on mountains and western slopes, often along roads, in grassland and woodland. Qld, NSW. Summer.

Brachycome angustifolia

Spreading stoloniferous perennial herb to 35cm high. **Leaves** narrow-oblanceolate, 3–5cm long, scattered along upright stems. **Flowerheads** to 2cm across, with yellow disc florets surrounded by numerous pink, blue or mauve ray florets. Widespread from coast to mountains and farther inland, mainly in open forest, often on sandy soils. NSW, Vic, Tas, SA. Spring, autumn.

Brachycome ciliaris | Variable Daisy

Spreading perennial herb to 45cm high; stems usually covered with short glandular hairs. **Leaves** pinnate, to 5cm long, with 3-9 linear pointed lobes. **Flowerheads** about 3cm across, with yellow central disc florets and white to mauve ray florets, borne singly on slender stalks. Widespread in inland areas, mainly on plains. All States. Throughout the year.

Brachycome formosa | Pilliga Daisy

Small rhizomatous perennial herb to 15cm high. **Leaves** circular to obovate in outline, to 3cm long, with 3-11 lobes, dark green, sometimes with purple tinges. **Flowerheads** solitary, to 3cm across, with yellow disc florets and deep pink petal-like ray florets. Inland, mainly in open forest and woodland. NSW. Spring.

Ammobium alatum

Brachycome angustifolia

Brachycome ciliaris

Brachycome formosa

Brachycome goniocarpa | Dwarf Daisy

Annual herb to 20cm high; stems pubescent. **Leaves** basal and along the stems, to 4cm long, lobed or divided into narrow segments. **Flowerheads** to 1cm across, with yellow central discs and white ray florets, singly on slender leafy stalks. Widespread in inland districts. Qld, NSW, Vic, SA, WA. Winter, spring.

Brachycome iberidifolia | Swan River Daisy

Erect annual herb to 50cm high. **Leaves** pinnate, to 3cm long, light green with very narrow segments. **Flowerheads** to 2cm across, with central yellow discs and white, blue or purple ray florets. Widespread in winter rainfall districts, in a variety of habitats. SA, WA, NT. Spring, summer.

Brachycome multifida | Cut-leaf Daisy

Spreading annual or perennial herb to 45cm high. **Leaves** to 7cm long, deeply dissected into 7–10 segments. **Flowerheads** 2cm across, with yellow central disc florets and white, pink or mauve ray florets, solitary. Widespread in grassland or open forest. Qld, NSW, Vic. Throughout the year.

Brachycome obovata |

Loosely tufted or shortly creeping herb to 30cm high. **Leaves** linear to narrow–oblanceolate, to 12cm long and 5mm wide, mostly basal; upper stem leaves sessile and much smaller. **Flowerheads** 2–3cm across, with yellow disc florets and white or pale mauve ray florets, solitary. At higher elevations in the Australian Alps, usually in wet places and along stream banks. NSW, Vic. Summer.

Brachycome scapigera | Tufted Daisy

Erect tufted perennial herb to 40cm high. **Leaves** basal, linear to oblanceolate, 6–15cm long to 1.5cm wide with the midrib prominent on the underside; old leaves persistent at the base of the plant. **Flowerheads** 1–2cm across, with yellow disc florets and white or pale violet ray florets, solitary. Widespread on mountains in a variety of habitats, to alpine herbfields, to open forest, frequently in moist areas. Qld, NSW, Vic. Spring, summer.

Brachycome tadgellii | Snow Daisy

Formerly *B. nivalis* var. *alpina*. Stoloniferous perennial herb, to about 20cm high. **Leaves**, basal oblong to narrow–spathulate, to 9cm long, margins entire or irregularly toothed; stem leaves to 3cm long. **Flowerheads** 2–4cm across, with yellow disc florets and white ray florets, solitary. Alpine and subalpine tracts, in marshy boggy areas. NSW. Summer.

Brachycome goniocarpa

Brachycome iberidifolia

Brachycome multifida

Brachycome obovata

Brachycome scapigera

Brachycome tadgellii

Brachycome trachycarpa | Smooth Daisy

Erect slender perennial herb to 40cm high; stems glandular. **Leaves** linear, 1–3.5cm long to 1.5mm wide, sessile, margins entire or finely lobed. **Flowerheads** about 1.5cm across, yellow disc florets and white to lilac ray florets. Widespread in inland districts, often on sandy and rocky soils. Qld, NSW, Vic, SA, WA. Throughout the year.

Bracteantha bracteata | Golden Everlasting

Formerly *Helichrysum bracteatum*. Erect annual or short-lived perennial herb, usually single-stemmed to 1m high. **Leaves** oblanceolate to narrow–lanceolate, to 10cm long and 2cm wide, dark green, minutely hairy, margins entire. **Flowerheads** bright yellow, about 5cm across, with a yellow centre surrounded by several rows of shiny petal-like papery bracts, often reflexed at maturity. Widespread open woodland and forest. All States. Spring, summer.

Bracteantha papillosum |

Formerly *Helichrysum papillosum*. Erect annual or biennial herb to 80cm high; stems glandular. **Leaves** oblong–lanceolate, 3–6cm long and 1–2cm wide, sessile, rough and warty. **Flowerheads** solitary, about 3cm across, with white papery bracts and a few pink or greenish outer bracts. Coastal districts in heath and on cliffs. Vic, Tas. Spring, summer.

Bracteantha viscosa | Sticky Everlasting

Formerly *Helichrysum viscosum*. Erect sticky annual or short-lived perennial herb to 80cm high; stems branched and rough. **Leaves** narrow–linear to lanceolate, 3–9cm long and less than 1cm wide, dark green with a varnished appearance. **Flowerheads** solitary or up to 3 together, bright yellow with several rows of yellow petal-like papery bracts, sometimes with brownish outer bracts. Woodland and open forest, often on shallow stony soils. NSW, Vic. Spring.

Calocephalus knappii |

Annual or short-lived perennial herb to 20cm high; stems white woolly. **Leaves** linear to lanceolate, to 2cm long and 4mm wide, sessile, densely hairy. **Flowerheads** globular to ovate, yellow or orange, to 1.5cm across, with 7–15 tubular florets per head. Widespread in arid and semi-arid areas. Qld, SA, WA, NT. Winter, spring.

Calocephalus platycephalus | Yellow Top

Annual or perennial herb to 45cm high; stems woolly white. **Leaves** linear to lanceolate, to 3cm long and 2mm wide, sessile, glabrous to densely hairy. **Flowerheads** yellow globular with slightly flattened top, 1–3cm across; 12–22 tubular florets per head. Widespread in arid and semi-arid areas. Qld, NSW, SA, WA, NT. Winter, spring.

Brachycome trachycarpa

Bracteantha bracteata

Bracteantha papillosum

Bracteantha viscosa

Calocephalus knappii

Calocephalus platycephalus

Calotis cuneifolia | Purple Burr-daisy

Erect or spreading perennial herb to 60cm high; stems covered with stiff hairs. **Leaves** wedge-shaped, to 4cm long and 2cm wide with 3–6 pointed lobes near the tip, sessile. **Flowerheads** to 2cm across, with yellow centre and white, blue or purple ray florets, borne singly, axillary or terminal on slender stalks, prolific. **Fruit** with 2–4 erect barbed spines. Widespread, on grassland and open forest. Qld, NSW, Vic, SA, NT. Spring, also other times.

Calotis glandulosa |

Spreading to erect hairy herb about 35cm high. **Leaves** wedge-shaped, lobed, about 3cm long and 1cm wide with glandular hairs, sessile. **Flowerheads** to 2cm wide, yellow centre and white to blue ray florets. **Fruit** with 4 or 5 erect spines of unequal length. Grassland and dry forest at high altitudes. NSW. Summer.

Calotis lappulacea | Yellow Burr-daisy

Erect perennial, multi-branched herb or subshrub to 50cm high. **Leaves**, basal wedge-shaped, toothed or lobed, to 6cm long, soon withering; stem leaves linear, entire or lobed to 2.5cm long and 4mm wide, sessile. **Flowerheads** to 2cm across, with a yellow centre and yellow ray florets, prolific. **Fruit** with 2 long erect spines and several shorter spreading ones. Widespread in woodland, open forest and cleared land. All mainland States. Throughout the year.

Cassinia arcuata | Chinese Shrub

Aromatic shrub to 2m high; branches slender and covered in fine white hairs. **Leaves** narrow–linear, to 1.5cm long and 1mm wide, stocky above, hairy below, margins revolute, tip rounded. **Flowerheads**, small reddish-brown, each with 2–3 tubular florets, in terminal, drooping panicles to 7cm long. Widespread in a wide variety of habitats; invasive on cleared and disturbed ground. NSW, Vic, SA, WA. Spring, autumn.

Cassinia denticulata | Stiff Cassinia

Erect shrub to 2m high; stems with glandular hairs. **Leaves** ovate to elliptic, to 2.5cm long and 6mm wide, slightly stem-clasping, shiny above, hairy below, spreading or reflexed, margins finely toothed. **Flowerheads** pale yellow, each with 12–14 florets clustered into a dense terminal corymb, 10cm diameter, which is almost flat-topped. Confined to central coast and tablelands, mainly in open forest on sandstone and sandy soils. NSW. Spring, summer.

Cassinia laevis | Cough Bush

Aromatic open shrub to 3m high; stems woolly white. **Leaves**, narrow–linear, 1–5cm long to 1mm wide, shiny above, margins revolute concealing pubescent undersurface. **Flowerheads** creamy-white, each with 2–4 florets borne in loose pyramidal panicles, 5–10cm diameter. Widespread from coast to ranges and farther inland, in open forest and woodland in shallow stony soils, also in mallee communities. Qld, NSW, SA. Spring, autumn.

Calotis cuneifolia

Calotis glandulosa

Calotis lappulacea

Cassinia arcuata

Cassinia denticulata

Cassinia laevis

Cassinia longifolia | Shiny Cassinia

Aromatic spreading shrub to 3m high; stems with glandular hairs. **Leaves** oblong to narrow–lanceolate, 4–8cm long, 2–6mm wide, glabrous above, matted white hairs below. **Flowerheads** white, each with 5 or 6 florets arranged in a dense terminal corymb to 12cm diameter. Dry open forest and partly cleared sites. NSW, Vic, Tas. Summer, autumn.

Cassinia subtropica |

Erect shrub to 2m high; stems with fine woolly hairs. **Leaves** lanceolate to ovate, 1–3cm long, 3–7mm wide, dark green and shiny above, white to rusty tomentose below. **Flowerheads** creamy-white or pale brown, each with 1–2 florets arranged in a dense pyramidal panicle to 10cm long and 6cm wide. Open forest and rainforest margins, or in open rocky situations at fairly high elevations. Qld, NSW. Autumn, winter.

Cassinia uncata | Sticky Cassinia

Sticky shrub 1–3m high; stems covered in short glandular hairs. **Leaves** linear, 1–3cm long, 1mm wide, glabrous and somewhat resinous above with tightly revolute margins obscuring pubescent lower surface, tip hooked. **Flowerheads** white to cream, each with 5 or 6 florets arranged in a compact, almost flat corymb to 8cm across. Open forest and woodland, often on hillsides and ridges in gravelly soil. NSW, Vic, SA. Spring.

Celmisia asteliifolia | Snow Daisy

Tufted silvery-white perennial herb to 45cm high. **Leaves** mainly basal, linear, 10–20cm long to 1cm wide, silvery-green above with silvery-white hairs below, margins revolute. **Flowerheads** to 5cm across, disc florets yellow, ray florets white, singly on erect stalks to 45cm high. Common and abundant in alpine regions, where it forms extensive mats, usually in damp places. NSW, Vic, Tas. Summer.

Chrysocephalum apiculatum | Common Everlasting

Formerly *Helichrysum apiculatum*. Variable, erect or spreading perennial herb to 60cm high; stems often matted with woolly white and glandular hairs. **Leaves** linear–lanceolate to lanceolate, 1–6cm long, 1–3cm wide, sessile, hairy above, sometimes denser below, tip finely pointed. **Flowerheads** golden-yellow, about 1.5cm across, surrounded by short, pointed petal-like bracts, in terminal compact clusters, on short stalks. Widespread and common in grassland and open woodland. All States. Spring, but also at other times.

Chrysocephalum baxteri | Fringed Everlasting

Formerly *Helichrysum baxteri*. Perennial herb to 20cm high, stems woolly white. **Leaves** narrow–linear, 1.5–3cm long, grey-green, margins revolute, tip pointed. **Flowerheads** solitary, 2–4cm across, central disc florets yellow surrounded by white bracts, sometimes buff-coloured (rarely pale pink), on slender woolly stalks to 20cm long. Widespread in southern Australia, mostly in coastal heath and dry open forest farther inland. NSW, Vic, SA. Spring, summer.

Cassinia longifolia

Cassinia subtropica

Cassinia uncata

Celmisia asteliifolia

Chrysocephalum apiculatum

Chrysocephalum baxteri

Chrysocephalum semipapposum | Clustered Everlasting

Formerly *Helichrysum semipapposum*. Variable perennial herb to 60cm high; stems sticky with fine cottony and glandular hairs when young. **Leaves** linear, to 5cm long and 1–3mm wide, hairy, margins flat or recurved, tip pointed. **Flowerheads** about 7mm across, golden-yellow grouped in compact clusters of 50–100 heads per cluster. Smaller clusters in the second flush of flowering. Widespread from coast to ranges and farther inland, in grassland, woodland and mallee communities. All States. Spring, summer.

Craspedia costiniana |

Erect herb to 50cm high. **Leaves** basal, spathulate, to 12cm long and 2cm wide, densely covered with glandular and long fine hairs. **Flowerheads** globular, to 3.5cm diameter with up to 100 partial heads, each with 7–12 golden-yellow tubular florets, terminally on a single, cream to deep red, hairy stalk to 50cm long. High subalpine grassland and alpine herbfield. NSW. Summer.

Craspedia maxgrayii |

Robust herb to 50cm high covered in white woolly hairs. **Leaves** silvery-grey, oblanceolate to spathulate, 5–15cm long to 1.5cm wide with woolly white hairs on both surfaces. **Flowerheads** globular, to 4.5cm diameter with up to 120 partial heads, each with 9–11 yellow tubular florets, terminally, on a single reddish-brown hairy stalk to 50cm high Confined to Kosciusko area, mainly in grassland. NSW. Summer.

Leptorhynchos panaetioides | Woolly Buttons

Erect multi-branched, silvery-grey subshrub to 60cm high, stems with a dense covering of soft white hairs. **Leaves** linear to oblong, 1–1.5cm long to 1.5mm wide, sessile, silvery-grey and densely hairy. **Flowerheads** yellow, about 1cm across, solitary on flowering stems 2–5cm long. Semi-arid and arid regions in grassland and woodland, usually on heavy soils of flood plains. NSW, Vic. Spring, summer.

Leucochrysum albicans subsp. *albicans* | Hoary Sunray

Formerly *Helipterum albicans* subsp. *albicans*. Erect annual or sometimes perennial woolly herb to 30cm high. **Leaves** filiform to linear, sessile, 2–10cm long, to 1cm wide, cottony or woolly. **Flowerheads** solitary, 2–3cm across, disc florets yellow surrounded by golden-yellow inner papery bracts and pale brown outer bracts. Widespread in a range of communities and habitats. Qld, NSW, Vic. Tas. Spring, summer.

Leucochrysum albicans subsp. *alpinum* | Alpine Sunray

Formerly *Helipterum albicans* subsp. *alpinum*. Spreading perennial herb to 20cm often form-ing extensive patches. **Leaves** obovate or oblanceolate, 1–5cm long to 1cm wide, silvery and densely hairy. **Flowerheads** solitary, to 4cm across, disc florets yellow-orange surrounded by white papery inner bracts. Strongly perfumed. Common in alpine and subalpine regions. NSW, Vic. Summer.

Chrysocephalum semipapposum

Craspedia costiniana

Craspedia maxgrayii

Leptorhynchos panaetioides

Leucochrysum albicans subsp. *albicans*

Leucochrysum albicans subsp. *alpinum*

Minuria leptophylla | Minnie Daisy

Erect or ascending, multi-branched perennial herb to 40cm high becoming woody at base. **Leaves** narrow–linear, to 4cm long and about 1mm wide, becoming smaller on upper stems, bright green, sessile, tip pointed. **Flowerheads** to 2cm across, with white, pink or purple ray florets and yellow disc florets, terminal on short hairy stalks, profuse. Common in semi-arid regions in open forest and woodland. Qld, NSW, Vic, SA, WA, NT. Throughout the year.

Olearia microphylla | Small-leaved Daisy Bush

Erect shrub to 2m high. **Leaves** spoon-shaped, 2–7mm long to 3mm wide, crowded, dark green, glandular above, woolly-hairy below, margins strongly revolute, tip rounded. **Flowerheads** solitary, about 1.7cm across, ray florets white in a single row; disc florets yellow, terminal. Widespread from coast to mountains, heath and dry open forest. Qld, NSW. Winter, spring.

Olearia pannosa | Silver-leaved Daisy Bush

Shrub to 2m high; young growth covered with dense white hairs. **Leaves** broad–oblong or elliptic, 3–10cm long and 1.5–5cm wide, deep green, sometimes with a thin coating of hair above, silvery and hairy below, margins entire, tips blunt. **Flowerheads** to 5.5cm across, with 12–25 white or rarely pale mauve ray florets borne singly on terminal stalks to 30cm long. Southern Australia in open forest and woodland. Vic, SA. Spring.

Olearia pimeleoides | Mallee Daisy Bush

Shrub to 2m high; young growth and stems covered with grey woolly hairs. **Leaves** linear, elliptic or obovate, to 2.5cm long and 6mm wide, dark green above and grey woolly below, margins entire or irregularly toothed, tips pointed or rounded. **Flowerheads** to 4cm across, with 8–25 white ray florets, borne singly or in terminal clusters. Common in semi-arid regions of southern Australia, often in open forest and woodland. Qld, NSW, Vic, SA, WA. Winter, spring.

Olearia ramulosa | Twiggy Daisy Bush

Aromatic shrub to 1.5m high; young growth and stems greyish hairy and somewhat sticky. **Leaves** narrow–elliptic or narrow–obovate, to 1cm long and 2.5mm wide, green and minutely warty above, grey woolly below, margins entire, tip rounded. **Flowerheads** to 2cm across, 2–13 pale blue, mauve or white ray florets, singly on short axillary branches, sometimes terminal. Widespread in southern Australia, from the coast to the ranges and inland plains. NSW, Vic, Tas, SA. Spring, summer, autumn.

Olearia rudis | Azure Daisy Bush

Small somewhat resinous shrub to 1.3m high. **Leaves** elliptic, ovate or obovate, to 1.5cm long and 4mm wide, both surfaces bright green and hairy, margins entire or toothed, tips pointed or rounded. **Flowerheads** to 4cm across, with up to 75 pale blue, mauve or purple ray florets, singly or a few together in terminal clusters. Common in semi-arid regions of southern Australia, often in woodland and mallee communities. NSW, Vic, SA, WA. Winter, spring.

Minuria leptophylla

Olearia microphylla

Olearia pannosa

Olearia pimeleoides

Olearia ramulosa

Olearia rudis

Olearia stellulata | Snow Daisy Bush

Formerly *O. lirata*. Shrub to 3m high. **Leaves** broad–elliptic or ovate, 5–15cm long to 3cm wide, upper surface dark green and reticulate, lower surface greyish hairy, margins entire or toothed, tips pointed or rounded. **Flowerheads** numerous, 2–5cm across, with 11–16 white ray florets, in showy terminal clusters. Wet and dry forests, often in moist situations. Qld, NSW, Vic, Tas. Spring, summer.

Olearia teretifolia | Cypress Daisy Bush

Slender somewhat sticky shrub to 1.5m high; stems many, short. **Leaves** compressed, linear, 2–5mm long, less than 1mm wide, deep green above, slightly grooved below. **Flowerheads** solitary, to 1.5cm across, 4–8 white ray florets, at branch ends. Mallee, woodland and dry forest. Vic, SA. Spring, summer.

Olearia tomentosa | Toothed Daisy Bush

Shrub to 2m high; stems hairy. **Leaves** ovate, 1.5–8cm long to 2.5cm wide, dark green and rough above, woolly white or rusty below, margins toothed or shallowly lobed, tip blunt or rounded. **Flowerheads** to 6cm across, with 13–29 white or pale blue ray florets, in loose terminal clusters, on brown furry stalks to 4cm long. Widespread from the coast to the mountains, in heath, shrubland and dry open forest. NSW. Spring, summer, autumn.

Olearia viscidula | Wallaby Weed

Erect somewhat resinous shrub to 2.5m high. **Leaves** narrow–elliptic or ovate, 1.5–9cm long to about 1cm wide, dark green and sticky above and grey felted below, margins entire. **Flowerheads** to 2cm across, with 8–21 white ray florets, in small axillary clusters. Dry forest and woodland. NSW, Vic. Winter, spring.

Ozothamnus diosmifolius | Ball Everlasting

Formerly *Helichrysum diosmifolium*. Large branched shrub 2–5m high. **Leaves** linear, 1–2.5cm long and no more than 2.5mm wide, dark green and hairless above and shortly hairy below, margins revolute. **Flowerheads** to 3mm across, in numerous dense clusters to 7cm diameter. The broad papery bracts are white or tinged with pink. Widespread and common in heath, open forest and rainforest margins. Qld, NSW. Spring, summer.

Ozothamnus hookeri | Kerosene Bush

Formerly *Helichrysum hookeri*. Highly inflammable aromatic bushy shrub to 2m high with white woolly branches. **Leaves** small, triangular to ovate, 3mm long and 1mm wide, sessile and closely appressed to the stem, bright green and sticky above, woolly-hairy below, margins revolute. **Flowerheads** creamy, to 2mm across, in small terminal clusters about 1.5cm across. Common in subalpine areas, often in heaths and boggy situations. NSW, Vic, Tas. Summer.

Olearia stellulata

Olearia teretifolia

Olearia tomentosa

Olearia viscidula

Ozothamnus diosmifolius

Ozothamnus hookeri

Ozothamnus obcordatus | Grey Everlasting

Formerly *Helichrysum obcordatum*. Erect shrub to 1.5m high; branches with grey woolly hairs. **Leaves** obovate to obcordate, 3–15mm long and 3–7mm wide, dark green and shiny above, woolly and grey below. **Flowerheads** yellow, about 4mm long, in dense terminal clusters. Widespread from coast to ranges and farther inland, in heath and open forest on low stony ridges. Qld, NSW, Vic, Tas. Spring, summer.

Ozothamnus purpurascens |

Formerly *Helichrysum purpurascens*. Erect compact shrub to 2m high; young growth densely covered with white woolly hair. **Leaves** narrow linear, 1.5cm long and 2mm wide, hairy, dark green above, white below, margins recurved, tip blunt; strongly aromatic. **Flowerheads** white, about 5mm across, in many dense terminal clusters to 4cm across. Endemic in Tasmania where it is common in the south. Tas. Summer.

Ozothamnus rosmarinifolius | Rosemary Everlasting

Formerly *Helichrysum rosmarinifolium*. Shrub to 1.5m high; stems woolly white. **Leaves** linear, often crowded, 1.5–5cm long and to 2mm wide, dark green and rough above, pale grey or white hairy below, margins revolute, tip pointed. **Flowerheads** white, about 3mm across, in terminal hemispherical clusters about 3cm across. Widespread in southeast and common in Tasmania, mostly in heath and open forest, often beside watercourses. NSW, Vic, Tas. Spring, summer.

Ozothamnus secundiflorus | Cascade Everlasting

Formerly *Helichrysum secundiflorum*. Aromatic spreading shrub 2.5m high to 3m wide; branches whitish-grey and often arching. **Leaves** oblong to narrow–oblanceolate, to 1.5cm long and 2mm wide, dark grey and hairy above, pale grey and woolly below, margins slightly recurved, tip pointed. **Flowerheads** white, about 2mm across, in rounded clusters on short lateral branchlets. Heath and open forest on mountain slopes. NSW, Vic. Summer, autumn.

Ozothamnus thyrsoideus | Sticky Everlasting

Formerly *Helichrysum thyrsoideum*. Shrub to 2m high; branches spreading, greyish hairy. **Leaves** narrow–linear, 1.5–3cm long, 1–2mm wide, dark green and slightly resinous above, pale yellowish-green and hairy below, margins slightly recurved. **Flowerheads** white, about 5mm across, in dense heads on the upper side of short lateral branchlets. Widespread in subalpine areas in open forest. NSW, Vic, Tas. Spring, summer.

Polycalymma stuartii | Poached Eggs

Formerly *Myriocephalus stuartii*. Erect annual herb 10–50cm high, stems woolly-hairy. **Leaves** linear or linear–lanceolate, 2–7cm long to 5mm wide, grey-green, woolly to almost glabrous above, hairy below, tip slightly pointed. **Flowerheads** hemispherical, 2–4cm across, deep yellow disc florets surrounded by several rows of white papery bracts. Widespread and common on inland sandy plains and sand dunes. Qld, NSW, Vic, SA, NT. Winter, spring.

Ozothamnus obcordatus

Ozothamnus purpurascens

Ozothamnus rosmarinifolius

Ozothamnus secundiflorus

Ozothamnus thyrsoideus

Polycalymma stuartii

Pterocaulon serrulatum

Erect aromatic perennial herb to 90cm high; stems and leaves covered with a combination of woolly and glandular hairs. **Leaves** lanceolate to ovate, 3–5cm long to 2mm wide, often toothed and continuing down stem as wings. **Flowerheads** oblong, 2–3.5cm long, comprise many white to mauve tubular florets, terminal. Semi-arid and arid regions. Qld, SA, WA, NT. Winter, spring.

Pterocaulon sphacelatum | Applebush

Aromatic short-lived perennial herb to 1.2m high; stems and leaves covered with a combination of woolly and glandular hairs. **Leaves** oblanceolate to oblong, 1–5cm long and to 1.5cm wide, continuing down the stem as wings, margins entire or shallowly toothed. **Flowerheads** globular, to 2cm across, comprise many white to pinkish tubular florets, terminal. Widespread and common in dry inland areas, in low-lying areas and along roadsides. Qld, NSW, SA, WA, NT. Winter, spring.

Pycnosorus globosus | Drumsticks

Formerly *Craspedia globosa*. Tufted perennial herb with 1 or more erect flowering stems to 1.2m high. **Leaves** mainly basal, also along stem, linear, 10–30cm long, 4–12mm wide covered with fine woolly white hairs on both surfaces. **Flowerheads** bright yellow globular, to 3.5cm diameter, comprising a large number of partial heads each with 3–6 florets. Semi-arid regions, mostly open grassland and woodland, moist low-lying areas. Qld, NSW, SA, Vic. Spring, summer.

Rhodanthe anthemoides | Chamomile Sunray

Formerly *Helipterum anthemoides*. Erect bushy perennial herb to 30cm high. **Leaves** linear or narrow–oblong, to 1cm long and 2mm wide, crowded along the stems, tip pointed. **Flowerheads** solitary, about 2.5cm across, with numerous yellow disc florets surrounded by white papery petal-like inner bracts, terminal; outer bracts usually straw-coloured with a purple or pale brown midrib. Widespread in southeastern Australia, mainly at higher altitudes in rocky places. Qld, NSW, Vic, Tas. Summer.

Rhodanthe chlorocephala subsp. rosea | Rosy Sunray

Formerly *Helipterum roseum*. Upright tufted annual to 60cm high. **Leaves** linear, 1–6cm long and to 7mm wide, green to grey-green, tip blunt or pointed. **Flowerheads** 3–6cm across, with numerous yellow disc florets surrounded by white, pale deep pink petal-like papery bracts. Widespread in the southwest, usually slightly inland in sandy soils. WA. Winter, spring.

Rhodanthe manglesii | Pink Sunray

Formerly *Helipterum manglesii*. Slender annual herb to 50cm high; stems wiry and smooth. **Leaves** heart-shaped, about 5cm long, stem-clasping, green to grey-green. Pendent silvery buds open to **flowerheads** 2.5cm across, with numerous yellow disc florets surrounded by white to deep pink petal-like inner bracts; outer bracts are silky white. Widespread in the wheatbelt and mulga country. WA. Winter, spring.

Pterocaulon serrulatum

Pterocaulon sphacelatum

Pycnosorus globosus

Rhodanthe anthemoides

Rhodanthe chlorocephala subsp. *rosea*

Rhodanthe manglesii

Rhodanthe tiekensii | Sand Sunray

Formerly *Helipterum tiekensii*. Erect woolly annual herb to 40cm high. **Leaves** linear, 2–6cm long to 2–6mm wide, grey-green, hairy; upper leaves stem-clasping, margins sometimes wavy. **Flowerheads** yellow, cylindrical, about 5mm long, lacking prominent bracts, congested in globular terminal clusters about 2cm across. Widespread and common on sandy soils in semi-arid regions. NSW, SA, WA, NT. Winter, spring.

Schoenia cassiniana | Pink Everlasting

Formerly *Helichrysum cassinianum*. Small aromatic annual herb to 50cm high. **Leaves** linear–lanceolate, 3–7cm long to 1.5cm wide, densely hairy, mostly basal with a few shorter leaves along the stem. **Flowerheads** 2–3cm across, yellow disc florets surrounded by pink papery bracts, in terminal clusters of 5–10; outer bracts golden-brown. Widespread in arid and semi-arid regions, often in mulga and other *Acacia* shrublands. SA, WA, NT. Spring.

Senecio anethifolius | Feathery Groundsel

Erect aromatic shrub to 1m high. **Leaves** pinnate, 5–8cm long, 2–6cm wide, divided into 7–15 narrow linear segments, which are sometimes further divided. **Flowerheads** yellow, in terminal clusters, each with about 10 tubular florets about 5mm longer than the cylindrical involucre. Arid regions, near creek beds or on rocky hillsides in *Acacia* shrublands. NSW, SA. Spring.

Senecio gregorii | Annual Yellowtop

Erect annual herb 10–40cm high; stems hairless. **Leaves** broad–linear, 2–7cm long, 2–6mm wide, bluish-green, entire, fleshy. **Flowerheads** yellow, about 5cm across, with 8–12 ray florets. Germination and growth is dependent on favourable autumn and winter rainfall. Widespread in arid and semi-arid regions in mallee and mulga communities. All mainland States. Winter, spring.

Senecio lautus subsp. *alpinus* |

Perennial herb about 45cm high with erect or shortly creeping stems. **Leaves** pinnate, spoon-shaped in outline, 3–6cm long, deeply divided with entire or toothed lobes. **Flowerheads** yellow, to 2.5cm across, with 9–14 ray florets and slightly darker disc florets, in loose clusters. Alpine and subalpine regions. NSW, Vic, Tas. Summer.

Senecio lautus subsp. *dissectifolius* | Variable Groundsel

Erect perennial herb to 70cm high. **Leaves** linear or narrow–lanceolate, entire or deeply dissected into narrow lobes with entire or toothed margins. **Flowerheads** yellow, with 8–14 ray florets and dark yellow centre, in loose terminal clusters. Mainly inland in grassland, woodland and open forest. All States. Winter, spring.

Rhodanthe tiekensii

Schoenia cassiniana

Senecio anethifolius

Senecio gregorii

Senecio lautus subsp. *alpinus*

Senecio lautus subsp. *dissectifolius*

Senecio linearifolius | Fireweed Groundsel

Perennial herb or subshrub to 1.5m high. **Leaves** variable, linear, elliptic to obovate, 5–15cm long and 5–15mm wide, sessile or slightly stem-clasping, entire or sparsely toothed. **Flowerheads** yellow, 4–8 ray florets and 8–12 disc florets, numerous in terminal clusters. Wet sclerophyll forest and rainforest margins. NSW, Vic, Tas. Throughout the year.

Senecio magnificus | Showy Groundsel

Erect perennial herb or shrub to 1.5m high. **Leaves** spoon-shaped or oblanceolate, 5–9cm long and 1–3cm wide, blue-green, fleshy; lower leaves toothed, upper leaves toothed to entire, sometimes stem-clasping. **Flowerheads** yellow, 4–8 ray florets and darker yellow centre, numerous in showy terminal clusters. Widespread in inland regions, often near streams along drainage lines and roadsides. All mainland States. Winter, spring.

BAUERACEAE

Small family of shrubs of only 1 genus, *Bauera*, consisting of 4 species, all endemic to eastern Australia. Leaves opposite, 3-foliate, appearing in whorls of 6. Flowers regular, bisexual. Sepals and petals 4–10. Stamens 4 to numerous. Ovary superior to half-inferior. Fruit a flattened capsule that opens at maturity. The family is named after the 19th-century botanical artists Franz and Ferdinand Bauer.

Bauera rubioides | Wiry Bauera

Scrambling multi-branched shrub to 2m high. **Leaves** divided into 3 narrow leaflets, about 1cm long, opposite and appearing whorled, margins slightly toothed. **Flowers** pink or occasionally white, about 2cm across, 8–10 petals, on slender hairy stalks in leaf axils. Widespread on coast and ranges usually in wet situations, often on sandy soils. Qld, NSW, Vic, Tas, SA. Throughout the year.

Bauera sessiliflora | Grampians Bauera

Erect bushy shrub 2–3m high, branches hairy. **Leaves** divided into 3 oblong leaflets to 2.5cm long, opposite and appearing whorled, hairy, margins entire. **Flowers** magenta, open-petalled, about 1.5cm across, crowded in sessile clusters. Endemic to the Grampians, in shaded gullies in open forest. Vic. Spring, summer.

Senecio linearifolius

Senecio magnificus

Bauera rubioides

Bauera sessiliflora

BIGNONIACEAE

Large family of mostly woody climbers of about 120 genera and 650 species, mainly centred in tropical America. About 10 genera and 17 species are represented in Australia. Leaves opposite (rarely in whorls) often pinnate; stipules absent. Flowers irregular, bisexual tubular to trumpet-shaped, usually 5–numerous. Stamens 4 and paired. Ovary superior. Fruit an oblong capsule.

Pandorea jasminoides | Bower Vine

Vigorous woody climber with long twining stems. **Leaves** opposite, pinnate with 4–? ovate to lanceolate leaflets, each 4–6cm long and 1.5–3cm wide, margins entire, tip pointed. **Flowers** trumpet-shaped, 4–6cm long, white or pink with reddish-pink hairy throat, in terminal sprays to 12cm long. Subtropical and dry rainforest. Qld, NSW. Spring, summer, autumn.

Pandorea pandorana | Wonga Wonga Vine

Woody scrambling shrub or climber with twining stems. **Leaves** pinnate, 3-9 linear to ovate leaflets, each 2.5-8cm long to 3cm wide, margins entire, tip pointed. Juvenile leaflets of 8-17 per leaf are much smaller, margins bluntly toothed. **Flowers** tubular, 1-3cm long, white, cream, pink or brownish with purplish-red hairy throat, in loose terminal sprays to 15cm long. Rainforest, sheltered forest and woodland. All mainland States. Winter, spring, summer.

BLANDFORDIACEAE | Christmas Bell family

A small family of 1 genus, *Blandfordia*, comprising 4 endemic species confined to eastern Australia, and commonly known as Christmas Bells. They are tufted perennial herbs with bell shaped flowers borne in terminal racemes. Flowers usually red with yellow lobes, but some forms with pure yellow flowers. Fruit a dry capsule containing numerous brown velvety seeds. Leaves are not illustrated in this family as they are too similar for identification purposes.

Blandfordia cunninghamii | Mountain Christmas Bell

Tufted perennial herb. **Leaves** grass-like, to 1m long and 1cm wide, margins smooth. **Flowers** tubular, to 4.5cm long and 3cm wide, narrow toward the base, in terminal racemes of 7-18 flowers. Stamens 6, attached to the floral tube below its middle. Damp situations in sandstone areas. NSW. Summer.

Blandfordia grandiflora | Northern Christmas Bell

Tufted perennial herb. **Leaves** grass-like, to 80cm long and 4mm wide; margins rough and toothed. **Flowers** funnel-shaped, waxy, to 6cm long and 4cm wide, narrowing gradually toward the base, in terminal racemes of 3-10 flowers. Wet heathland. Qld, NSW. Summer.

Pandorea jasminoides

Pandorea pandorana

Blandfordia cunninghamii

Blandfordia grandiflora

Blandfordia nobilis | Christmas Bell

Tufted perennial herb. **Leaves** grass-like, to 80cm long and 5mm wide; margins rough and shallowly toothed. **Flowers** somewhat cylindrical, waxy, to 3.5cm long and 1cm wide in terminal racemes of 3–10 flowers. Damp sandstone areas. NSW. Summer.

Blandfordia punicea | Tasmanian Christmas Bell

Stout tufted perennial herb. **Leaves** narrow–linear, to 1m long and 1cm wide, margins slightly toothed and recurved. **Flowers** tubular, waxy, to 4cm long and 2cm wide, numerous in a cluster at the end of a stout stem up to 1m long. Moist acid soils in heaths. Tas endemic. Summer.

BORAGINACEAE | Forget-me-not family

Large family of mostly perennial herbs, but also includes some shrubs, trees and climbers. There are about 156 genera and 2500 species widely distributed throughout the world. The family is poorly represented in Australia, where there are 19 genera and about 63 species. All parts of the plants are usually covered with stiff rough hairs. Leaves alternate, sometimes in a basal rosette, without stipules. Flowers regular, bisexual. Sepals 5, free or united at the base. Corolla tubular with 5 lobes. Stamens 5, alternate with corolla lobes. Ovary superior. Fruit a drupe that splits into 4 nutlets. The family contains the widely naturalised Paterson's Curse.

Echium plantagineum | Paterson's Curse

Erect annual or biennial herb to 1m high; stems and leaves hairy. **Leaves** obovate, to 30cm long in the rosette, but becoming shorter and lanceolate, with heart-shaped base on the stems. **Flowers** purplish-blue, tubular, about 3cm long, in spreading cymes. Widely naturalised and has become a major weed of agricultural land. Native of Europe. All States. Spring, summer

Halgania cyanea | Rough Halgania

Small suckering shrub to 90cm high and to 2m across. **Leaves** linear to wedge-shaped or narrow–obovate, 2cm long, 5mm wide, covered with appressed glandular hairs, margins toothed. **Flowers** deep blue with 5 spreading lobes, to 5cm across, in short clusters. Widespread in low-rainfall regions, usually in mallee communities. NSW, Vic, SA, WA, NT. Winter

Blandfordia nobilis

Blandfordia punicea

Echium plantagineum

Halgania cyanea

Halgania preissiana

Open, often suckering shrub to 60cm high. **Leaves** oblong to wedge-shaped or obovate, to 2.5cm long and 1cm across, hairy with prickly toothed margins. **Flowers** purple-blue, to 2cm across, in small clusters of 2–3 flowers. Widespread in the southwest. WA. Spring, summer.

Trichodesma zeylanicum | Cattle Bush

Erect annual or perennial herb to 1m high, usually covered by long stiff hairs. **Leaves** oblong–linear or narrow–ovate, 4–10cm long to 2cm wide, grey-green, sessile, tip pointed. **Flowers** pale blue, about 2cm across, with 5 spreading lobes, nodding in loose clusters at the ends of branches. Widespread in low-rainfall regions, usually in mulga communities. Qld, NSW, SA, WA, NT. Winter, spring.

CAESALPINIACEAE | Senna family

A large family of mostly shrubs and trees of about 150 genera and 2500–3000 species widely distributed in tropical and subtropical regions of the world. About 20 genera and 85 species are found in Australia in all States, except Tasmania. Leaves alternate, mostly pinnate or sometimes bipinnate, rarely simple. Flowers slightly irregular, often large and showy. Petals 5, free. Stamens 10, often of unequal size. Ovary superior. Fruit commonly a pod. This family is often included as the subfamily Caesalpinioideae of the family Fabaceae.

Senna aciphylla | Australian Senna

Formerly *Cassia aciphylla*. Spreading shrub to 2m high. **Leaves** pinnate, 3–5cm long divided into 8–12 pairs of leaflets; each leaflet linear to elliptic to 2.5cm long and 4mm wide, margins revolute, tips almost pungent-pointed. Hairlike glands present between all pairs of leaflets. **Flowers** yellow, to 2.5cm across, in small umbels of 2–3. Stamens 10, of equal size. Widespread in woodland and forest. Qld, NSW, Vic. Spring, summer, autumn.

Senna artemisioides subsp. *artemisioides* | Silver Cassia

Formerly *Cassia artemisioides*. Erect silvery shrub 1–2m high. **Leaves** pinnate, 2–4cm long, divided into 2–8 pairs of grey-green or silvery leaflets, each terete or linear, 1–4cm long, margins incurved. A flat gland is present between lowest pair of leaflets. **Flowers** yellow, to 1.5cm across, in axillary clusters. Stamens 10. **Fruit** a flat oblong pod 4–8cm long and 6–10mm wide. Widespread in inland districts. Qld, NSW, SA, WA, NT. Winter, spring.

Halgania preissiana

Trichodesma zeylanicum

Senna aciphylla

Senna artemisioides subsp. artemisioides

Senna artemisioides subsp. *filifolia* | Desert Cassia

Formerly *Cassia eremophila* var. *eremophila*. Shrub 1–3m high. **Leaves** pinnate, 4–8cm long, divided into 1–4 pairs of leaflets, each terete, sparsely hairy when young. **Flowers** bright yellow, about 1.5cm across, in short axillary clusters. **Fruit** a thin flat pod 2–8cm long and less than 1cm wide. Widespread in inland districts. All mainland States. Winter, spring.

Senna artemisioides subsp. *helmsii* | Blunt-leaved Cassia

Formerly *Cassia helmsii*. Small shrub to 80cm high. **Leaves** pinnate, grey-green and densely hairy, 2.5–5cm long, divided into 2–4 pairs of ovate leaflets, each 1–2.5cm long with a blunt or notched tip. **Flowers** deep golden-yellow, to 2.5cm across in axillary clusters. **Fruit** a broad oblong pod 2–4cm long and 2cm wide. Widespread in inland areas. Qld, NSW, SA, WA, NT. Winter, spring.

Senna artemisioides subsp. *oligophylla* | Oval-leaf Cassia

Formerly *Cassia oligophylla*. Dense shrub to 2m high and across. **Leaves** pinnate, grey-green, silky-hairy and waxy, divided into 2 or 3 pairs of ovate leaflets, each 1–2cm long with a rounded or notched tip. **Flowers** bright yellow, to 1.5cm across, in clusters of 6–20 in the upper leaf axils. **Fruit** a slightly curved pod to 7cm long and 2.5cm wide. Widespread in desert regions. Qld, NSW, SA, WA, NT. Winter, spring.

Senna artemisioides subsp. *sturtii* | Grey Cassia

Formerly *Cassia sturtii*; *Cassia desolata* var. *desolata*. Grey-green shrub 1–2m high. **Leaves** pinnate, 3–6cm long divided into 2–8 pairs of linear–elliptic densely hairy leaflets, each 1.5 to 2.5cm long with upturned margins. **Flowers** golden-yellow, 2.5cm across, in clusters in the upper leaf axils. **Fruit** a flat straight pod to 7cm long and 1cm wide. Widespread throughout the inland. Qld, NSW, SA, WA, NT. Throughout the year.

Senna artemisioides subsp. *zygophylla* |

Formerly *Cassia eremophila* var. *zygophylla*. Erect shrub 1–3m high. **Leaves** pinnate, 4–8cm long with 1–2 pairs of linear–elliptic leaflets, each about 4cm long, initially downy but becoming hairless with age. **Flowers** bright yellow, about 1.5cm across, in short axillary clusters. **Fruit** a thin flat pod 2–8cm long and less than 1cm wide. Inland plains and rocky slopes. All mainland States. Winter, spring.

Senna coronilloides |

Formerly *Cassia coronilloides*. Shrub to 2m high. **Leaves** pinnate, 5–9cm long, divided into 9–12 pairs of elliptic leaflets, each about 2cm long and 8mm wide, sparsely hairy, 1 or 2 glands present between lowest pairs. **Flowers** bright yellow, 2–3cm across in axillary clusters of 3–5 flowers. **Fruit** a slightly curved pod 6–8cm long and 4–6mm wide. Woodland and dry open forest. Qld, NSW. Spring, summer, autumn.

Senna artemisioides subsp. *filifolia*

Senna artemisioides subsp. *helmsii*

Senna artemisioides subsp. *oligophylla*

Senna artemisioides subsp. *sturtii*

Senna artemisioides subsp. *zygophylla*

Senna coronilloides

Senna notabilis | Cockroach Bush

Formerly *Cassia notabilis*. Small spreading shrub to 1.5m high, densely covered with long and short hairs. **Leaves** pinnate, 10–16cm long, divided into 6–12 pairs of ovate leaflets, each 1.5–4.5cm long and to 1.5cm wide, tip pointed with a small bristle. **Flowers** numerous bright yellow in axillary, spike-like racemes held well above the leaves. **Fruit** a black and yellowish oblong pod to 4cm long and 1.5cm wide with ridges over the seeds and resembling a cockroach. Widespread in inland and northern regions. Qld, WA, NT. Autumn, winter.

Senna odorata |

Formerly *Cassia odorata*. Sprawling shrub to 2.5m high. **Leaves** pinnate, 8–10cm long divided into 8–13 pairs of lanceolate to elliptic leaflets, each 1–3cm long and to 1cm wide, dark green, shiny, tips rounded, notched or pointed. Glands present between all pairs of leaflets. **Flowers** golden-yellow, about 2.5cm across in axillary clusters of 2–6 flowers. **Fruit** a flat straight pod 7–10cm long. Sheltered forests in coastal districts. Qld, NSW. Spring, summer.

Senna pleurocarpa | Fire Bush

Formerly *Cassia pleurocarpa*. Straggly hairless shrub 1–3m high; sometimes suckering. **Leaves** pinnate, 7–15cm long, divided into 5–7 pairs of linear or oblong leaflets, each 2–5cm long and 1cm wide. Glands absent. **Flowers** yellow, about 1.5cm across, in erect spike-like racemes 7–25cm long. **Fruit** a smooth oblong pod, 3–7cm long with raised ridges over the seeds. Widespread in inland sandy areas. Qld, NSW, SA, WA, NT. Throughout the year.

Senna venusta | Graceful Cassia

Formerly *Cassia venusta*. Straggly shrub to 2m high, covered with soft hairs. **Leaves** pinnate, 15–20cm long, divided into 6–15 pairs oblong leaflets, each 2–4cm long and 1–2cm wide. **Flowers** bright yellow, about 2cm across, in erect spike-like racemes up to 40cm long. The buds are enclosed by large deciduous bracts. **Fruit** an oblong pod 5–7cm long and 1cm wide with traverse ridges over the seeds. Inland and northern coastal areas. Qld, WA, NT. Winter, spring.

Senna notabilis

Senna odorata

Senna pleurocarpa

Senna venusta

CAMPANULACEAE | Bluebell family

Annual or perennial herbs usually with milky latex. About 35 genera and 600 species are centred mostly in northern temperate regions of the world and represented in Australia by the widespread bluebell genus *Wahlenbergia*. Leaves alternate, opposite or sometimes whorled, without stipules. Flowers regular, bisexual. Floral tube bell-shaped, with 5 spreading lobes. Ovary inferior. Fruit a capsule surmounted by persistent calyx lobes. The Lobeliaceae, sometimes included in this family, are treated in this book as a separate family.

Wahlenbergia communis | Tufted Bluebell

Small perennial herb to 75cm high; stems numerous, wiry. **Leaves** linear, to about 8cm long and 6mm wide, alternate, margins sometimes wavy, entire or slightly toothed. Lower leaves sometimes oblanceolate. **Flowers** blue, bell-shaped, about 1.5cm across. **Capsule** elongated, about 1cm long. Widespread in many open situations. All mainland States. Throughout the year.

Wahlenbergia gloriosa | Royal Bluebell

Erect perennial herb to 40cm high. **Leaves** opposite, obovate or oblanceolate, 1–3.5cm long to 1.5cm wide, margins wavy, entire or with a few small teeth. **Flowers** deep blue or purple, about 3cm across, solitary on slender stalks to 25cm long. **Capsule** elongated, about 1.2cm long. Subalpine regions in woodland and grassland. NSW, Vic. Summer.

Wahlenbergia stricta | Tall Bluebell

Perennial herb to 90cm high with a few branched stems. **Leaves,** lower, opposite, oblanceolate, to 7cm long, becoming alternate and linear up the stem, hairy, margins wavy, entire or with a few small teeth. **Flowers** blue within, sometimes paler on the outside, 2–3cm across. **Capsule** globular to egg-shaped, to 1cm long. Widespread from the coast to inland in woodland and open forest. Qld, NSW, Vic, SA, WA. Throughout the year.

Wahlenbergia communis

Wahlenbergia gloriosa

Wahlenbergia stricta

CHENOPODIACEAE | Saltbush family

Large family of more than 100 genera and 1500 species of mostly herbs and shrubs, sometimes succulent, often inhabiting saline soils around the world. Australia has 29 genera and about 300 species commonly known as saltbushes, bluebushes or samphires. Leaves usually alternate, frequently covered with scales, fine hairs or mealy bloom; stipules absent. Some species appear leafless with very reduced leaves and fleshy, jointed stems. Flowers small, mostly regular, bisexual or unisexual. Perianth with 1–5 segments arranged in a single whorl. Stamens 5 or fewer, opposite the perianth segments. Ovary usually superior. Fruit may be dry, berry-like, winged or spined. Many of the saltbushes and bluebushes are valuable fodder plants, especially in dry inland regions. Members of this family have a characteristic fruiting body, which is illustrated below to facilitate identification.

Atriplex nummularia | Old Man Saltbush

Large shrub 2–3m high and 4–5m across. **Leaves** circular to ovate, 1–2.5cm long, bluish-grey, margins entire or shallowly toothed. **Flowers** small, in terminal panicles, unisexual, usually on separate plants. **Fruiting body** fan-shaped or broad–triangular, to 1cm long, entire or shallowly toothed. Widespread in dry inland areas; usually on heavy soils in low-lying situations. All mainland States. Throughout the year.

Chenopodium curvispicatum | Cottony Saltbush

Formerly *Rhagodia gaudichaudiana*. Mealy-white spreading shrub to 1m high. **Leaves** mostly opposite, triangular or spear-shaped, 1–1.5cm long, covered in a silvery layer of hairs. **Flowers** small, in spike-like clusters. **Fruit** a bright red berry. Open forest and woodland. NSW, Vic, SA, WA. Summer.

Einadia nutans | Climbing Saltbush

Formerly *Rhagodia nutans*. Prostrate or scrambling perennial with weak woody stems. **Leaves** opposite or alternate, shaped like an arrow-head, to 3cm long. **Flowers** mealy, few in short terminal or axillary spikes. **Fruit** a red or yellow globular berry. Widespread and common in many plant communities. All mainland States. Summer, autumn.

Atriplex nummularia

Chenopodium curvispicatum

Einadia nutans

Enchylaena tomentosa | Ruby Saltbush

Dome-shaped shrub to 1m high; stems hairy or smooth. **Leaves** succulent, almost terete, to 1.5cm long, downy. **Flowers**, small solitary in the leaf axils. **Fruit** fleshy, 4–6mm diameter, green at first then yellow or red, drying black. Widespread in drier areas in a variety of habitats. All mainland States. Throughout the year.

Maireana pyramidata | Black Bluebush

Formerly *Kochia pyramidata*. Dome-shaped shrub to 1.5cm high. **Leaves** succulent, obovate to almost terete, to 5mm long, blue-green with short hairs. **Flowers** small, solitary, mostly unisexual. **Fruiting body** with a horizontal wing, about 1.2cm across, often with 1 slit, at first creamy-green, then brown or black when dry, upper part pyramidal and softly hairy. Widespread in drier areas. NSW, Vic, SA, WA. Spring.

Maireana sedifolia | Pearl Bluebush

Formerly *Kochia sedifolia*. Dome-shaped shrub to 1.5m high; branches covered with close woolly hairs. **Leaves** succulent, obovoid, to 8mm long, bluish-grey, tip rounded. **Flowers** in pairs, axillary, usually only 1 maturing. **Fruiting body** with a faintly veined horizontal wing, about 1cm across, with 1 slit, straw-coloured or pink at first, then pale brown. Widespread in drier areas. NSW, Vic, SA, WA, NT. Winter, spring.

Maireana tomentosa | Felty Bluebush

Formerly *Kochia tomentosa*. Erect shrub to 1m high; branches woolly-hairy. **Leaves** succulent, almost terete, to 1.2cm long, loosely hairy, tip blunt or pointed. **Flowers** solitary, axillary, bisexual. **Fruiting body** with a translucent horizontal wing, about 1cm across, sparsely lobed and no slit, creamy-green at first then brown when dry. Low-lying saline areas and along creeks. NSW, WA, NT. Winter, spring.

Sclerolaena birchii | Galvanized Burr

Formerly *Bassia birchii*. Dome-shaped shrub to 1m high; branches densely hairy. **Leaves** obovate, flat, to 1.5cm long covered with short white hairs. **Flowers** solitary, axillary. **Fruiting body** woolly, about 3mm in diameter, with 4–5 spreading spines; 3 larger spines to 9mm long, 2 smaller spines to 4mm long. Widespread in drier areas on sandy soils. Qld, NSW, SA, NT. Throughout the year.

Sclerolaena cornishiana |

Formerly *Bassia cornishiana*. Much-branched small shrub 30–60cm high; branches densely woolly. **Leaves** ovate or oblong, to 1.5cm long. **Fruiting body** densely woolly 3–5mm diameter, with 6 horizontally spreading spines to 8mm long, 5 of them of equal length. Slightly saline habitats. Qld, SA, WA, NT. Throughout the year.

Enchylaena tomentosa

Maireana pyramidata

Maireana sedifolia

Maireana tomentosa

Sclerolaena birchii

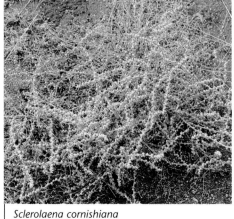

Sclerolaena cornishiana

CHLOANTHACEAE

Endemic Australian family consisting of 10 genera and about 100 species. Perennials, shrubs or subshrubs, often densely clothed with much-branched hairs. Leaves opposite or whorled, often wrinkled, margins entire. Flowers regular or irregular, bisexual, each with a bract and 2 bracteoles. Calyx 4–8 lobed, densely hairy outside. Corolla tubular with 4–8 equal lobes or unequally lobed or 2-lipped. Stamens 4–8. Ovary superior. Fruit dry, rarely a drupe. This family has previously been treated as a tribe of Verbenaceae, but differs in having 2 bracteoles at the base of each flower, and dry fruit.

Cyanostegia corifolia

Branching shrub to 1.5m high; stems and leaves resinous. **Leaves** oblong or narrow–elliptic, 2–4cm long to 1.5cm wide, margins toothed. **Flowers** 2cm across, in open panicles. Corolla deep blue, subtended by a papery disc-like calyx, which is purple and the most conspicuous part of the flower. Sandy or gravelly heath in the southwest. WA. Spring.

Dicrastylis exsuccosa

Shrub to 1.5m high, densely covered in thick golden–yellow hairs. **Leaves** lanceolate to ovate–lanceolate, 3–10cm long and to 2.5cm wide, usually in pairs, rough and wrinkled above, hairy beneath. **Flowers** tubular, yellow, in terminal panicles, each about 5mm long, almost hidden in densely hairy calyx. **Capsule** obovoid, about 4mm diameter, hairy. Arid regions on sand plains and dunes. WA, NT. Autumn, winter, spring.

Newcastelia hexarrhena | Lambs Tails

Erect shrub 60–90cm high. **Leaves** lanceolate to oblanceolate, 3–6cm long, opposite, sessile, densely woolly, margins revolute, tip pointed. **Flowers** lilac, in woolly white oblong spikes to 14cm long; conspicuous bracts deciduous as flowers open. Dry inland areas on sandstone. WA. Winter, spring.

Newcastelia interrupta

Low branching shrub to 60cm high, covered with dense short woolly hairs. **Leaves** oblong–lanceolate, 1–3.5cm long and to 6mm wide, in pairs or in whorls of 3, opposite, sessile, hairy, margins recurved, tip pointed. **Flowers** purple, with 5 or 6 narrow lobes, solitary or in branched interrupted spikes to 18cm long. Confined to the Darling Downs, mainly in open forest. Qld. Winter, spring.

Cyanostegia corifolia

Dicrastylis exsuccosa

Newcastelia hexarrhena

Newcastelia interrupta

Newcastelia spodiotricha

Erect shrub to 2m high; stems with grey hairs. **Leaves** broad–ovate to elliptic–ovate, 3–6cm long and to 3cm wide, in opposite pairs, covered in whitish-grey hairs, margins revolute. **Flowers** purple or blue, in cylindrical spikes 3–8.5cm long; style and stamens exserted and conspicuous. Arid regions in red sandy soils. Qld, SA, WA, NT. Winter, spring.

Pityrodia uncinata

Low, spreading shrub to 60cm high; stems and branches covered with whitish woolly hairs. **Leaves** dark green, linear to linear–lanceolate, 1–5cm long and to 5mm wide, sessile, dark green, wrinkled and woolly, margins revolute. **Flowers** tubular, pink to red (rarely yellow), 5-lobed, single or in groups of 3 in upper leaf axils; calyx lobes deeply divided and hairy. Widespread on sandy soils in the southwest. WA. Winter, spring.

CONVOLVULACEAE | Morning Glory family

A cosmopolitan family of herbaceous or woody plants usually with long trailing or twining stems. There are about 55 genera and 1650 species mainly in tropical and subtropical regions of the world. Australia is well represented with 20 genera and about 130 species. Leaves alternate, often lobed or deeply divided. Flowers regular, bisexual. Sepals 5, rarely 3 or 4, usually free. Corolla tubular or funnel-shaped. Stamens 5, fused toward the base of the corolla tube, alternating with lobes. Ovary superior. Fruit a capsule. The family contains the important food crop, *Ipomoea batatas*, cultivated for its edible tubers.

Ipomoea muelleri | Poison Morning Glory

Perennial herb with trailing and twining stems. **Leaves** broadly ovate to ovate–lanceolate, heart-shaped at base, 2–8cm long and 3–7cm wide, dark green and glabrous. **Flowers** pink or purple with darker throat, funnel-shaped, to 4.5cm long and 3.5cm across, 1–3 per cyme. **Capsule** somewhat globular, about 1.5cm across, containing 4 hairy seeds. Central inland and northern tropical areas. Qld, SA, WA, NT. Autumn, winter.

Ipomoea pes-caprae subsp. brasiliensis | Goats-foot Morning Glory

Prostrate perennial vine with long trailing stems to 5m long. **Leaves** broad–oblong to almost circular, 5–12cm long and 4–12cm wide, with 2 large equal lobes sometimes folded lengthwise. **Flowers** rose-purple with darker throat and mid-petal bands, funnel-shaped, 3–6.5cm long. **Fruit** globular, to 2cm across, containing 4 hairy seeds. Northern coastal sand dunes. Qld, NSW, WA, NT. Throughout the year.

Newcastelia spodiotricha

Pityrodia uncinata

Ipomoea muelleri

Ipomoea pes-caprae subsp. *brasiliensis*

DASYPOGONACEAE

A family of 8 genera and 64 species found in Australia, New Guinea and New Caledonia, with its greatest concentration in southwest Western Australia. Perennial herbs, shrubs or trees Leaves often large and grass-like, basal, along the stem or in a terminal rosette. Flowers in large compound spikes, heads or singly. Perianth segments 6, stamens 6. Ovary superior usually 3-celled. Fruit a capsule or indehiscent nutlet containing 1 to several orange, red or brown seeds. This family is often included in Lomandraceae or in the Xanthorrhoeaceae Leaves are not illustrated in this family as they are too similar for identification purposes.

Calectasia cyanea | Blue Tinsel Lily

Perennial subshrub 30–60cm high. **Leaves** narrow, to 1.5cm long, and 1mm wide, acute **Flowers** solitary, brilliant metallic blue or purple, to 3.5cm across, with 6 papery petals and 6 stamens with yellow anthers, aging orange or red. Widespread in southwest, in sandy heaths Vic, SA, WA. Spring, summer.

Dasypogon bromeliifolius | Pineapple-leaved Dasypogon

Tufted shrub with a short caudex to 1m high. **Leaves** tough, grass-like, to 30cm long and 1cm wide, margins slightly toothed and tapering to a point. **Flowerheads** globular, cream-coloured, to 3cm in diameter, terminal on thick, hairy stalks to 40cm long. Coastal plain and jarrah forest of the southwest. WA. Spring, summer.

Dasypogon hookeri | Pineapple Bush

Erect tufted perennial with a slender caudex to 4m high. **Leaves** tough, grass-like and tapering, to 1m long with rough margins and overlapping leaf bases. **Flowerheads** globular creamy-white, to 3cm diameter, terminal on tall hairy stalks. Jarrah forest of the southwest WA. Spring, summer.

Kingia australis | Black Gin

Erect woody perennial, usually with a solitary trunk, 2–8m high. **Leaves** grass-like, to 60cm long, grey-green and angular in cross-section, hairy when young. Dead leaves form a grass-like skirt. **Flowerheads** globular, cream and grey, to 6cm across, on stout stalks to 50cm long covered with silky bracts. Widespread in the southwest. WA. Winter, spring.

Calectasia cyanea

Dasypogon bromeliifolius

Dasypogon hookeri

Kingia australis

Lomandra leucocephala | Woolly Mat-rush

Tufted perennial herb to 60cm high. **Leaves** narrow, flat, 20–60cm long to 3mm wide with loose fibres along the margins, tips rounded or pointed. **Flowers** cream, grouped in dense globular or cylindrical woolly heads, 2–6cm long on unbranched flower stems shorter than the leaves. Open forest on dry sandy soils. Qld, NSW. Spring, summer.

Lomandra longifolia | Spiny-headed Mat-rush

Tussock-forming perennial herb to 1m high. **Leaves** tough, narrow, flat or slightly inrolled, to 1m long and 75mm wide. **Flowers** creamy-yellow, almost cylindrical, 3–4mm long grouped in clusters 1–2cm long along a flattened branched inflorescence, usually half the length of the leaves. Spiny bracts, 1–2cm long, present beneath the flowers. Widespread from coast to mountains in a wide range of habitats. Qld, NSW, Vic, Tas, SA. Spring, summer.

Lomandra multiflora | Many-flowered Mat-rush

Tussock-forming perennial herb to 90cm high. **Leaves** rigid, flat or slightly concave, 40–70cm long, tip rounded. **Flowers** yellowish, bell-shaped; male flowers clustered on a stalk to 1cm long on branched flower stem 5–30cm high; female flowers are stalkless and smaller. Widespread in open forest and woodland. Qld, NSW, Vic, NT. Winter, spring, summer.

DILLENIACEAE | Guinea Flower family

Family of shrubs, sometimes trees or climbers of about 400 species in 12 genera found chiefly in tropical and subtropical regions of Southeast Asia. Australia has 5 genera and 110 species, with many in the temperate zones; the most widespread genus is *Hibbertia*, commonly known as guinea flowers. Leaves alternate, mostly entire, rarely toothed or lobed. Flowers regular, bisexual, mostly yellow. Sepals usually 5. Petals usually 5. Stamens 3 to numerous, but usually 5. Ovary superior. Fruit a cluster of follicles.

Hibbertia cuneiformis | Cut-leaf Guinea Flower

Erect bushy shrub to 3.5m high. **Leaves** oblong to obovate, 2–4cm long to 1cm wide, with a few teeth toward the tip. **Flowers** bright yellow, 3–4cm across, singly at branch ends; stamens united into 5 bundles. Widespread in coastal districts of the southwest and common in karri forest. WA. Spring, summer.

Lomandra leucocephala

Lomandra longifolia

Lomandra multiflora

Hibbertia cuneiformis

Hibbertia dentata | Twining Guinea Flower

Light climber with wiry stems to 2m long. **Leaves** ovate to elliptical, 3–9cm long and 2–3cm wide, dark green or purplish, hairy when young, becoming glabrous, margins toothed. **Flowers** solitary, bright yellow, 3cm across, axillary or terminal; stamens numerous surrounding 3 carpels. Widespread on coast and ranges in open forest or rainforest margins Qld, NSW, Vic. Winter, spring.

Hibbertia hypericoides | Yellow Buttercups

Small spreading shrub to 1m high. **Leaves** linear, to 1.5cm long and to 5mm wide, dark green and slightly rough above, stellate hairy beneath, margins revolute. **Flowers** solitary in axils, yellow, to 2.5cm across, with deeply notched petals; stamens 10–15 grouped on one side of the carpels. Common on coastal plain and jarrah forest in the southwest WA. Winter, spring.

Hibbertia linearis |

Erect or sprawling shrub to 2m high. **Leaves** linear–oblong to obovate, 1–3cm long, to 5mm wide, entire, tip blunt or tapering to a point. **Flowers** bright yellow, to 2cm across, sessile, singly or on short stalks to 3mm long; stamens 15–25 grouped around the carpels. Widespread in coastal areas, extending to tablelands with isolated occurrence in Pilliga Scrub Qld, NSW. Spring, summer.

Hibbertia microphylla |

Small arching shrub to 80cm high. **Leaves** ovate, 2–3mm long and 1.5mm wide, dark green and shiny, reflexed, margins curved down. **Flowers**, yellow, to 1cm across, singly or slender stalks to 2cm long in upper leaf axils; stamens 8–10 grouped on one side of the carpels. Southern coastal heath. WA. Spring, summer.

Hibbertia dentata

Hibbertia hypericoides

Hibbertia linearis

Hibbertia microphylla

Hibbertia miniata | Orange Guinea Flower

Small erect shrub to 40cm high. **Leaves** broadly linear, 2–4cm long and 1cm wide greyish-green above, paler below, margins sometimes recurved, tip blunt. **Flowers** solitary deep orange, to 3cm across, on short stalks; stamens numerous with purple anther surrounding the carpels. Rare and confined to northern jarrah forests. WA. Spring, summer

Hibbertia obtusifolia | Hoary Guinea Flower

Erect or sprawling shrub to 60cm high. Young growth with short greyish hairs. **Leave** oblanceolate, 1–3cm long and to 1cm wide, margins usually recurved, tips rounded often notched and with a fine point. **Flowers** bright yellow, to 4cm across, singly, sessile, termina or in leaf axils on short branches; stamens numerous surrounding the carpels. An extreme variable species, of which some forms may be defined into separate species in future botanical revision. Widespread from coast to the ranges, in heath and open forest. Qld, NSW Vic, Tas. Spring, summer.

Hibbertia pedunculata |

Prostrate or erect shrub with widely sprawling stems to 1.5m long. **Leaves** linea 3–6mm long and less than 1mm wide, hairy, dark green, margins recurved, tip pointed **Flowers** bright yellow, to 1.5cm across, terminal on stalks to 1–5mm long; stamens 15–2 surrounding the carpels; sepals conspicuously hairy. Widespread from the coast to mountain and farther inland, mostly in open forest. Qld, NSW, Vic. Spring, summer, autumn.

Hibbertia prostrata | Bundled Guinea Flower

Small erect or sprawling shrub to 50cm high. **Leaves** narrow–linear, 5mm–2cm lon to 1.5cm wide, clustered in groups, hairy, margins curve upward, tip pointed. **Flowers** brigh yellow, 1–2cm across, sessile and terminal on short side shoots; stamens 8–12 grouped aroun 2 or 3 carpels. Coastal districts and slightly inland, in open forest, often on sandy soil. Vic, Tas, SA. Winter, spring, early summer.

Hibbertia miniata

Hibbertia obtusifolia

Hibbertia pedunculata

Hibbertia prostrata

Hibbertia riparia | Erect Guinea Flower

Small usually erect shrub to 60cm high; stems hairy when young. **Leaves** narrow-linear, to 1cm long and to 2mm wide, dark green with short hairs, margins strongly revolute, tip blunt. **Flowers** deep yellow, about 2cm across, axillary or terminal on short shoots; sepals silky-hairy or rough; stamens 6–16 on one side of the carpels. Widespread from coast to the mountains and farther inland, often in heath on sandy soils. Qld, NSW, Vic, Tas, SA, WA. Spring, summer.

Hibbertia scandens | Climbing Guinea Flower

Vigorous climber with stems to 4m long. **Leaves** ovate to obovate, 3–9cm long 1–3cm wide, sessile, dark green and glossy above, silky beneath, margins entire, tip blunt or tapering to a point. **Flowers** bright yellow, to 5cm across, singly on short stalks; stamens numerous surrounding the carpels. Mainly coastal on sand dunes, also open forest and rainforest margins. Qld, NSW. Throughout the year.

Hibbertia sericea | Silky Guinea Flower

Erect or spreading shrub to 1m high; stems silky hairy. **Leaves** linear to narrow-lanceolate, 5mm–2cm long and 2–5mm wide, both surfaces densely hairy with hairs o different lengths, margins strongly recurved. **Flowers** yellow, to 3cm across, crowded in upper leaf axils; sepals conspicuously hairy; stamens 10–16 on one side of the carpels. Widespread from the coast to farther inland, mostly in open forests and heath on sandy soils. Qld, NSW, Vic, SA. Winter, spring, summer.

Hibbertia vestita | Hairy Guinea Flower

Prostrate or erect shrub to 30cm high. **Leaves** oblong to lanceolate, 4–7mm long to 2mm wide, dark green, minutely hairy, margins recurved, tip blunt. **Flowers** bright yellow 1–3cm across, sessile and terminal; sepals silky-hairy; stamens about 30 surrounding the carpels. Coastal heath or farther inland in dry open forest. Qld, NSW. Winter, spring.

Hibbertia riparia

Hibbertia scandens

Hibbertia sericea

Hibbertia vestita

Hibbertia villosa

Small spreading shrub to 50cm high. **Leaves** oblanceolate, 1–2.5cm long to 1cm wide, dark grey-green with whitish shaggy hairs, margins entire or occasionally toothed. **Flowers** bright yellow, 2–4cm across, sessile in leaf axils; stamens 15–20 in 3 groups around the carpels. Confined to the northern ranges, usually in dry open forest. NSW. Winter, spring, summer.

Hibbertia virgata | Twiggy Guinea Flower

Small erect shrub to 1m tall. **Leaves** narrow–linear, 7–25mm long to 5mm wide, smooth or with crinkly hairs, margins rolled upward. **Flowers** yellow, to 2.5cm across, sessile in leaf axils or terminal on short shoots; stamens 10–12 grouped around the carpels. Widespread in coastal heath and farther inland in woodland. NSW, Vic, Tas, SA, WA. Winter, spring.

DORYANTHACEAE | Spear Lily family

An endemic family consisting of the single genus *Doryanthes* with 2 species noted for their very tall flower stems bearing large blood-red flowers arranged in terminal globular heads or oblong racemes. Leaves in a large tussock. Fruit a dry capsule containing numerous, winged, reddish-brown seeds. Leaves are not illustrated in this family as they are too similar for identification purposes.

Doryanthes excelsa | Gymea Lily; Giant Lily

Tall perennial herb to 1.5m high. **Leaves** linear, thick and leathery, to 1.5m long and 10cm wide, in a basal rosette. **Flowers** red, in terminal globular head about 30cm across, on stem to 5m high. Each flower has 6 narrow perianth segments, to 10cm long, fused at the base. Common in sandstone areas around Sydney. NSW. Winter, spring, summer.

Doryanthes palmeri | Spear Lily

Tall perennial herb, 1–3m high. **Leaves** linear–lanceolate, to 3m long and 20cm wide, erect in a basal rosette. **Flowers** dark red, in terminal spike-like raceme to 1m long, on stem 2–5m high. Each flower has 6 broad perianth segments to 6cm long, surrounded by deep reddish-brown bracts. Mountain slopes. Qld, NSW. Spring.

Hibbertia villosa

Hibbertia virgata

Doryanthes excelsa

Doryanthes palmeri

DROSERACEAE | Sundew family

Small insectivorous herbs of 4 genera and about 100 species widespread in temperate an
tropical parts of the world. They are very well developed in Australia with 2 genera
Aldrovanda, a monotypic genus, and *Drosera*, which has about 70 species. Leaves in a basa
rosette and/or along the stems, covered with sticky glandular hairs. Flowers regula
bisexual. Petals 4 or 5, sometimes more. Stamens 4 or 5 free. Ovary superior with
chamber. Fruit a capsule, enclosed in the persistent calyx; seeds many, small.

Drosera auriculata | Tall Sundew

Erect herb to 30cm high, but can be taller. **Lower leaves** almost circular, to 1.2cm
long, in a flat rosette; **stem leaves** rounded with 2 distinct lobes, 4–6mm across, peltate
Flowers white or pale pink, to 1.5cm across, 2–8 per terminal cyme; sepals hairless. Wide
spread in southeast, often in moist places. Qld, NSW, Vic, Tas, SA. Winter, spring, summer.

Drosera binata | Forked Sundew

Small perennial herb to 60cm high. **Leaves** linear, covered with reddish glandula
hairs, erect, usually forked one or more times, on slender hairless stems to 30cm high. **Flower**
white or pink, about 2.5cm across, numerous, on erect stalk to 50cm long. Common in pea
swamps, creek banks and other wet places. Qld, NSW, Vic, Tas, SA. Winter, spring.

Drosera glanduligera | Pimpernel Sundew

Tiny ephemeral herb to 5cm high when in flower. **Leaves** almost circular, 8–12mm
across, yellowish-green, in basal rosette, margins fringed with glandular hairs. **Flowers** orang
or red, cup-shaped, 6–10 per raceme, on erect sticky stalks to 5cm tall. Moist banks an
swampy areas. NSW, Vic, Tas, SA, WA. Winter, spring.

Drosera peltata | Pale Sundew

Perennial herb to 50cm high. **Lower leaves** spoon-shaped, 4–15mm long, pale gree
in flat rosette; **stem leaves** round with 2 acute lobes, 4–7mm long, peltate. **Flowers** white o
pale pink, to 1.5cm across, 5–10 per raceme. Sepals hairy with fringed margins, whicl
separates this species from the similar *D. auriculata*. Widespread in damp places. All mainlan
States. Winter, spring, summer.

Drosera auriculata

Drosera binata

Drosera glanduligera

Drosera peltata

EPACRIDACEAE | Heath family

Family of mainly small shrubs and a few trees, of about 32 genera and more than 420 species, mostly in Australia and Indomalaysia. It is well developed in Australia with 29 genera and about 355 species, many of which occur in coastal heaths and sandplain communities. Leaves alternate or in spirals, narrow rigid and often pungent-pointed with several longitudinal veins. Flowers regular, bisexual or sometimes unisexual. Sepals 4 or 5. Petals 4 or 5, partly or wholly fused forming a bell-shaped or tubular flower with 4 or . lobes. Stamens 4 or 5 alternating with corolla lobes and often projecting beyond the tube. Ovary superior. Fruit a drupe or a dry capsule.

Astroloma conostephioides | Flame Heath

Small erect shrub to 1m high; stems hairy. **Leaves** linear or linear–lanceolate, 1–2cm long, margins revolute, tip sharply pointed. **Flowers** bright red and tubular, to 2cm long, often drooping, solitary in leaf axils; petals silky-hairy; stamens enclosed. Heath and open forest. Vic, SA. Winter, spring, summer.

Astroloma pinifolium | Pine Heath

Small erect or spreading shrub to 1m high; stems hairy. **Leaves** linear, 1–2.5cm long; midrib prominent on lower surface, tip finely pointed. **Flowers** reddish or yellow with green tips and lobes, tubular, to 2cm long, solitary, often appearing in clusters; stamens enclosed. Heath and open forest on sandy soils. NSW, Vic, Tas. Autumn, winter, spring.

Brachyloma daphnoides | Daphne Heath

Erect shrub to 1.5m high. **Leaves** ovate, obovate to lanceolate, 5–15mm long to 4mm wide, flat or slightly concave, tip blunt or pointed. **Flowers** white, about 5mm long, tubular with 5 spreading lobes, often grouped in leaf axils, strongly scented. Heath, open forest and woodland on sandy soils. Qld, NSW, Vic, Tas, SA. Winter, spring, summer.

Cyathodes parvifolia |

Erect dense shrub to 1m high. **Leaves** linear–lanceolate, about 6mm long, dark green above, striate below, tip with sharp point. **Flowers** very small, cream, bell-shaped, singly in leaf axils; male and female flowers on separate plants. **Berries** globular, pink to red, on female plants only. Endemic to Tasmania; common on rocky hillsides. Tas. Summer.

Astroloma conostephioides

Astroloma pinifolium

Brachyloma daphnoides

Cyathodes parvifolia

Dracophyllum secundum

Small erect or spreading shrub to 1m high. **Leaves** lanceolate, 5–15cm long to 1cm wide, base sheathing, margins sometimes finely toothed, tip tapering to long point. **Flower** white or pink, tubular, to 1cm long, in narrow panicles to 15cm long, usually on one side of the stem. Mainly coastal on sandstone and damp rock faces. NSW. Spring, summer.

Epacris breviflora

Erect shrub to 1m or more high; stems hairy. **Leaves** ovate, 4–8mm long to 4mm wide, spreading or reflexed, tip pungent-pointed. **Flowers** white, tubular, to 2cm long, crowded in upper leaf axils. Beside creeks and swampy places. Qld, NSW, Vic. Spring, summer

Epacris glacialis

Low-growing or prostrate shrub to 50cm high; stems smooth. **Leaves** diamond-shaped to obovate, 2–4mm long to 2.5mm wide, thick, flat or slightly concave. **Flower** white, bell-shaped, about 1cm across, crowded in the upper leaf axils. Alpine and subalpine regions, in wet or swampy places. NSW, Vic. Summer.

Epacris impressa | Common Heath

Erect shrub to 1.2m high; stems usually hairy. **Leaves** spreading, linear–lanceolate to ovate, 8–15mm long to 3mm wide, margins entire or minutely hairy, tip pungent-pointed **Flowers** white, pink or red, tubular, to 2cm long, often pendent, crowded in the upper leaf axils or forming a leafy spike. Coastal heath and open forest farther inland. NSW, Vic, Tas, SA Autumn, winter, spring.

Epacris longiflora | Fuchsia Heath

Erect or sprawling shrub to 2m high; stems hairy. **Leaves** ovate to heart-shaped 5–15mm long to 6mm wide, spreading, flat, margins entire or minutely toothed, tip pointed **Flowers** red with white spreading lobes, tubular, to 2.5cm long, becoming pendent along the upper stems. Heath, woodland and open forest. Qld, NSW. Autumn, winter, spring.

Epacris obtusifolia | Blunt-leaf Heath

Erect shrub to 1m tall; stems softly hairy. **Leaves** elliptic, about 1cm long to 3mm wide, thick, flat or slightly concave, tip blunt. **Flowers** white, tubular, to 1.5cm long, crowded along the upper leaf axils forming a leafy spike. Common on coastal heaths, usually in swampy places. Qld, NSW, Vic, Tas. Winter, spring.

Dracophyllum secundum

Epacris breviflora

Epacris glacialis

Epacris impressa

Epacris longiflora

Epacris obtusifolia

Epacris paludosa | Swamp Heath

Erect shrub to 1m high; stems with stiff hairs. **Leaves** elliptic or ovate, 5–12mm long to 3mm wide, thick, flat, tip tapering to point. **Flowers** white or pinkish, tubular, to 6mm long, crowded to form small terminal clusters. Heath, woodland and mountain forest in swampy places. NSW, Vic, Tas. Spring, summer.

Leucopogon ericoides | Pink Beard-heath

Slender spreading or erect shrub to 90cm high. **Leaves** oblong, 5–15mm long to 3mm wide, margins recurved, tip shortly pointed. **Flowers** white to pinkish, tubular, about 2mm long, finely hairy at throat, in short axillary clusters. Widespread in open forest and heath on sandy soils. NSW, Vic, Tas. Winter, spring.

Leucopogon fraseri |

Prostrate shrub with branches to 20cm high. **Leaves** linear–lanceolate, 4–8mm long to 2.5mm wide, tip pungent-pointed. **Flowers** white, tubular, to 8mm long, softly hairy on the inside, 1 or 2 in the leaf axils along the stems. Widespread in open forest and heath, often among rocks. NSW, Vic, Tas. Winter, spring.

Leucopogon montanus |

Small bushy shrub to 40cm high. **Leaves** narrow–oblong, 6–8mm long to 2.5mm wide, margins entire and often translucent. **Flowers** small, white, tubular, to 2mm long, clustered in short terminal spikes. **Fruit** a globular red drupe. Alpine areas, heath, grassland and rocky slopes. NSW, Vic, Tas. Summer, autumn.

Epacris paludosa

Leucopogon ericoides

Leucopogon fraseri

Leucopogon montanus

Leucopogon parviflorus | Coastal Beard-heath

Tall erect shrub 1–5m high. **Leaves** elliptic to oblanceolate, 1–3cm long to 8mm wide, dark green above, paler beneath, margins and tip recurved. **Flowers** white (rarely pink), tubular, to 2cm long, in dense axillary clusters. **Fruit** an ovoid white drupe. Widespread in coastal districts on sand dunes and in heaths. Qld, NSW, Vic, Tas, SA, WA. Winter, spring.

Leucopogon thymifolius | Thyme Beard-heath

Small bushy shrub to 60cm high; stems hairy. **Leaves** lanceolate to oblong, 5–15mm long to 3mm wide, hairy, margins recurved, tip pointed and recurved. **Flowers** white, tubular with spreading hairy lobes, to 5mm across, in spikes in the upper leaf axils. Widespread in heath and open forest in the Grampians and Little Desert. Vic. Winter, spring, summer.

Leucopogon verticillatus | Tassel Flower

Erect shrub 1–4m high; stems reddish and smooth. **Leaves** elliptic to ovate, 5–15cm long to 2.5cm wide, appear whorl-like, tip pointed. **Flowers** pink or reddish, about 5mm long, in axillary many-flowered spikes about 8cm long. Karri and jarrah forest, in moist sandy places. WA. Spring.

Leucopogon virgatus |

Small shrub to 45cm high; stems wiry and hairy. **Leaves** narrow–ovate, to 2cm long, margins entire or sparsely toothed, concave, tip finely pointed. **Flowers** small, white, tubular, to 2mm long, in short dense clusters in upper leaf axils. Widespread on coast and ranges, in heath, open forest and woodland. Qld, NSW, Vic, Tas, SA. Winter, spring, summer.

Melichrus urceolatus | Urn Heath

Small erect shrub to 1.5m high. **Leaves** narrow–ovate, to 1.5cm long and 6mm wide, sessile, concave, margins translucent, lower surface marked with parallel veins, tip sharply pointed. **Flowers** small, white to greenish, urn-shaped, about 1cm long, singly without stalks in leaf axils. **Drupe** globular, about 6mm across, greenish or brown. Widespread from the coast to drier inland areas, in woodland and open forest. Qld, NSW, Vic. Winter, spring.

Richea continentis | Candle Heath

Small branched shrub to 1m high; stems spreading and often taking root. **Leaves** ovate, 2–4cm long to 7mm wide, crowded, sheathing at the base, margins entire, tip pungent-pointed. **Flowers** creamy-white, ovoid, about 8mm long, do not fully open, in terminal spikes 5–15cm long. Alpine and subalpine regions, common in sphagnum bogs. NSW, Vic. Summer.

Leucopogon parviflorus

Leucopogon thymifolius

Leucopogon verticillatus

Leucopogon virgatus

Melichrus urceolatus

Richea continentis

Sprengelia incarnata | Pink Swamp Heath

Erect shrub to 2m high. **Leaves** ovate to lanceolate, 5–20mm long to 6mm wide, sheathing at the base, tip tapering to fine point. **Flowers** pink, lobes narrow and spreading, to 1cm across, in dense axillary clusters. Widespread from coast to the ranges, often in heath in swampy places. NSW, Vic, Tas, SA. Winter, spring.

Styphelia adscendens

Semi-prostrate shrub to 50cm high; stems hairy. **Leaves** elliptic to oblanceolate, to 2.5cm long to 5mm wide, margins finely toothed, tip tapering to stiff point. **Flowers** cream, green or occasionally pink or red, cylindrical, to 1.5cm long, with curled hairy lobes; stamens exserted. Open scrub and dry forest on sandy soils. NSW, Vic, Tas, SA. Winter, spring.

Styphelia tubiflora | Red Five-corners

Small erect or spreading shrub to 90cm high. **Leaves** oblong or obovate, to 2.5cm long to 4mm wide, tip pungent-pointed. **Flowers** red or occasionally cream or green, cylindrical, to 2.5cm long with red curled lobes; stamens exserted. Widespread from coast to ranges in heath and open forest, on sandy soils. NSW. Autumn, winter.

Woollsia pungens | Woollsia

Erect shrub to 1m or more high; stems pubescent. **Leaves** ovate, 4–12mm long, 2–6mm wide, crowded and reflexed, tip tapering to rigid pungent point. **Flowers** white, pale pink or deep pink, tubular with overlapping lobes, to 1.5cm across, in upper leaf axils, sweetly scented; lobes contorted in bud. Widespread in coastal districts in open forest, heath and behind dunes. Qld, NSW. Winter, spring, summer.

Sprengelia incarnata

Styphelia adscendens

Styphelia tubiflora

Woollsia pungens

FABACEAE | Pea family

Very large family of herbs, shrubs, trees and climbers of about 490 genera and more than 12,000 species found throughout the world. The family includes many species that are important economically, for food, timber, animal fodder, dyes, medicines and horticulture. About 143 genera and 1115 species are widely distributed throughout Australia. Leaves alternate, simple or usually variously compound with stipules. Flowers strongly irregular. Corolla of 5 unequal petals, the upper one large and conspicuous (standard), the 2 smaller lateral petals (wings), and the 2 basal ones united into a boat-shaped structure (keel). Stamens 10; filaments free or more often 9 fused with 1 free. Ovary superior. Fruit a pod. In some classifications other pod-bearing plants Mimosaceae (wattles) and Caesalpiniaceae (sennas) are included in this family as subfamilies.

Bossiaea cordigera | Wiry Bossiaea

Prostrate or low straggling shrub to 20cm high; stems wiry and minutely hairy. **Leaves** almost heart-shaped, about 5mm long, in opposite pairs, tip finely pointed. **Flowers** pea-shaped, about 1cm long, standard golden-yellow, keel red, singly on a fine stalk. **Pod** to 2cm long and 5mm wide on long stalk. Heath and mountain forests, often in damp situations. Vic, Tas. Spring, summer.

Bossiaea walkeri | Cactus Pea

Upright rigid leafless shrub to 2m high; stems flat and distinctly winged. **Leaves** reduced to scales, less than 2mm long. **Flowers** pea-shaped, red, standard much shorter than the keel, which is about 2cm long, singly on short stalks. **Pod** oblong, about 6cm long and 1cm wide, shortly stalked. Drier inland areas, mainly in mallee communities. NSW, Vic, SA, WA. Winter, spring.

Brachysema celsianum | Dark Bush Pea

Formerly *B. lanceolatum*. Small spreading shrub or semi-climber to 1.5m high; stems silvery hairy. **Leaves** lanceolate, to 10cm long, dark green and smooth above, silvery hairy below. **Flowers** pea-shaped, red, about 2.5cm long, solitary or in clusters of 2-3; calyx with short silver hairs. **Pod** about 1.5cm long. Woodland and mallee in southwest. WA. Winter, spring.

Brachysema latifolium | Broad-leaved Brachysema

Prostrate trailing shrub to 3m across; stems often hairy. Leaves leathery, ovate, to 5cm long, dark green and smooth above, silky-hairy below. Flowers pea-shaped, about 2.5cm long standard golden-yellow, keel red, singly or in clusters of 2–3; calyx with silky hairs. Pod about 1cm long. Slightly inland in the southwest, mainly on plains and ridges. WA. Winter, spring.

Bossiaea cordigera

Bossiaea walkeri

Brachysema celsianum

Brachysema latifolium

Brachysema praemorsum

Prostrate trailing shrub to 2m across; stems hairy when young. **Leaves** fan-shaped, to 3cm long, dark green or purplish above, paler below, tip cut-off with small recurved point. **Flowers** pea-shaped, about 3.5cm long, in opposite pairs, initially cream then aging to dark red. **Pod** ovate, to 2cm long. Southwest. WA. Autumn, winter, spring.

Brachysema subcordatum

Dense shrub to 1.5m high; new growth silky. **Leaves** rounded to heart-shaped, about 2cm long, margins wavy, underside silky. **Flowers** pea-shaped, dark red, about 2cm long, solitary or in small clusters; calyx silky-hairy. Southwest. WA. Winter, spring.

Canavalia rosea | Coastal Jack Bean

Climbing or trailing herb; stems thin and wiry to 3m long. **Leaves** trifoliate; each leaflet circular to oblong, 4–12cm long to 3–10cm wide. **Flowers** pea-shaped, mauve or white, to 2.5cm long in erect racemes 15–30cm long. **Pod** oblong, 10–25cm long and 2.5cm wide. Widespread, often on coastal sand dunes. Qld, NSW, WA, NT. Autumn, winter.

Castanospermum australe | Black Bean

Tree to 35m high. **Leaves** pinnate, 30–60cm long, divided into 9–17 leaflets; each leaflet oblong–elliptic, 7–20cm long and 3–5cm wide, upper surface glossy. **Flowers** pea-shaped, orange to red, 3–4cm long, in racemes usually on old wood; standard reflexed and larger than the lower petals. **Pods** large, woody, 10–20cm long and 4–6cm in diameter. Widespread in rainforest, often common along rivers. NSW, Qld. Spring.

Chorizema cordatum | Heart-leaved Flame Pea

Erect shrub or semi-climber with stems to 1.5m long. **Leaves** heart-shaped, up to 7cm long and 5cm wide, margins flat or wavy, prickly toothed. **Flowers** pea-shaped, orange, red and pink, to 1.5cm across, in terminal racemes to 15cm long; standard rounded, orange-red, keel deep pink. **Pod** ovoid. Heath or low woodland in the southwest. WA. Winter, spring, summer.

Chorizema dicksonii | Yellow-eyed Flame Pea

Small shrub to 1m high; stems numerous erect or spreading. **Leaves** ovate–lanceolate to 2cm long, tip pungent-pointed. **Flowers** pea-shaped, orange-red, to 2cm across, in loose terminal racemes of about 4 flowers; standard rounded, orange-red with basal yellow blotch. Mainly on gravelly soil in open forest in the southwest. WA. Winter, spring, summer.

Brachysema praemorsum

Brachysema subcordatum

Canavalia rosea

Castanospermum australe

Chorizema cordatum

Chorizema dicksonii

Chorizema ilicifolium | Holly Flame Pea

Erect or sprawling shrub 1–3m high. **Leaves** to 4cm long and 2.5cm wide, margins wavy and prickly toothed, tip elongated and triangular. **Flowers** pea-shaped, to 1cm across in loose racemes of 1–4 flowers; standard rounded, orange-red, keel deep pink or red. Coastal regions in the southwest. WA. Winter, spring, summer.

Crotalaria cunninghamii | Green Birdflower

Erect shrub 1–3m high; stems velvety. **Leaves** ovate or obovate, 3–8cm long and 2–4.5cm wide, velvety hairy on both surfaces. **Flowers** pea-shaped, green or yellow-green streaked with fine black lines, to 4.5cm long, in terminal racemes up to 22cm long; calyx densely hairy; keel longer than the standard. **Pod** inflated, 4–5cm long, hairy. Widespread in inland areas. Qld, NSW, WA, NT. Winter, spring.

Crotalaria novae-hollandiae | New Holland Rattlepod

The glabrous form in *C. novae-hollandiae* subsp. *novae-hollandiae* was formerly *C. crassipes*. Small erect shrub to 1.5m high; branches smooth or with grey woolly hairs. **Leaves** ovate to obovate, 5–8cm long and to 3cm wide, smooth or hairy, base heart-shaped or tapered, tip blunt. **Flowers** pea-shaped, yellow, to 1.5cm long, in terminal racemes; calyx smooth or hairy. **Pod** 3–4cm long. Widespread in northern Australia in a variety of habitats. Qld, WA, NT. Autumn, winter.

Crotalaria retusa | Wedge-leaf Rattlepod

Erect perennial herb to 1m high; branches minutely hairy and somewhat ribbed. **Leaves** obovate, 3–8cm long to 2.5cm wide, smooth above, hairy below, tip rounded or notched. **Flowers** pea-shaped, yellow, to 2cm long, in terminal racemes; calyx shortly hairy, standard broad to almost circular. **Pod** 3–4cm long. Widespread in northern Australia, often in wet sandy soils. Qld, WA, NT. Autumn, winter.

Crotalaria smithiana |

Small subshrub with erect or prostrate stems to 50cm long; stems densely hairy. **Leaves** obovate to elliptic, 1–4cm long to 2.5cm wide, densely hairy when young. **Flowers** pea-shaped, yellow, often with fine reddish stripes, to 1cm long, in terminal racemes to 12cm long; calyx covered with dense hairs; standard circular; keel shortly beaked. **Pod** 1–2cm long. Widespread in dry inland regions. Qld, NSW, SA, NT. Autumn, winter.

Daviesia brevifolia | Leafless Bitter Pea

Small erect shrub to 1.5m high; stems bluish-green, rounded stiff and ridged. **Leaves** few and distant, about 5mm long, thorn-like and continuous with the branches. **Flowers** small, pea-shaped, apricot to red, in small clusters. **Pod** swollen, triangular, to 12mm long. Common from coast to farther inland, in heath or rocky slopes. Vic, SA, WA. Winter, spring.

Chorizema ilicifolium

Crotalaria cunninghamii

Crotalaria novae-hollandiae

Crotalaria retusa

Crotalaria smithiana

Daviesia brevifolia

Daviesia latifolia | Hop Bitter Pea

Erect shrub 1–3m high with open habit. **Leaves** broad ovate to lanceolate, to 14cm long and 2–5cm wide, margins wavy, net veins prominent. **Flowers** small, pea-shaped, orange-yellow with brown centres, to 6mm across, in many-flowered axillary racemes to 8cm long. **Pod** smooth, to 1cm long and to 7mm wide. Widespread in mountain forests. Qld, NSW, Vic, Tas. Spring.

Daviesia pachyphylla | Ouch Bush

Small shrub to 1.5m high; branches open or arching. **Leaves** crowded, very thick, terete, 1–2cm long, tip pungent-pointed. **Flowers** pea-shaped, yellow, orange and red, about 8mm across, in small clusters in the upper leaf axils. **Pod** triangular and inflated, about 1.5cm long. Sand heaths in the southwest. WA. Winter, spring.

Daviesia ulicifolia | Gorse Bitter Pea

Erect prickly shrub 1–2m high, branchlets spine-tipped. **Leaves** vary from narrow–ovate to narrow–elliptic, 5–20mm long, stiff, tip sharply pointed. **Flowers** pea-shaped, yellow with red-brown centres, about 8mm across, solitary or in small axillary clusters. **Pod** triangular, 5–8mm long. Widespread and common in southern Australia in a variety of habitats. Qld, NSW, Vic, Tas, SA, WA. Winter, spring.

Dillwynia floribunda |

Small erect shrub to 1m high. **Leaves** narrow–linear, to 2cm long, rough, crowded and somewhat twisted. **Flowers** pea-shaped, yellow and orange, about 1cm across, sessile and crowded in pairs in the upper leaf axils; standard kidney-shaped, broader than long. **Pod** inflated, 3–4mm long. Common in swampy heaths and gullies. Qld, NSW. Winter, spring, summer.

Dillwynia juniperina | Prickly Parrot Pea

Erect prickly shrub 1–3m high; stems covered in short hairs. **Leaves** linear, 7–15mm long, spreading out from the stems, somewhat triangular in cross-section and grooved above, tip pungent-pointed. **Flowers** pea-shaped, golden-yellow with red markings, about 1cm across, in small terminal or axillary clusters; standard much larger than other petals. **Pod** inflated, about 6mm long. Widespread in dry open forest. Qld, NSW, Vic. Winter, spring.

Dillwynia phylicoides |

(Also known as *D. retorta* subsp. *B*). Prostrate or small erect shrub to 1.5m high. Stems, leaves and calyx covered with short stiff hairs. **Leaves** linear to narrow–oblong, 3–8mm long, rough and spirally twisted. **Flowers** pea-shaped, golden-yellow and red, about 1–2cm across, mostly stalkless, singly or in tight clusters in the upper leaf axils. **Pod** inflated, to 7mm long. Widespread in open forest and woodland. Qld, NSW, Vic. Winter, spring.

Daviesia latifolia

Daviesia pachyphylla

Daviesia ulicifolia

Dillwynia floribunda

Dillwynia juniperina

Dillwynia phylicoides

Dillwynia retorta

Spreading to erect shrub to 3m high; stems lightly hairy. **Leaves** linear to narrow oblong, 4–12mm long, mostly smooth or minutely warty, spreading out from the stems and somewhat twisted. **Flowers** yellow and red, to 1.5cm across, on short stalks, singly or in clusters in the upper leaf axils. **Pod** inflated, to 7mm long. Heath and open forest. Qld, NSW. Winter, spring.

Dillwynia sericea | Showy Parrot Pea

Erect shrub to 1m high; stems covered with silky white hairs, especially when young. **Leaves** linear, 5–20mm long, minutely warty, glabrous or hairy. **Flowers** pea-shaped, golden-yellow or orange with red markings, to 1.5cm across, stalkless, singly or in pairs in the upper leaf axils; calyx often silky-hairy. **Pod** to 4mm long, sparsely hairy. Widespread in heath, woodland and open forest. Qld, NSW, Vic, Tas, SA. Winter, spring.

Erythrina vespertilio | Bat's Wing Coral Tree

Deciduous tree 6–12m high with thick corky bark and usually scattered with thorns. **Leaves** trifoliate; each leaflet roughly triangular and usually 3-lobed, 2–10cm long and 4–12cm wide. **Flowers** pea-shaped, scarlet, tubular, 3–5cm long, in dense racemes 10–30cm long. **Pod** linear, 5–10cm long with pointed tip. Widespread in woodland, open forest and rainforest margins. Qld, NSW, WA, NT. Winter, spring, summer.

Eutaxia cuneata

Open or bushy shrub 1–2m high; stems reddish. **Leaves** in pairs at right angles, wedge-shaped, to 1.5cm long, slightly concave, tip rounded. **Flowers** pea-shaped, orange-yellow, streaked red or purple, to 1cm across, solitary in the leaf axils. **Pod** ovoid, slightly hairy, to 5mm long. Coastal heath in the south. WA. Winter, spring.

Eutaxia obovata

Bushy spreading shrub to 2.5m high; stems twiggy. **Leaves** in pairs, obovate–oblong, 2cm long and 4–7mm wide, concave, tip pointed. **Flowers** pea-shaped, yellow and red, to 1.5cm across, in small clusters in upper leaf axils. **Pod** flat, to 8mm long. Coastal heath and karri forest in the south. WA. Winter, spring, summer.

Glycine clandestina | Twining Glycine

Weak trailing perennial herb with faintly hairy stems to 2m long. **Leaves** trifoliate; leaflets narrow–linear to oblong–lanceolate, 1–8cm long and 2–10mm wide, tip blunt or pointed. **Flowers** pea-shaped, pale mauve to purple, about 8mm across, in loose axillary racemes. **Pod** straight, 2–5cm long. Widespread from coast to mountains and farther inland in a variety of habitats. Qld, NSW, Vic, Tas, SA. Throughout the year.

Dillwynia retorta

Dillwynia sericea

Erythrina vespertilio

Eutaxia cuneata

Eutaxia obovata

Glycine clandestina

Gompholobium glabratum | Dainty Wedge Pea

Low spreading or ascending shrub to 60cm high; stems slender, warty and often sparsely hairy. **Leaves** pinnate with 5–7 linear leaflets, each 7–15mm long and to 1.5mm wide, margins rolled under. **Flowers** pea-shaped, pale yellow, to 1.5cm across, solitary or in small axillary clusters; standard kidney-shaped and larger than other petals. **Pod** ovoid, about 18mm long. Widespread in heath and dry open forest on sandy soils. NSW, Vic. Winter, spring.

Gompholobium latifolium | Golden Glory Pea

Erect shrub to 3m high. **Leaves** trifoliate; leaflets linear, to 5cm long and 6mm wide, margins flat or recurved, tip pointed or blunt. **Flowers** pea-shaped, yellow, about 3cm across, solitary or in small clusters; standard kidney-shaped and larger than other petals; keel conspicuously fringed with white hairs. **Pod** 15–18mm long. Widespread from coast to ranges in dry open forest on sandy soils. Qld, NSW, Vic. Spring, summer.

Gompholobium scabrum | Painted Lady

Formerly *Burtonia scabra*. Erect shrub 1–3m high. **Leaves** trifoliate; leaflets narrow–linear, to 1.5cm long, margins recurved. **Flowers** pea-shaped, deep pink, about 2cm across, solitary, in upper leaf axils. Standard kidney-shaped and larger than other petals. **Pod** globular, about 5mm in diameter. Widespread in sandheath and open forest in southwest. WA. Spring.

Goodia lotifolia | Golden-tip

Open shrub to 4m high. **Leaves** trifoliate; leaflets obovate, 1–3cm long, on slender stalk to 2cm long. **Flowers** pea-shaped, yellow with brown centre, about 1.5cm across, in loose racemes to 8cm long. **Pod** ovate, to 3cm long, brown. Widespread in moist sheltered sites in open forest and rainforest margins. Qld, NSW, Vic, Tas, SA. Spring.

Hardenbergia comptoniana | Wild Sarsaparilla

Climber with slender stems to 2m long. **Leaves** trifoliate; leaflets linear–lanceolate to ovate, to 15cm long and 1–6cm wide, dark green and strongly veined. **Flowers** pea-shaped, mauve or purple, about 1cm across, in showy axillary racemes. **Pod** oblong, about 3.5cm long. Common in jarrah forest and coastal plains in southwest. WA. Spring.

Hardenbergia violacea | Purple Coral Pea

Climbing or prostrate shrub with tough wiry stems to 2m long. **Leaves** a single leaflet, ovate to narrow–lanceolate, 3–10cm long and 1–5cm wide, dark green and strongly veined. **Flowers** pea-shaped, violet or rarely pink or white, about 1cm across, in showy axillary racemes, often forming terminal panicles. **Pod** oblong, 2–5cm long. Very widespread and common in a variety of habitats from coast to ranges. Qld, NSW, Vic, Tas, SA. Winter, spring.

Gompholobium glabratum

Gompholobium latifolium

Gompholobium scabrum

Goodia lotifolia

Hardenbergia comptoniana

Hardenbergia violacea

Hovea acutifolia

Tall slender shrub to 4m high; stems covered in grey or rusty hairs. **Leaves** narrow–elliptic, 2–8cm long, 3–12mm wide, tapering at both ends, margins slightly recurved smooth above and finely veined, rusty hairs below, tip pointed. **Flowers** pea-shaped, pale mauve to purple, about 1cm across, in short axillary racemes. **Pod** sparsely hairy, about 15mm long. Moist sheltered sites in forest and on rainforest margins. Qld, NSW. Winter, spring.

Hovea chorizemifolia | Holly-leaved Hovea

Small erect shrub to 1m high; stems often rusty hairy. **Leaves** ovate to lanceolate 3–7cm long, 1–3cm wide, margins prickly toothed, strongly veined. **Flowers** pea-shaped mauve or purple, about 1cm across, in small axillary clusters. **Pod** smooth, about 1cm long Gravelly soils of the Darling Range and Avon District. WA. Winter, spring.

Hovea elliptica | Tree Hovea

Tall slender shrub to 4.5m high; stems rusty hairy. **Leaves** elliptic to lanceolate 3–11cm long and 1–5cm wide, dark green and smooth above, rusty hairy below. **Flowers** pea shaped, blue to purple, to 1.5cm across, in short axillary racemes; calyx rusty hairy. **Pod** globular, about 1cm long. Karri and jarrah forest of the southwest. WA. Spring.

Hovea linearis | Common Hovea

Small erect or spreading shrub to 50cm high; stems covered in dense grey hairs. **Leaves** narrow–linear, 2–6cm long, 2–4mm wide, upper surface strongly veined and glabrous sparsely hairy below, tip pointed and often recurved. **Flowers** pea-shaped, mauve, about 1.2cm across, 1 or 2 together in the upper leaf axils. **Pod** globular, about 1cm long. Widespread from coast to ranges in heath and open forest. Qld, NSW, Vic, Tas, SA. Winter, spring.

Hovea longifolia | Rusty Pods

Erect shrub 1–2m high; stems covered in grey or rusty curled hairs. **Leaves** linear to narrow–elliptic, 2–9cm long and 4–6mm wide, midrib channelled, dark green and smooth above, sparsely hairy below, margins recurved, tip pointed. **Flowers** pea-shaped, blue or purple with darker veins, about 8mm across, in short axillary clusters of 2–3. **Pod** globular, to 1.5cm long. Shady moist creek banks, mainly coastal. NSW. Winter, spring.

Hovea pungens | Devil's Pins

Erect shrub 1–2m high. **Leaves** linear to lanceolate, 1–2.5cm long to 3mm wide spreading, dark green and glabrous above, hairy below, tip pungent-pointed. **Flowers** pea-shaped, purple, about 1cm across, solitary or in small axillary clusters. **Pod** globular, about 1cm long. Widespread in the southwest; common in jarrah forest. WA. Winter, spring.

Hovea acutifolia

Hovea chorizemifolia

Hovea elliptica

Hovea linearis

Hovea longifolia

Hovea pungens

Indigofera australis | Austral Indigo

Slender erect or spreading shrub to 2.5m high. **Leaves** pinnate, about 10cm long divided into numerous leaflets; each leaflet oblong to obovate, 1–4cm long to 1cm wide, ti blunt or with small point. **Flowers** pea-shaped, mauve to purple, to 12mm across, in axillar racemes to 15cm long. **Pod** cylindrical, to 4cm long and 3mm wide, brown. Widespread an common in a variety of habitats, often in dry forest. All States. Winter, spring.

Jacksonia scoparia | Dogwood

Tall open shrub or small tree to 3m high; branches angular or winged, mostly leafless often drooping. **Leaves** usually reduced to small scales. **Flowers** pea-shaped, orange-yellow and red, about 13mm across, profuse in terminal and axillary racemes, perfumed. **Pod** oblong about 1cm long, hairy. Widespread from coast to mountains and inland plains, mostly in heat and woodland. Qld, NSW. Spring.

Kennedia beckxiana |

Robust woody climber; stems twining, glabrous. **Leaves** trifoliate; leaflets ovate 2–5cm long, slightly wavy and strongly veined. **Flowers** pea-shaped, red with a green centre about 5cm long, singly or in short axillary racemes with conspicuous bracts at the base of th flower stalk. **Pod** cylindrical, about 7cm long. Confined to the Israelite Bay region, on granit sand. WA. Winter, spring.

Kennedia macrophylla | Augusta Kennedia

Robust woody climber; stems twining and covered with silky hairs. **Leaves** trifoliate leaflets light green, obovate to orbicular, to 7cm long, margins slightly wavy, venation conspicuous. **Flowers** pea-shaped, red with a yellow centre, 2cm across, in showy racemes o stalks to 20cm long. **Pod** cylindrical, about 4cm long, ending in long curved point. Between Augusta and Cape Leewin in the southwest. WA. Spring.

Kennedia microphylla |

Prostrate creeper to 1.5m across; stems hairy when young. **Leaves** trifoliate; leaflet dark green, almost orbicular, about 1.5cm long and 1cm across, with a broad shallow notc at the tip. **Flowers** pea-shaped, red with greenish-yellow centre, 12mm across, usually singl on slender stalks. **Pod** linear. Moist situations in the southwest, often in sandy soil WA. Winter, spring.

Kennedia nigricans | Black Coral Pea

Robust woody climber or trailer; stems twining, glabrous. **Leaves** single or trifoliate leaflets ovate to ovate–lanceolate, 3–10cm long and 2–7mm wide, venation conspicuous **Flowers** pea-shaped, black with yellow on reflexed standard, about 4cm long, usually in pairs **Pod** flat, 4–8cm long, densely hairy. Widespread in southern coastal areas in heath and wood land. WA. Winter, spring.

Indigofera australis

Jacksonia scoparia

Kennedia beckxiana

Kennedia macrophylla

Kennedia microphylla

Kennedia nigricans

Kennedia prostrata | Running Postman

Prostrate creeping subshrub to 5m across; stems silky-hairy. **Leaves** trifoliate; leaflets circular to obovate, 1–3cm long and across, margins conspicuously wavy, undersurface slightly hairy, veins prominent. **Flowers** pea-shaped, bright red with yellow centre, about 2cm long, singly or in pairs in leaf axils. **Pod** cylindrical, 3–5cm long, dark brown, hairy. Widespread and common in temperate regions, mainly in heath and open forest. NSW, Vic, Tas, SA, WA. Winter, spring.

Kennedia retrorsa |

Vigorous climber with long twining stems; rusty hairy when young. **Leaves** trifoliate; leaflets obovate to almost circular, 3–13cm long and 5–6cm wide, deep green and slightly hairy above, paler and hairy below. **Flowers** pea-shaped, bright pink-purple with a white spot, about 2cm across, in axillary racemes to 25cm long. **Pod** flat, to 6cm long, hairy. Confined to a mountain west of Muswellbrook, rare. NSW. Spring, summer.

Kennedia rubicunda | Dusky Coral Pea

Vigorous climber; stems tough and twining to 4m long, initially hairy. **Leaves** trifoliate; leaflets obovate to almost circular, 3–10cm long and to 3.5cm wide, glabrous to silky-hairy on both surfaces. **Flowers** pea-shaped, deep red with a reflexed standard, about 4cm long, in racemes 4–5cm long. Pod flat, 5–10cm long, hairy. Widespread along coastal regions in a variety of habitats. Qld, NSW, Vic. Spring.

Oxylobium ellipticum | Common Shaggy Pea

Erect or spreading shrub to 2m high; stems initially hairy. **Leaves** mostly elliptic, to 3cm long, opposite or in irregular whorls, rough and veined above, silky-hairy below, margins and tip recurved. **Flowers** pea-shaped, golden-yellow, sometimes with reddish markings, about 1cm across, in short dense, terminal or axillary racemes. **Pod** ovoid, about 8mm long, densely hairy. Open forest and woodland, mostly in mountainous regions. Qld, NSW, Vic, Tas. Spring, summer.

Oxylobium robustum | Tree Shaggy Pea

Erect or spreading shrub or small tree to 3m high; stems hairy. **Leaves** linear to narrow–lanceolate, 2–8cm long and less than 1cm wide, opposite or often in whorls, rough and veined above, hairy below, margins recurved. **Flowers** pea-shaped, golden-yellow with or without reddish markings, about 1cm across, in short terminal and axillary racemes. **Pod** oblong, to 1cm long. Open forests in coastal regions. Qld, NSW. Spring, summer.

Platylobium obtusangulum | Common Flat Pea

Erect or spreading shrub to 1m high; stems wiry, brown. **Leaves** triangular or arrow-head-shaped, to 3cm long, veins prominent, tips of the 3 angles finely pointed. **Flowers** pea-shaped, orange-yellow and red, subtended by brown overlapping bracts, singly or 2–3 together in upper leaf axils. **Pod** oblong, to 2cm long, dark brown, hairy. Widespread and common in southeast in heath, woodland and open forest. Vic, Tas, SA. Spring.

Kennedia prostrata

Kennedia retrorsa

Kennedia rubicunda

Oxylobium ellipticum

Oxylobium robustum

Platylobium obtusangulum

Platylobium scandens | Netted Shaggy Pea

Formerly *Oxylobium scandens*. Prostrate shrub; stems trailing to 60cm long, initially hairy. **Leaves** elliptic or obovate, 2–6cm to long, glabrous and veined above, paler and sparsely hairy below, often shallowly toothed, tip pointed. **Flowers** pea-shaped, golden-yellow with reddish markings, about 1cm across, in terminal and axillary racemes, on slender stalks extending beyond the leaves. Widespread in coastal regions, mostly in open forest. Qld, NSW. Spring

Pultenaea costata | Ribbed Bush Pea

Erect shrub to 1m high; stems shortly hairy. **Leaves** broad–lanceolate, crowded 7–15mm long, glabrous above, 3–5 longitudinal veins below, margins concave, tip pungent pointed. **Flowers** pea-shaped, orange-yellow with deep red markings, to 1.5cm across, in dense terminal heads; calyx hairy. Endemic in the Grampians, mainly in light open forest Vic. Spring–early summer.

Pultenaea cunninghamii |

Spreading shrub to 1m high; stems mostly glabrous. **Leaves** broadly ovate, to 2cm long, in whorls of 3 encircling the stem, tip pungent-pointed. **Flowers** pea-shaped, orange-yellow, about 1.5cm across, solitary in upper leaf axils, on stalks to 5mm long. **Pod** swollen to 7mm long. Widespread in woodland and open forest. Qld, NSW, Vic. Spring, summer.

Pultenaea daphnoides | Large-leaf Bush Pea

Erect shrub to 3m high; stems pubescent. **Leaves** obovate or wedge-shaped, 1–4cm long and to 1cm wide, margins mostly flat, tip rounded with a short soft point. **Flowers** pea-shaped, golden-yellow and red, to 3cm across, sessile in dense terminal heads; calyx densely hairy. **Pod** flat, 5–7mm long. Widespread in heath and sheltered forests from the coast to the mountains. NSW, Vic, Tas, SA. Spring, summer.

Pultenaea flexilis |

Erect shrub to 3m high; stems sparsely hairy. **Leaves** alternate, narrow–obovate, to 2cm long and about 2mm wide, tip distinctly pointed. **Flowers** pea-shaped, yellow, about 1cm across, in upper leaf axils; calyx hairless. **Pod** swollen, to 1cm long. Widespread and common on coast and ranges in open forest. Qld, NSW. Spring.

Pultenaea humilis | Dwarf Bush Pea

Small erect shrub to 30cm high; stems densely hairy. **Leaves** linear–lanceolate, crowded, to 1cm long and about 2mm wide, smooth above and hairy below, margins slightly incurved, tip pointed. **Flowers** pea-shaped, apricot-orange with dark red markings, about 2cm across, in clusters in upper leaf axils; calyx hairy. Widespread in heath and open forest often in damp situations. Vic, Tas. Spring, summer.

Platylobium scandens

Pultenaea costata

Pultenaea cunninghamii

Pultenaea daphnoides

Pultenaea flexilis

Pultenaea humilis

Pultenaea myrtoides

Erect or spreading shrub to 60cm high; stems downy. **Leaves** narrow–obovate, 1–2.5 b
5mm wide, green, glabrous above, paler and hairy below, margins and tip recurved. **Flowers** pea
shaped, golden with red markings, 1.5cm across, sessile in dense terminal heads; calyx densely hair
Pod flat, to 6mm long. Heath, open forest, swampy coastal situations. Qld, NSW. Winter, spring.

Pultenaea rosmarinifolia | Rosemary Bush Pea

Erect straggly shrub to 1m tall; upper stems downy. **Leaves** alternate, linear to elliptic
2–4cm long to 5mm wide, dark green and mainly glabrous above with depressed midveir
paler below, margins and tip recurved. **Flowers** pea-shaped, yellow with red markings, abou
1cm across, in dense terminal heads; bracts persistent and silky-hairy. **Pod** flat, about 8mr
long. Heath and open forest mainly in coastal regions. NSW. Spring.

Pultenaea scabra | Rough Bush Pea

Erect bushy shrub 1–2m tall; stems covered in dense spreading hairs. **Leaves** wedge
shaped and usually bilobed at the tip, 3–16mm long and 4–6mm wide, dark green and short
ly hairy above, paler and densely hairy below, margins and tip recurved. **Flowers** pea-shapec
orange-yellow with deep red markings, about 1.5cm across, in loose terminal clusters; caly
densely hairy. **Pod** flat, about 7mm long. Heath and open forest. NSW, Vic, SA. Spring.

Pultenaea villosa | Bronze Bush Pea

Prostrate or erect shrub to 1–2m; stems covered in long, soft, rust-coloured hairs. **Leave**
alternate, narrow–oblong to obovate, 3–10mm long and 2–3mm wide, margins concave, tip most
rounded. **Flowers** pea-shaped, golden-yellow and red, about 1.5cm across, in small axillary head
Pod swollen, to 6mm long. Heath and open forest, mainly near coast. Qld, NSW, Vic. Spring.

Swainsona formosa | Sturt's Desert Pea

Formerly *Clianthus formosus*. Prostrate spreading annual or short-lived perennial herk
stems densely pubescent with long, fine hairs. **Leaves** pinnate, 10–15cm long, with about 1
leaflets; each leaflet elliptic to obovate, 1–3cm long, densely hairy on the underside, tip roundec
often with minute point. **Flowers** pea-shaped, red, about 9cm long, in erect racemes of 2–
flowers; standard pointed with glossy black dome at base. **Pod** swollen, oblong, 4–9cm long t
about 1cm wide. Widespread in dry parts of the inland. Qld, NSW, SA, WA, NT. Winter, spring

Swainsona galegifolia | Smooth Darling Pea

Perennial subshrub to 1m high; stems glabrous. **Leaves** pinnate, 5–10cm long divide
into about 21–29 pairs of leaflets; each leaflet narrow–obovate, 6–20mm long and 2–5mr
wide, glabrous, tip rounded, often with a small point. **Flowers** pea-shaped, white, pink, purpl
and occasionally yellow or brownish, about 1.5cm long, in racemes of 15–20 flowers up t
20cm long. **Pod** swollen, elliptic, 2–4cm long to 2.5cm wide. Widespread in a variety c
habitats on coast, tablelands and farther inland. Qld, NSW, Vic. Spring, summer.

Pultenaea myrtoides

Pultenaea rosmarinifolia

Pultenaea scabra

Pultenaea villosa

Swainsona formosa

Swainsona galegifolia

Swainsona greyana | Darling Pea

Formerly *S. greyana* subsp. *bracteata*. Perennial subshrub to 1.5m high; stems with fine spreading hairs. **Leaves** pinnate, 5–10cm long with about 19–25 obovate leaflets, tip rounded often with small point. **Flowers** pea-shaped, white, pink or pale purple, about 2cm long in showy erect racemes to 40cm long with 20 or more flowers. **Pod** swollen, elliptic, to 5cm long and 2.5cm wide. Mainly along the lower Murray River and its associated floodplains and the Darling River and its major tributaries. Qld, NSW, Vic, SA. Spring.

Templetonia retusa | Cockies' Tongues

Spreading shrub to 1.5m high; stems leafy. **Leaves** obovate, 2–4cm long to 2.5cm wide, leathery, grey-green with waxy bloom, margins entire, tip rounded or notched with small point. **Flowers** deep pink, red and occasionally cream, up to 6cm long, in the upper leaf axils; standard narrow and reflexed. **Pod** linear–oblong, 4–5cm long. Coastal regions of the southwest and southern Australia. WA, SA. Winter, spring.

GERANIACEAE | Pelargonium family

Family of perennial herbs and shrubs of 7 genera and about 750 species globally distributed, mostly in temperate zones. Three genera and an estimated 36 species occur in Australia. Leaves alternate or opposite or in a basal rosette, often pinnately or palmately lobed or dissected. Flowers irregular or regular. Sepals 5, united toward the base. Petals 5 free. Stamens 10, in 2 whorls. Ovary superior; style with 5 lobes. Fruit a dry slender capsule which splits on maturity into 5 separate segments called mericarps, each 1-seeded and bearing a terminal spiral awn or beak. The family contains many exotic species and hybrids of *Pelargonium* and *Geranium* cultivated as ornamental plants.

Geranium neglectum |

Prostrate or decumbent perennial herb with stems to 1.5m long. **Stem leaves** 1–3cm long to 5cm wide, palmately divided into 5–7 lobes, each lobe is again divided toward the tip, both surfaces sparsely hairy. **Basal leaves** larger. **Flowers** regular, pink with darker veins, about 3cm across, solitary on slender stalks to 10cm long. **Fruit** to 2cm. Mainly on the ranges along creek banks and swampy situations. Qld, NSW, Vic. Summer, autumn.

Geranium solanderi | Native Geranium

Creeping or slightly ascending perennial herb with hairy stems to 50cm long, sometimes taking root at the nodes. **Stem leaves** 1–3cm long and 2–5cm across, palmately dissected into 5–10 lobes, each lobe is again divided toward the tip. **Basal leaves** larger. **Flowers** regular, pink with paler centres, about 1.5cm across, in pairs on slender stalks to 4cm long. **Fruit** to 2.5cm long. Widespread in temperate Australia Qld, NSW, Vic, Tas, SA, WA. Spring, summer.

Swainsona greyana

Templetonia retusa

Geranium neglectum

Geranium solanderi

Pelargonium australe | Native Storksbill

Sprawling or slightly ascending perennial herb to 70cm high; stems downy. **Leaves** ovate to circular, 2–9cm long and across, shallowly lobed, margins wavy and toothed. **Flowers** pale pink in umbels of 4–12, pale pink, each about 1.5cm across; the slightly larger 2 upper petals have dark pink veins. **Fruit** downy, to 1.5cm long. Widespread from coastal regions to mountains and farther inland. Qld, NSW, Vic, Tas, SA, WA. Spring, summer, autumn.

Pelargonium drummondii |

Spreading or slightly ascending perennial herb to 50cm high; stems softly hairy. **Basal leaves** hairy, almost circular, 4cm long and 3cm across, shallowly lobed, margins wavy. **Stem leaves** smaller. **Flowers** pink with darker veins on the upper petals, in umbels of 3–8. **Fruit** to 1.5cm long. Rocky crevices in granite outcrops in southern regions. WA. Autumn, winter, spring.

Pelargonium rodneyanum | Magenta Storksbill

Low perennial herb to 40cm high; stems softly hairy. **Leaves** ovate to narrow–ovate, 2–5cm long to 4cm wide, with 5–7 shallow lobes, veins sparsely hairy, margins faintly toothed. **Flowers** deep pink with darker veins on the upper petals, in umbels of 2–7, on slender stalks 5–12cm long. **Fruit** to 2cm long. Rocky slopes in open forest and woodland. NSW, Vic, SA. Summer, autumn.

GOODENIACEAE |

Family of mostly herbs and low shrubs of 13 genera and about 390 species, chiefly in the Southern Hemisphere and most of which are confined to Australia. Leaves mostly alternate and simple. Flowers irregular, bisexual, usually 5-merous. Corolla shortly tubular with 5 united petals, tube slit almost to the base on one side. The lobes may spread evenly as in *Scaevola*, but mostly are 2-lipped with the upper lip 2-lobed and the lower one 3-lobed as in *Dampiera*, *Goodenia* and *Velleia*. Stamens 5. Ovary inferior to superior. The style bears a unique 2-lipped cup (indusium) surrounding the stigma, which collects the pollen before the flower opens. Fruit a capsule, drupe or nut.

Coopernookia barbata ` | Purple Goodenia

Small erect shrub to 80cm high; stems glandular and hairy. **Leaves** linear, 1–3cm long and about 2mm wide, sessile, with scattered hairs, becoming rough, margins entire or slightly toothed, revolute. **Flowers** blue to mauve, about 1.5cm long; lobes unequal and broadly winged with long bristles inside. **Fruit** a capsule. Dry open forest. NSW, Vic, Tas. Spring, summer.

Pelargonium australe

Pelargonium drummondii

Pelargonium rodneyanum

Coopernookia barbata

Dampiera adpressa | Bushy Dampiera

Multi-stemmed perennial subshrub to 1m high; stems covered in close white down when young. **Leaves** sessile, ovate–elliptic, 1–5cm long to 2cm wide, sessile, entire or faintly toothed. **Flowers** blue or mauve, with silvery hairy exterior, about 2cm across, in groups o 3–5; lobes with winged margins. **Fruit** a ribbed nut to 5mm long. On ranges and western slopes, mostly in dry open forest and woodland. Qld, NSW. Winter, spring, summer.

Dampiera alata | Winged-stem Dampiera

Erect perennial subshrub to 1m high; stems flattish with wings to 1cm wide. **Leave** oblanceolate, 1–6cm long to 1cm wide, entire or slightly toothed, dark green and glabrou above, dense white hairs below. **Flowers** purple-blue with greyish hairy exterior, abou 2cm across, in groups of 1–3; lobes broadly winged. **Fruit** a wrinkly nut, about 4mm ir diameter. Variety of habitats in the southwest. WA. Winter, spring.

Dampiera candicans |

Erect shrub to 70cm high; stems covered in dense grey to brownish hairs. **Leaves** elliptic to obovate, about 3.5cm long and 2cm wide, glabrous above, hairy below, margins with a few shallow teeth. **Flowers** purple-blue with greyish-brown hairy exterior, about 1cm across, in leaf-less spikes; lobes with narrow wings. **Fruit** a globular hairy nut to 2.5mm long. In dry regions o northern Australia, on sandy or stony soil often with Porcupine Grass. WA, NT. Autumn, winter

Dampiera diversifolia |

Prostrate mat-forming perennial subshrub with spreading stems to 2m across. **Basa leaves** linear–oblong to oblong–lanceolate, to 5cm long and 8mm wide, sessile, with a few teeth toward the tip; **stem leaves** oblanceolate and smaller. **Flowers** purple-blue, about 1.5cm across, in leaf axils; exterior smooth (unlike other species of *Dampiera*, which usually have hair on the outside of the flowers). Mainly in southern district, in sandy heath. WA. Winter, spring

Dampiera eriocephala | Woolly-headed Dampiera

Erect clump-forming perennial herb to 30cm high; stems densely covered with wooll white hairs. **Leaves** obovate or elliptic, to 7cm long and 3cm wide, glabrous above, densel woolly below. **Flowers** blue with silky-hairy exterior, about 2.5cm across, in loose termina racemes on branched leafless stalks. Widespread in wheatbelt and goldfields regions of south west, in heath and mallee. WA. Spring.

Dampiera lanceolata | Grooved Dampiera

Erect perennial subshrub to 1m high and across; stems terete, slightly grooved, initiall woolly-white. **Leaves** linear to oblong, 1–5cm long to 2.5cm wide, sessile, margins entire o slightly toothed and sometimes slightly revolute, glabrous above when mature, hairy below **Flowers** deep blue with dark grey hairy exterior, about 1.5cm across, in axillary clusters c 3–9. Mainly inland in dry forest and woodland. Qld, NSW, Vic, SA. Winter, spring.

Dampiera adpressa

Dampiera alata

Dampiera candicans

Dampiera diversifolia

Dampiera eriocephala

Dampiera lanceolata

Dampiera lavandulacea | Lavender Dampiera

Perennial subshrub to 70cm high; stems prominently ribbed. **Leaves** linear to oblong-elliptic, to 2.5cm long and about 1cm wide, sessile, margins mostly entire and recurved sometimes with a few teeth, hairy below. **Flowers** blue-purple with yellow throat and hairy exterior, about 1.5cm across, in axillary clusters of up to 3. *D. preissii* is included with this species. Widespread in southwest and farther inland, in woodland and heath. WA. Winter, spring.

Dampiera leptoclada |

Erect perennial subshrub to 60cm high; stems angled, glabrous. **Leaves** oblong to linear, to 5cm long and 1cm wide, sessile, margins entire or slightly toothed, glabrous. **Flowers** blue or mauve with greyish-brown hairy exterior, about 2cm across, in axillary clusters of 1–3 flowers. *D. subspicata* is included with this species. Widespread in southwest often in damp situations. WA. Winter, spring.

Dampiera linearis | Common Dampiera

Perennial subshrub to 60cm high; stems erect and slightly ribbed. **Leaves** linear to obovate, 1–4cm long to 1.5cm wide, sessile, margins entire or irregularly lobed, glabrous. **Flowers** pale blue to purple with greyish hairy exterior, about 2cm across, in terminal clusters of 1–7 flowers. *D. cuneata* is included with this species. Widespread and common in the southwest, in a variety of habitats. WA. Winter, spring.

Dampiera purpurea |

Erect perennial subshrub to 1m high; stems ribbed and hairy or rough. **Leaves** elliptic to obovate, 1–6cm long to 4cm wide, sessile, margins entire or irregularly toothed, usually glabrous above, hairy below. **Flowers** purple with dark grey hairy exterior, about 2.5cm across, in axillary or terminal clusters of 3–5 flowers. Widespread on coast and ranges in heath and open forest. Qld, NSW, Vic. Winter, spring, summer.

Dampiera rosmarinifolia | Wild Rosemary

Perennial prostrate or erect subshrub to 60cm high; stems ribbed and densely hairy. **Leaves** linear to linear–oblong, about 2.5cm long and 5mm wide, sessile, margins strongly revolute, glabrous above, densely hairy below. **Flowers** mauve or purple with hairy exterior, about 2cm across, in axillary clusters. Sandy soils in relatively low-rainfall regions. Vic, SA. Winter, spring.

Dampiera stricta |

Erect perennial subshrub to 60cm high; stems 3-angled and mostly glabrous. **Leaves** linear to elliptic, 2–4.5cm long and to 2cm wide, sessile, margins entire or with a few small teeth. **Flowers** blue or mauve with rusty hairy exterior, about 2.5 across, singly or in pairs in the leaf axils. Widespread in eastern States, from coast to ranges, usually in heath on sandy soils. Qld, NSW, Vic, Tas. Winter, spring, summer.

Dampiera lavandulacea

Dampiera leptoclada

Dampiera linearis

Dampiera purpurea

Dampiera rosmarinifolia

Dampiera stricta

Dampiera trigona | Angled-stem Dampiera

Erect perennial herb to 40cm high; stems 3-angled, glabrous, slender and wiry. **Leaves** linear–lanceolate, 2–4cm long and 2–5mm wide, sessile, margins entire or sometimes with a few teeth, glabrous. **Flowers** blue or purple with finely hairy exterior, about 2cm across, singly or in pairs in the leaf axils. In near-coastal areas in southwest. WA. Spring, summer.

Goodenia affinis | Cushion Goodenia

Erect or spreading perennial herb to 20cm high. **Leaves** mostly basal, oblanceolate, oblong–lanceolate or obovate, 2–4cm long to 1.5cm wide, densely woolly on both surfaces, margins toothed. **Flowers** yellow with woolly exterior, about 2cm across, singly or in racemes to 5cm long. Widespread in dry southern regions, in mallee. WA, SA. Winter, spring, summer.

Goodenia cycloptera | Serrated Goodenia

Annual or perennial herb to 30cm high; stems ascending to spreading, softly hairy. **Basal leaves** obovate to oblong, 4–10cm long to 2cm wide, coarsely toothed or lobed, hairy; **stem leaves** smaller and sometimes entire. **Flowers** yellow with hairy throat and exterior, about 2cm across, solitary, on stalks to 5cm long. Widespread in dry inland regions, mostly on sandy soils. Qld, NSW, SA, WA, NT. Throughout the year.

Goodenia glomerata |

Erect perennial herb to 50cm high; stems covered with greyish hairs when young. **Leaves** mostly toward the base, elliptic to oblanceolate, 6–20cm long to 2cm wide, margins toothed; stem leaves smaller. **Flowers** yellow with hairy interior and star-like hairs outside, about 2cm across, in compact spikes to 12cm long. South coast and nearby ranges, in swampy situations on sandstone. NSW. Spring, summer.

Goodenia grandiflora | Large-flowered Goodenia

Erect shrub to 1.5m high; stems angular, sticky when young. **Leaves** ovate to circular, 2.5–5cm long to about 5cm wide, hairy, margins regularly toothed. **Flowers** yellow with purplish-brown stripes and pubescent exterior, about 3cm across, singly or in leafy racemes. Widespread from coast to ranges and farther inland, often on rocky sites. Qld, NSW, WA, NT. Winter, spring.

Goodenia hederacea | Ivy Goodenia

Prostrate trailing herb with stems to 80cm long. **Basal leaves** obovate to circular, 3–10cm long to 2.5cm wide, dark green and usually glaucous on both surfaces, margins lobed, toothed or entire. **Stem leaves** smaller and irregularly toothed. **Flowers** yellow, about 2cm across, solitary, on slender stalks to 3cm long, along the stems. Widespread on the coast and ranges in heath, woodland and open forest. Qld, NSW, Vic. Spring, summer, autumn.

Dampiera trigona

Goodenia affinis

Goodenia cycloptera

Goodenia glomerata

Goodenia grandiflora

Goodenia hederacea

Goodenia lunata | Hairy Goodenia

Perennial herb to 20cm high; stems hairy, erect or spreading and taking root to form plantlets. **Leaves** mainly basal, linear to ovate, 4–12cm long to 3cm wide, margins toothed or deeply lobed; young and outer radical leaves entire. **Flowers** yellow, about 2cm across, exterior hairy, solitary, on hairy stalks of which several may arise together from the leaf axils. Widespread in dry inland regions. All mainland States. Winter, spring.

Goodenia ovata | Hop Goodenia

Erect or scrambling shrub to 2m high; stems slender, glossy and sticky. **Leaves** mostly ovate to elliptic, 3–8cm long and 1–4cm wide, light green, margins toothed, venation conspicuous. **Flowers** yellow, 2cm across, in axillary racemes of 3–6 flowers on stalks to 4cm long. Widespread on the coast and ranges in woodland and moist forest, sometimes near the sea. Qld, NSW, Vic, Tas, SA. Spring, summer.

Goodenia pinnatifida | Cut-leaf Goodenia

Erect to spreading annual or perennial herb to 40cm high. **Leaves** mainly basal, oblong to oblanceolate, 5–8cm long to 2cm wide, margins toothed to narrowly lobed. **Flowers** bright yellow and densely bearded, to 4cm across, in racemes or sometimes umbels on stalks to 12cm long. Widespread mainly in dry inland districts. Qld, NSW, Vic, SA, WA. Autumn, winter, spring.

Goodenia rotundifolia |

Low spreading or erect perennial herb to 50cm high; stems glabrous, slightly hairy or sticky. **Leaves** circular to obovate, 1–2cm long and wide, margins toothed or lobed. **Flowers** yellow with brownish throat and hairy exterior, to 1.5cm across, singly or in groups of 3, on stalks to 2.5cm long. Woodland and open forest. NSW, Qld. Spring, summer, autumn.

Goodenia stelligera | Spiked Goodenia

Erect perennial herb to 50cm high. **Leaves** mainly in basal rosette, linear to narrow–oblanceolate, 5–25cm long and about 1cm wide, sessile, usually glossy above, margins entire or irregularly toothed. **Flowers** yellow with hairy exterior, to 1.5cm across, in spike-like clusters on almost leafless stalks to 50cm high. Mainly coastal in wet situations in heath and open forest. Qld, NSW. Winter, spring, summer.

Lechenaultia biloba | Blue Lechenaultia

Open spreading shrub to 1m high; often suckering stems erect. **Leaves** linear to terete, to 1cm long and 1mm wide, often crowded. **Flowers** in various shades of blue, rarely white, to 3cm across; lobes almost equal, spreading and broadly winged. **Capsule** ribbed to 3.5cm long. Widespread and common in a variety of habitats in the southwest. WA. Winter, spring.

Goodenia lunata

Goodenia ovata

Goodenia pinnatifida

Goodenia rotundifolia

Goodenia stelligera

Lechenaultia biloba

Lechenaultia formosa | Red Lechenaultia

Prostrate suckering shrub to 50cm across; stems spreading or erect. **Leaves** linear t terete, to 1cm long and 1mm wide, fleshy, often crowded, tip pointed. **Flowers** in shades c red, orange yellow, pink and cream as well as combinations of these, about 2.5cm across, a branch ends. **Capsule** to 3cm long. Widespread along the southern coast and farther inlanc WA. Winter, spring.

Lechenaultia laricina | Scarlet Lechenaultia

Small erect or spreading shrub to 80cm high, often suckering. **Leaves** linear, t 1cm long and 1mm wide, rather soft, crowded, tip pointed. **Flowers** tubular, red or orange red with a paler centre, about 2.5cm across, in clusters of up to 3 flowers. **Capsule** 4-valvec about 3cm long. Confined to the Avon district of the southwest, usually in woodlanc WA. Spring, summer.

Lechenaultia macrantha | Wreath Lechenaultia

Prostrate perennial herb to 1m across, growing annually from a rootstock. **Leaves** lin ear, to 3.5cm long and 1cm wide, erect, grey-green, tip pointed. **Flowers** tubular, yellow an deep pink or reddish, to 4cm across, massed in dense clusters around the perimeter of th plant forming a wreath-like display. Wheatbelt region north of Perth, in open areas, usually i sandy or red gravelly soil. WA. Spring.

Scaevola aemula | Fairy Fan Flower

Prostrate or spreading perennial herb to 50cm high; stems coarsely hairy. **Leaves** ovat to obovate, 2–8cm long and to 2.5cm wide, margins coarsely toothed. **Flowers** fan-shapec blue or mauve with yellow at the base, in leafy spikes to 24cm long; style cup (indusiun with long purplish hairs. Mainly in coastal districts on sandy soils. NSW, Vic, SA. Sprin₁ summer, autumn.

Scaevola albida | Pale Fan Flower

Low spreading perennial herb to 50cm high. **Leaves** obovate to elliptic, to 5cm lon and 2.5cm wide, sessile, margins entire or toothed. **Flowers** fan-shaped, pale blue, mauve c white in leafy spikes in the upper leaf axils; style cup (indusium) with silvery hairs at the bas Widespread from the coast and ranges in open forest and woodland. Qld, NSW, Vic, SP Throughout the year.

Scaevola calendulacea | Dune Fan Flower

Prostrate shrub with ascending branches to 40cm high. **Leaves** semi-succulen oblanceolate to obovate, to 8cm long to 2.5cm wide, margins mostly entire. **Flowers** fan shaped, bright blue with yellow centres, in terminal spikes to 8cm long. **Fruit** a white an purplish berry. Widespread in coastal districts on sand dunes near the sea. Qld, NSW, Vi Spring, summer, autumn.

Lechenaultia formosa

Lechenaultia laricina

Lechenaultia macrantha

Scaevola aemula

Scaevola albida

Scaevola calendulacea

Scaevola parvibarbata

Erect densely hairy perennial herb to 50cm high. **Leaves** oblanceolate to circular, 1–4cm long to 2cm wide, sessile, hairy, margins usually toothed. **Flowers** fan-shaped, lilac with densely bearded throat, in spikes to 25cm long; style cup (indusium) with short white hairs. Widespread in dry inland districts, mostly on sandy soils. Qld, NSW, SA, NT. Winter, spring.

Scaevola ramosissima | Purple Fan Flower

Prostrate perennial herb to 40cm high; stems wiry with glandular hairs. **Leaves** sessile, linear to oblanceolate, 2–10cm long to 1cm wide, sessile, margins entire or toothed. **Flowers** fan-shaped, pale violet to purple with bearded throat, solitary or in clusters of 3 on a slender stalk; style cup (indusium) with short white hairs. Mainly coastal, in heath and open forest, usually on sandy soils. Qld, NSW, Vic. Spring, summer, autumn.

Scaevola striata | Royal Robe

Prostrate suckering perennial herb to 1m across; stems hairy. **Leaves** ovate to linear, 3–5cm long and to 2cm wide, sessile, hairy and coarsely toothed toward the tips. **Flowers** fan-shaped, purple with prominent striations on the petals, about 3cm across; style cup (indusium) with short yellowish hairs. Common in the Darling Range and jarrah forests of the south coast. WA. Spring, summer.

Scaevola taccada | Pipe Tree

Formerly *S. sericea*. Erect shrub or small tree 2–4m high; stems smooth. **Leaves** oblong to obovate, 8–20cm long and 2–9cm wide, spirally arranged, glossy, light green and smooth, usually entire, tip rounded. **Flowers** fan-shaped, white and bearded inside, 2–3cm across, in clusters in the upper leaf axils; style cup (indusium) with a few white hairs. **Fruit** a fleshy white drupe to 13mm long. Common on coastal sand dunes just above high water mark, in northern Australia. WA, NT, Qld. Throughout the year.

Velleia montana

Small prostrate perennial herb. **Leaves** in basal tufts, oblanceolate to obovate, 2–8cm long to 3cm wide, margins toothed or entire. **Flowers** tubular, yellow, split almost to the base on the upper side. **Fruit** a globular capsule to 2mm across. Subalpine grasslands and woodland usually in moist situations. NSW, Vic, Tas. Summer.

Scaevola parvibarbata

Scaevola ramosissima

Scaevola striata

Scaevola taccada

Velleia montana

HAEMODORACEAE | Kangaroo Paw family

A relative small family of perennial herbs with rhizomes, bulbs or tubers, of about 14 genera and 100 species occurring mainly in Africa and Australia. Australia has about 7 genera and 85 species, with many confined to the southwestern botanical province of Western Australia. Leaves mainly basal, base sheathing, flat, triangular in cross-section or terete; stem leaves smaller or absent. Flowers regular or irregular, bisexual. Perianth of 6 segments or in 1 or 2 whorls, free or partly fused into a short or long woolly tube. Stamens 3 or 6. Ovary inferior or half inferior. Fruit a capsule. The family is noted for its colourful and long-lasting kangaroo paws (*Anigozanthos* species) grown for the nursery and florist trade. Leaves are not illustrated in this family as they are too similar for identification purposes.

Anigozanthos bicolor | Little Kangaroo Paw

Small rhizomatous perennial herb to 35cm high; leaves die down over summer. **Leaves** flat and strap-like to 35cm long and 1cm wide, glabrous. **Flowers** tubular with split on lower side, 3–7cm long, green with reddish (rarely yellow) base, densely hairy, arranged in a terminal racemes on an unbranched flowering stalk 10–70cm long. Near granite outcrops in the Darling Ranges, usually in woodland and forest. WA. Spring.

Anigozanthos flavidus | Tall Kangaroo Paw

Clumping rhizomatous perennial herb to 1m high. **Leaves** strap-like to 1m long and 2cm wide, glabrous, margins hairy in young plants. **Flowers** tubular, 3-4.5cm long, yellowish-green, or sometimes red, densely hairy, on branched flowering stalk to 2m tall. Common in southwest in high-rainfall forested regions, also woodland and heath. WA. Spring, summer.

Anigozanthos humilis | Cat's Paw

Small rhizomatous perennial herb to 20cm high; leaves may die down in winter. **Leaves** flat, sickle-shaped, to 20cm long and 1.5cm wide, margins hairy. **Flowers** tubular, to 5cm long, yellow suffused with red or salmon (rarely pure yellow), hairy, in a single terminal spike on flowering stalk to 30cm long. Widespread in the southwest in heath, woodland and occasionally forest. WA. Winter, spring.

Anigozanthos manglesii | Red and Green Kangaroo Paw

Tufted rhizomatous perennial herb to 40cm high. **Leaves** flat and strap-like, 10–40cm long to 1.2cm wide, grey-green, glabrous. **Flowers** tubular, split on lower side with reflexed lobes, 6-10cm long, bright green with scarlet base and stem, in a single (occasionally branched) terminal spike on slightly curved flowering stalk to 1m long. Common in coastal and near-coastal regions in sand plains, heath, woodland and forest of southwest. WA. Winter, spring.

Anigozanthos bicolor

Anigozanthos flavidus

Anigozanthos humilis

Anigozanthos manglesii

Anigozanthos pulcherrimus | Yellow Kangaroo Paw

Clumping rhizomatous perennial herb to 60cm high; leaves die down in summer. **Leaves** strap-like, to 60cm long and 1.5cm wide, grey-green, glabrous or tomentose. **Flowers** tubular 2–3.5cm long, yellow, hairy, on branched flowering stalk to 1.5m tall. Northern sandplains and low heath in seasonally wet sand. WA. Spring, summer.

Anigozanthos rufus | Red Kangaroo Paw

Clumping rhizomatous perennial herb 20–40cm high. **Leaves** strap-like, to 40cm long and 6mm wide, dull green, glabrous, margins rough. **Flowers** tubular, 2–3.5cm long, deep red or purple (rarely yellow), woolly, on branched flowering stalk to 1m tall. Mainly between the Stirling Range and Israelite Bay in the southwest in low heath and open mallee. WA. Spring, summer.

Anigozanthos viridus | Green Kangaroo Paw

Rhizomatous perennial herb to 50cm high; leaves die down in summer. **Leaves** semi-terete 5–50cm long to 5mm wide, grey-green and glabrous. **Flowers** tubular, split on lower side with reflexed lobes, 5–7cm long, green or yellow-green, hairy, on slightly curved unbranched flowering stalk to 50cm tall. Swan Coastal Plain and Darling Plateau, in heath, woodland and forest, in winter-wet situations. WA. Winter, spring.

Blancoa canescens | Winter Bell

Tufted rhizomatous perennial herb to 25cm high. **Leaves** linear, to 25cm long, grey pubescent, when young. **Flowers** tubular, pendulous, to 4cm long, with 6 spreading equal lobes, red and hairy outside, golden-orange interior in short racemes. Common in low woodland and heath in deep sand, north of Perth. WA. Winter, spring.

Anigozanthos pulcherrimus

Anigozanthos rufus

Anigozanthos viridus

Blancoa canescens

Conostylis aculeata |

Tufted perennial herb to 60cm high. **Leaves** flat, to 60cm long and 1cm wide, margins with widely spaced bristly spines along length. **Flowers** tubular, to 12mm long, yellow, hairy, in dense terminal globular heads, on simple or branched flowering stalk, usually longer than the leaves. A variable species with about 10 subspecies. Widespread in southwest, in heath, woodland and forest. WA. Winter, spring, summer.

Conostylis candicans | Grey Cottonheads

Tufted perennial herb to 40cm high. **Leaves** flat, 20–40cm long and 2–6mm wide, densely covered in greyish hairs. **Flowers** tubular, to 13mm long, yellow, hairy in dense heads mostly on unbranched stalks longer than the leaves. Common and widespread in coastal areas of southwest in heath and woodland. WA. Winter, spring, summer.

Conostylis prolifera | Mat Cottonheads

Tufted perennial herb to 10cm high; stems stoloniferous often forming dense mats. **Leaves** flat, linear, to 10cm long and 2mm wide, soft, margins sometimes with small bristles. **Flowers** tubular, pale yellow and cream inside, to 12mm long, hairy outside, in dense or loose heads on unbranched stalks as long or much longer than the leaves. Widespread north of Perth in heath and open woodland. WA. Spring, summer.

Conostylis robusta |

Tufted perennial herb to 40cm high. **Leaves** linear, 15–40cm long and 1.5cm wide, bluish-green margins sometimes with small spines. **Flowers** tubular, to 12mm long, deep yellow, in terminal, rounded heads on stalks usually exceeding the leaves. Sand plains north of Perth in heath and low woodland. WA. Winter, spring.

Conostylis seorsiflora |

Prostrate perennial herb forming mats to 40cm across; stems stoloniferous. **Leaves** linear, to 15cm long and less than 2mm wide, hairy when young then mostly glabrous. **Flowers** star-like, to 1.5cm long, yellow, hairy outside, usually solitary, on short stems to about 5cm long. Southern sand plains usually in damp situations. WA. Spring, summer.

Conostylis aculeata

Conostylis candicans

Conostylis prolifera

Conostylis robusta

Conostylis seorsiflora

Conostylis setigera | Bristly Cottonheads

Low tufted perennial herb to 30cm high. **Leaves** flat, 10–30cm long and 4mm wide, margin with white hairs, longitudinal nerves prominent. **Flowers** pale yellow, tubular with spreading lobes, to 1.5cm long, densely hairy outside, in heads of 5–10 flowers on stalks usually shorter than the leaves. Common and widespread in southwest, in a variety of plant communities WA. Winter, spring.

Conostylis setosa |

Low tufted perennial herb to 30cm high. **Leaves** flat, 15-30cm long and 4mm wide, margins with long white bristly hairs. **Flowers** cream, white or pinkish, tubular with spreading lobes, to 2cm long, silky-hairy outside, in dense heads to 6cm across on stalks to 35cm long. Common in the Darling Range near Perth, in jarrah forest. WA. Spring.

Conostylis stylidioides | Mat Cottonheads

Low tufted perennial herb to 20cm high; stems branched and stoloniferous. **Leaves** flat or semi-terete, to 5cm long and 1cm wide, with whitish hairs when young. **Flowers** golden yellow, tubular, to 13mm long, densely hairy outside, in small dense heads on unbranched felted stalks usually much longer than the leaves. On or near the coast, mainly between Geraldton and Shark Bay region. WA. Winter, spring, summer.

Macropidia fuliginosa | Black Kangaroo Paw

Tufted perennial herb to 80cm high; stems densely covered with black hairs. **Leaves** flat 20–50cm long and 1.5cm wide, base sheathing, bluish-green, mostly glabrous. **Flower** greenish-yellow covered with black hairs, tubular, to 6cm long, with irregularly curled lobes on branched flowering stalks to 1.8m tall. North of Perth to Geraldton, usually in low heath woodland and open mallee. WA. Spring.

Conostylis setigera

Conostylis setosa

Conostylis stylidioides

Macropidia fuliginosa

IRIDACEAE | Iris family

Large family of monocotyledons of about 85 genera and 1500 species widely distribute throughout the world and including well-known ornamental plants, such as *Iris* and *Frees* species and hybrids. Australian Iridaceae consists of only 6 genera, although many foreig plants, mainly of African origin, have become naturalised. They are erect perennial herk arising from rhizomes or corms with fibrous roots. Leaves sword-shaped, basal or along th stems arranged in 2 ranks. Flowers have 6 perianth segments, 3 petals and 3 sepals, ofte united below into a tube. Stamens 3. Ovary inferior. Fruit a capsule. Leaves are not illu trated in this family as they are too similar for identification purposes.

Dietes robinsoniana | Wedding Lily

Erect clumping perennial herb to 2m tall. **Leaves** sword-shaped, to 1m long and 4–7cm wid in a flat fan-like arrangement. **Flowers** white, 5–8cm across, with 6 spreading segments an 3 expanded stamens, on branched flowering stalk to 1.5m tall. Endemic to Lord Howe Islan NSW. Spring, summer.

Orthrosanthus laxus | Morning Iris

Tufted perennial herb to 50cm high. **Leaves** basal, linear, erect, 12–50cm long and 3–5mr wide, margins roughened. **Flowers** regular, pale blue, about 4cm across, with spreadin segments shortly united at the base, on erect branched stalks to 70cm tall. Widespread i southwest. WA. Winter, spring.

Orthosanthus multiflorus | Morning Flag

Tufted perennial herb to 60cm tall. **Leaves** basal, grass-like, 20–60cm long and 2–6mm wid margins rough, especially near the base. **Flowers** pale blue, to 4cm across, with 3–7 flowe per branch on flowering stalk to 80cm tall. Widely distributed in southern Australia, mostl in coastal heath. Vic, SA, WA. Spring, summer.

Patersonia occidentalis | Long Purple Flag

Tufted perennial herb to 55cm high. **Leaves** sword-shaped to linear, flat, 10–55cm long an 2–10mm wide, glabrous with margins glabrous or with brown hairs. **Flowers** blue-viole with 3 broad conspicuous petal-like sepals, 4–7cm across, in terminal clusters enclosed b 2 large, brown bracts (spathes), which are mostly glabrous, on stalks to 80cm long Widely distributed in southern Australia in coastal heath and woodland. Vic, Tas, SA, WA Spring, summer.

Dietes robinsoniana

Orthrosanthus laxus

Orthosanthus multiflorus

Patersonia occidentalis

Patersonia sericea | Silky Purple Flag

Tufted perennial herb to 50cm high. **Leaves** sword-shaped, flat, 15–50cm long to 6mm wide, glabrous with margins hairy, especially at the base. **Flowers** purple with 3 broadly ovate petal-like sepals, 4–6cm across; spathes to 6cm long are brownish-black with white silky hairs. Widespread from coast to ranges in heath, woodland and open forest. Qld, NSW, Vic. Winter, spring, summer.

Patersonia umbrosa | Purple Flag

Tufted perennial herb to 90cm high. **Leaves** linear to sword-shaped, 30–90cm long to 6mm wide, glabrous with rough margins near the base. **Flowers** deep blue-violet with 3 ovate petal-like sepals, 5–7cm across; spathes to 8cm long, green to pale brown, mostly glabrous. Widespread in lower southwest, in heath, woodland and jarrah forest. WA. Winter, spring.

LAMIACEAE | Mint family

Large cosmopolitan family of aromatic plants of about 180 genera and 3500 species especially noted for its Mediterranean culinary herbs, such as basil, mint, rosemary and thyme. Australian Lamiaceae comprise 38 genera and about 250 species, the main representative being the mint bushes *Prostanthera* (about 100 species). Most species are shrubs or herbs; stems usually 4-angled, especially when young. Leaves mostly opposite, each pair at right angles to the next (rarely whorled), without stipules. Flowers irregular, bisexual, usually 2-lipped or 5-lobed. Sepals 5. Petals 5, united into a tube. Stamens 4, attached to the corolla tube. Ovary superior, usually 4-lobed, the style arising from between the lobes. Fruit, dry, comprising 4 segments (mericarps).

Ajuga australis | Austral Bugle

Perennial herb to 60cm high; stems erect hairy. **Basal leaves** obovate, 3–12cm long to 3.5cm wide, hairy, margins toothed or lobed; **stem leaves** sessile and smaller. **Flowers** violet to blue, to 1.2cm long with elongated 3-lobed lower lip and short upper lip, in axillary whorls of 6–20 flowers. Widespread in woodland and open forest. Qld, NSW, Vic, Tas, SA. Spring, summer.

Hemiandra pungens | Snake Bush

Prostrate or upright shrub to 1m high. **Leaves** sessile, linear to linear–lanceolate 1–3cm long to 5mm wide, strongly ribbed below, tip pungent-pointed. **Flowers**, white, pink or mauve with darker spots at the throat, to 2cm long, with 5 irregular spreading lobes, singly in the leaf axils. Widespread in coastal and nearby districts in the southwest. WA. Spring, summer.

Patersonia sericea

Patersonia umbrosa

Ajuga australis

Hemiandra pungens

Hemigenia purpurea | Common Hemigenia

Slender shrub 1–2m high. **Leaves** linear to terete, to 1.5cm long crowded in whorl of 3, channelled above, tip pointed. **Flowers** mauve to lilac, about 1cm long, with a short 2-lobed upper lip and a larger, spreading 3-lobed lower lip, singly in the upper leaf axil. Common in heath around Sydney and Blue Mountains. NSW. Winter, spring.

Prostanthera aspalathoides | Scarlet Mint Bush

Small erect shrub to less than 1m tall; branches terete, hairy. **Leaves** linear–terete, to 6mm long, margins entire, crowded on smaller branches, strongly scented. **Flowers** scarlet, occasionally yellow, about 2cm long, finely hairy outside with a large upper lip, singly in leaf axils. In dry regions, usually in mallee. Qld, NSW, Vic, SA. Spring.

Prostanthera baxteri |

Small erect shrub to 1m high; stems with short grey hairs. **Leaves** sessile, narrow-linear and incurved or terete, 1–2cm long, sessile, silky-hairy when young, channelled above. **Flowers** pale lavender with purplish lines at throat, about 3cm long, in upper leaf axils; calyx hairy, upper lip larger and longer than lower lip. Drier regions of southern Australia. WA, SA. Winter, spring.

Prostanthera calycina |

Small erect shrub to 80cm high; stems with short hairs. **Leaves** ovate to almost orbicular, to 1cm long, dark green above, paler and minutely scaly below, margins slightly recurved. **Flowers** red, about 2cm long, in upper leaf axils; calyx lobes broad and reddish, almost equal. Dry coastal areas from Port Lincoln to Streaky Bay on the Eyre Peninsula, SA. Spring, summer.

Prostanthera cuneata | Alpine Mint Bush

Dense, highly aromatic shrub to 1m or more high; stems hairy and glandular. **Leaves** sessile, obovate, 4–6mm long to 4mm wide, sessile, rather thick, glossy dark green above, pale and glandular below, tip rounded. **Flowers** white with purple blotches or spots at the throat, about 2cm long; lower lip large and spreading, upper lip shorter and erect. Subalpine heath and shrubland. NSW, Vic, Tas. Summer.

Prostanthera denticulata | Rough Mint Bush

Scrambling open shrub to 1m high and 2m across. **Leaves** narrow ovate, to 1cm long and 2–3mm wide, sessile, margins entire and recurved, often with small raised tubercle hairs on upper surface. **Flowers** purple to mauve, about 1cm long, in pairs in the upper leaf axils; calyx lobes broad, reddish and hairy. Chiefly coastal, in damp situations in open forest and woodland. NSW, Vic. Spring, summer.

Hemigenia purpurea

Prostanthera aspalathoides

Prostanthera baxteri

Prostanthera calycina

Prostanthera cuneata

Prostanthera denticulata

Prostanthera discolor

Open erect shrub to 3m high; stems hairy and glandular. **Leaves** narrow–lanceolate or oblong, to 3cm long and 5mm wide, margins entire dark green above, paler below, strongly aromatic. **Flowers** mauve to violet with a darker throat, to 1cm long, in terminal compact racemes. Dry open forest on the central slopes. NSW. Spring.

Prostanthera incana | Velvet Mint Bush

Erect dense shrub to 2.5m high; stems densely hairy. **Leaves** ovate, 1–2cm long and to 1.5cm wide, wrinkled, margins shallowly toothed and slightly recurved, densely hairy. **Flowers** violet to lilac, about 1cm long, in short racemes at branch ends; calyx lobes broad and almost equal. Near coastal districts in sheltered forest and woodland. NSW, Vic. Spring, summer.

Prostanthera incisa | Cut-leaved Mint Bush

Variable spreading shrub from 1–2m high; stems moderately hairy. **Leaves** ovate to narrow–ovate, 1–3cm long and to 12mm wide, margins coarsely toothed, minutely hairy, strongly aromatic when crushed. **Flowers** mauve, about 1cm long, in short axillary clusters; calyx lobes unequal. Chiefly in central coastal districts in moist, sheltered forest and on rainforest margins. NSW. Spring.

Prostanthera lasianthos | Victorian Christmas Bush

Tall shrub or small tree to 5m high. **Leaves** lanceolate to ovate, 4–12cm long to 3cm wide, finely toothed, dark green above, paler below, tip pointed. **Flowers** white to pale mauve spotted purple in throat, to 2cm long, in large showy racemes. Mainly in sheltered forest in moist gullies and along creeks on the coast, mountains and slopes. Qld, NSW, Vic, Tas. Summer.

Prostanthera discolor

Prostanthera incana

Prostanthera incisa

Prostanthera lasianthos

Prostanthera linearis | Narrow-leaved Mint Bush

Erect slender shrub 1–3m high. **Leaves** linear to narrow–ovate, 1–4.5cm long and 3mm wide, sessile, dark green and glabrous above, paler below, margins entire and slightly revolute. **Flowers** white to mauve, sometimes spotted at throat, about 12mm long, axillary or in terminal leafy clusters. Widespread from coast to mountains, in forest, often in gullies. NSW. Spring, summer.

Prostanthera magnifica | Magnificent Mint Bush

Erect shrub 1–2m high; stem pubescent when young. **Leaves** thick, elliptic, sometimes obovate, to 3cm long and 1cm wide, rather thick, tip pointed. **Flowers** pale mauve or pink, to 2.5cm long in dense axillary clusters or leafy racemes; calyx purple to red, upper lip highly coloured and greatly enlarged after flowering. Confined to the Mullewa and Geraldton areas in sandy situations. WA. Winter, spring.

Prostanthera nivea | Snowy Mint Bush

Erect bushy shrub to 3m high; branches ridged. **Leaves** linear, 1–5cm long to 2mm wide, sessile, flat, margins entire. **Flowers** white to mauve with yellow spotted throat, to 2cm long, in axillary clusters toward the end of branches. Calyx enlarged after flowering. Widespread from the coast to farther inland in dry forest, woodland and heath. Qld, NSW, Vic. Spring.

Prostanthera ovalifolia | Purple Mint Bush

Erect bushy shrub 2–4m high; branches angular, glandular and softly hairy. **Leaves** ovate to narrow–ovate, to 4cm long and 1cm wide, margins entire or slightly lobed. **Flowers** purple or mauve (rarely white) with darker spotted throat, to 1cm long, in short terminal racemes; calyx lobes equal in length and entire. Widespread on coast, tablelands and farther inland. Qld, NSW, Vic. Winter, spring.

Prostanthera linearis

Prostanthera magnifica

Prostanthera nivea

Prostanthera ovalifolia

Prostanthera phylicifolia

Erect bushy shrub to 2m high; branches ridged and covered with short hairs. **Leaves** narrow–ovate to oblong, to 1.5cm long and to 5mm wide, margins entire and recurved, tip rounded. **Flowers** white to lilac with purple spotted throat, about 1.5cm long in upper leaf axils. Heath and dry open forest often on granite outcrops and slopes. Qld, NSW, Vic. Spring, summer.

Prostanthera prunelloides | Prunella Mint Bush

Erect shrub to 2m high; branches ridged, glandular and shortly hairy. **Leaves** ovate 2–6cm long and 1–4cm wide, wavy, margins mostly entire, tip rounded, aromatic. **Flower** white or faintly mauve with yellow spots and darker mauve at the throat, about 1.5cm long in short terminal racemes. Scattered from coast to mountains and farther inland, often along creeks. NSW. Spring.

Prostanthera rotundifolia | Round-leaved Mint Bush

Tall compact, aromatic shrub to 3m high; branches shortly hairy and glandular. **Leaves** variable, ovate, obovate or almost circular, to 2cm long and 1.5cm wide, glandular margins entire or faintly toothed, tip rounded. **Flowers** pink, lilac to purple, about 1.5cm long in either axillary or terminal racemes. Widespread in open forest, woodland and rainforest margins. Qld, NSW, Vic, Tas. Spring.

Prostanthera scutellarioides

Small spreading shrub to 1m high; branches shortly hairy. **Leaves** linear, to 2.5cm long and 2mm wide, light green, margins entire and recurved, tip pointed. **Flowers** mauve or purple, to 1cm long, in upper leaf axils. Coast and nearby mountains, in open forest and woodland in scattered locations Qld, NSW. Spring, summer.

Prostanthera phylicifolia

Prostanthera prunelloides

Prostanthera rotundifolia

Prostanthera scutellarioides

Prostanthera staurophylla

Erect strongly aromatic shrub to 1.5m high; branches shortly hairy and glandular. **Leaves** terete, to 1.5cm long, with 2–5 terete lobes, sessile, glandular, margins entire and recurved. **Flowers** lilac to deep mauve, about 12mm long, crowded in upper leaf axils. Tenterfield area, in heath and open forest, often on granite outcrops. NSW. Spring, summer.

Prostanthera striatiflora | Streaked Mint Bush

Erect aromatic shrub to 2m high; branches sparsely hairy. **Leaves** lanceolate to narrow–lanceolate, 1–3cm long and to 1cm wide, pale green, rather thick and glandular, margins entire, tip often blunt. **Flowers** white with prominent purple lines within, about 2cm long, axillary or crowded into terminal leafy racemes. Widespread in dry inland regions in woodland, often in rocky areas. Qld, NSW, SA, WA, NT. Winter, spring.

Westringia fruticosa | Coast Rosemary

Compact shrub to 1.5m high. **Leaves** sessile, narrow–lanceolate, 1–3cm long to 5mm wide, sessile, mostly in whorls of 4, upper surface dark green and smooth, paler and densely hairy below, margins entire and recurved. **Flowers** white with purplish spots within, about 1.5cm long, in upper leaf axils. Heath, sand dunes and cliffs near the sea. NSW. Throughout the year.

Westringia longifolia

Erect open shrub to 3m high. **Leaves** narrow–linear, to 3.5cm long and 2mm wide, usually in whorls of 3, shiny green above, paler below, margins entire. **Flowers** pale mauve with pale brown spots, about 1cm long, in upper leaf axils; calyx green with triangular lobes. Coastal and farther inland in gullies often in rocky areas. Qld, NSW. Throughout the year.

Prostanthera staurophylla

Prostanthera striatiflora

Westringia fruticosa

Westringia longifolia

LOBELIACEAE | Lobelia family

A family of mostly annual or perennial herbs, rarely trees and shrubs, consisting of 2 genera and about 120 species centred in the tropical Americas and temperate regions in the Southern Hemisphere. Australia has 6 genera and about 50 species. A milky sap might be present. Leaves simple, mostly alternate, without stipules. Flowers usually irregular bisexual. Sepals 5, erect or spreading. Petals 5, united at the base of the corolla tube, which may be entire or slit to the base on the upper side. Stamens 5; anthers fused into a tube around the style. Ovary inferior. Fruit a capsule. This family is often considered to be subfamily of Campanulaceae, but differs in its irregular flowers and fused anthers.

Isotoma anethifolia

Small perennial herb to 50cm high; stems erect and wiry. **Leaves** narrow, 2–10cm long and to 4cm wide, deeply divided into linear segments, sometimes toothed. **Flowers** usually white, star-shaped with a tube to 2cm long, about 3cm across, solitary, on slender stalks to 12cm long. Damp sites in rocky crevices, especially granite. Qld, NSW. Spring, summer.

Isotoma axillaris | Showy Isotome

Small bushy perennial herb to 30cm high; stems slender with a milky sap. **Leaves** narrow, 2–15cm long to 3cm wide, deeply divided into toothed linear lobes. **Flowers** pale to deep blue (rarely white), star-shaped with equal lobes to 3cm across, on slender axillary stalks to 12cm long. Widespread in eastern Australia mainly in rocky sites, especially granite. Qld, NSW, Vic. Spring, summer.

Lobelia dentata

Erect annual herb to 40cm high; stems slender, smooth. **Lower leaves** ovate, 1–4cm long to 1cm wide, deeply lobed, mostly withering early, **upper leaves** scattered and narrow. **Flowers** deep blue to purple, about 2.5cm long, on 1-sided raceme of 8–10 flowers; middle lower lobe oblong and longer than the 2 lobes. Chiefly coastal, in open forest and woodland on sandy soils. NSW. Winter, spring, summer.

Lobelia trigonocaulis | Forest Lobelia

Low perennial herb to 40cm high; stems trailing, 3-angled. **Leaves** ovate–cordate to almost circular, 1–4cm long to 3.5cm wide, margins bluntly toothed or scalloped, tip pointed. **Flowers** mauve-blue, about 1.5cm long, in loose terminal racemes of 3–6 flowers; 3 lower lobes oblong. Sheltered moist situations in dry forest, and in or near rainforest. Qld, NSW. Spring, summer.

Isotoma anethifolia

Isotoma axillaris

Lobelia dentata

Lobelia trigonocaulis

Pratia pedunculata | Matted Pratia

Mostly mat-forming perennial herb; stems weak and trailing, often with adventitiou roots. **Leaves** ovate to almost circular, 6–10mm long to 7mm wide, margins usually toothed tip blunt. **Flowers** solitary, white or bluish-mauve, about 1cm long, 5-lobed, floral tube spli to the base on the upper side. In damp situations, from the coast to the ranges. NSW, Vic, Tas SA. Summer, autumn.

LORANTHACEAE | Mistletoe family

Partly parasitic shrubs or trees growing either on the stems or roots of host plants. Ther are about 65 genera and 900 species widely distributed in tropical and southern temperat regions of the world. Australia is well represented by 10 genera and 65 species, most o which are endemic. Leaves usually opposite, simple and entire. Some host-specific specie have leaves that mimic those of the host. Flowers mostly bisexual and mostly regula usually large and brightly coloured. Calyx lobed or truncated or reduced to a low rin (calyculus). Corolla tubular, fused or sometimes split to the base. Petals mostly 4–6 Stamens mostly 4–6 opposite to and attached to the petals. Ovary inferior. Fruit berry-like often 1-seeded, with an inner sticky layer that aids adherence to stems and dispersal b certain small birds that feed on them.

Amyema pendulum | Drooping Mistletoe

Aerial stem-parasitic shrub; stems pendent, mostly glabrous, except when youn **Leaves** lanceolate, 10–40cm long and to 2cm wide, tip pointed. **Flowers** red, 2–4cm lon with 5 free petals, axillary in umbels of 3–7 groups of 3 flowers (triad). The central flower c each triad is sessile, a feature that separates this species from the very similar *A. miquelii*. Ho tree many species of *Eucalyptus* and several *Acacia* species. Widespread from coast to inlan districts, in open forest and woodland. Qld, NSW, Vic, SA. Throughout the year.

Lysiana exocarpi | Harlequin Mistletoe

Aerial stem-parasitic shrub; stems pendent, glabrous. **Leaves** on short stalks, linear t narrow–oblong, 3–15cm long to 2cm wide, leathery, tip rounded. **Flowers** red (rarely yellow sometimes tipped green, to 5cm long, usually in a 2-flowered umbel on a short commo stalk. **Fruit** about 1cm long, red or black. Parasitic on a wide variety of hosts. Widesprea chiefly in inland regions. Qld, NSW, Vic, SA, WA, NT. Summer, autumn.

Pratia pedunculata

Lysiana exocarpi

Amyema pendulum

MALVACEAE | Hibiscus family

A large cosmopolitan family of herbs, shrubs and small trees of about 85 genera and 2000 species found mostly in warm–tropical and tropical regions. Widely cultivated for its brightly coloured flowers throughout warmer parts of the world, *Hibiscus* is the best known genus. *Gossypium* is the most important genus commercially, grown for cotton and cottonseed oil. All *Gossypium* species have seeds that are covered in long hairs. Australia has 24 genera and about 160 species. Most species have stems, leaves and other parts covered with stellate hairs. Leaves alternate, often variously lobed, palmately veined, with stipules. Flowers regular, bisexual with 5 colourful free overlapping petals. Calyx often subtended by an epicalyx (lower calyx whorl) of 3 or more segments. Stamens numerous, fused into a prominent tube surrounding the style, joined to the petals at the base; anthers free, with 1 chamber. Ovary superior. Fruit dry, breaking into segments, or a capsule.

Abelmoschus manihot |

Erect herb or shrub 1–3m high; stems mostly hairy. **Leaves** variable with 3–7 lobes from 10–25cm long and wide, lobes toothed or entire, glabrous to densely hairy. **Flowers** solitary, yellow (sometimes white) with small purple centre, 10–15cm across. **Capsule** ovoid 3–6cm long, densely hairy. Widespread, often close to rivers. Qld. Summer, autumn.

Abutilon leucopetalum | Lantern Bush

Shrub 30cm to 1m high; stems covered with felty and long hairs. **Leaves** ovate to circular, 2–8cm long and 3–6cm wide, base heart-shaped, margins coarsely toothed, densely hairy. **Flowers** to 4cm long, bright yellow, fading to white with age; calyx bell-shaped, ribbed, to 2cm long. **Fruit** angular, about 1.5cm across, breaks into 7–10 segments. Dry inland regions, often on rocky slopes. Qld, NSW, SA, WA, NT. Autumn, winter.

Aloygyne huegeli |

Spreading shrub to 2.5m high; stems with scattered stellate hairs. **Leaves** 2–7cm long deeply divided into 3–5 oblong lobes, margins irregularly toothed or lobed. **Flowers** lilac or reddish-purple (occasionally white or yellow), 7–10cm across, solitary, on stalks usually longer than the leaves. **Fruit** an ovoid, pubescent capsule, to 2cm across. Widespread from the southwest to the Lofty Ranges. SA, WA. Spring, summer.

Gossypium australe | Desert Rose

Erect shrub 1–2m high; stems with short dense hairs. **Leaves** ovate, 3–6cm long to 3cm wide, hairy. **Flowers** mostly mauve with a dark red central blotch, 4–6cm across; calyx bell-shaped deeply lobed; epicalyx has 3 long slender segments. **Capsule** hairy, about 2cm long. Seeds black, covered in spreading bristly hairs. Widespread in Central Australia. Qld, WA, NT. Autumn, winter, spring.

Abelmoschus manihot

Abutilon leucopetalum

Aloygyne huegeli

Gossypium australe

Gossypium sturtianum | Sturt's Desert Rose

Erect open shrub to 2m high; stems hairless with raised black spots. **Leaves** ovate to cir cular, 2.5–6cm long to 6cm wide, entire to deeply lobed. **Flowers** solitary, pink or mauve wit a dark red central blotch, 6–7cm across; calyx 5-lobed; epicalyx has 3 large triangular segments **Capsule** ovoid, about 2.5cm long. Seeds with flattened, white to greenish hairs. Floral emblem of NT. Widespread in dry inland regions. Qld, NSW, Vic, SA, WA, NT. Most of the year.

Hibiscus heterophyllus | Native Rosella

Shrub or small tree 3–6m high; stems prickly. **Leaves** leaves ovate or deeply lobed 5–20cm long to 10cm wide, upper leaves linear ovate. **Flowers** solitary, white with a pinkis tinge and crimson central blotch (occasionally yellow), 10–25cm across. **Capsule** ovoid, t 2cm long, densely hairy. Moist situations in open forest, in or near rainforest, mainly coasta Qld, NSW. Spring, summer, autumn.

Hibiscus panduriformis |

Erect open shrub 1–2m high; stems densely hairy. **Leaves** broadly ovate to heart shaped, 3–9cm long to 8cm wide, grey-green above, paler below, margins toothed. **Flower** solitary, bright yellow with maroon central blotch, 6–8cm across. **Capsule** ovoid, to 1.5cm long, densely hairy. Along banks of streams, margins of clay pans and in open savann woodland. Qld, WA, NT. Autumn, winter.

Hibiscus splendens | Pink Hibiscus

Tall shrub or small tree 3–6m high; stems velvety, prickles scattered. **Lower leave** 3–5 lobed, **upper leaves** ovate to lanceolate, 3–8cm long, hairy, margins entire or toothed **Flowers** solitary, pale pink with dark red central blotch, to 12cm across. **Capsule** ovoid, t 3cm long, densely hairy. Common in open forest and rainforest margins, usually on rock slopes. Qld, NSW. Winter, spring, summer.

Howittia trilocularis | Howittia

Erect shrub 1–3m high; stems covered with yellowish hairs. **Leaves** lanceolate t ovate, 2–10cm long and 1–5cm wide, base sometimes heart-shaped, dark green and hair above, paler below, margins entire or toothed. **Flowers** solitary, purple with darker centre about 2cm across, on long slender stalks. **Capsule** globular, about 8mm across. Open forest mainly in moist valleys near creeks. NSW, Vic. Winter, spring.

Sida platycalyx | Lifesaver Burr

Prostrate or low erect shrub; stems and leaves covered with stellate hairs. **Leaves** ovat to circular, sometimes with heart-shaped base, 1–4cm long, hairy on both sides, margin toothed. **Flowers** solitary, bright yellow, about 2cm across, on thick stalk. **Fruit** inflated, t 2.5cm across, with up to 20 segments, covered with spines. Dry inland regions, often on re soils in mulga country. Qld, NSW, NT, WA. Winter, spring.

Gossypium sturtianum

Hibiscus heterophyllus

Hibiscus panduriformis

Hibiscus splendens

Howittia trilocularis

Sida platycalyx

MIMOSACEAE | Wattle family

A large, widespread and common family, which is often treated as the subfamily Mimosoideae of the family Fabaceae. Worldwide the family consists of about 60 genera and 3000 species, centred chiefly in tropical and subtropical regions. About 17 genera and more than 750 species are widely distributed throughout Australia of which the wattles, *Acacia* species (about 750 species), are the most widespread and best known. They are mainly trees and shrubs or rarely climbers and herbs. Leaves usually bipinnate, especially in seedling stage, but in mature plants of many species the leaves are reduced to phyllodes, glands often present on upper margin of phyllodes or the axis or midrib of bipinnate leaves, stipules present, sometimes thorn-like. Flowers regular, small, in tight clusters. Petals free or fused into a short tube at base. Stamens mostly 10 or numerous, long, protruding and showy. Flowers arranged in racemes, spikes or globular heads. Fruit a pea-like pod.

For the purpose of identification the following wattles are arranged in 3 groups according to flower shape and leaf structure:

Group 1   Wattles with cylindrical flower spikes and phyllodes.
Group 2   Wattles with globular flowerheads and phyllodes.
Group 3   Wattles that retain bipinnate leaves when mature.

GROUP 1: WATTLES WITH CYLINDRICAL FLOWER SPIKES AND PHYLLODES

Acacia aneura | Mulga

Erect or spreading shrub or tree 4–10m high with a short trunk. **Phyllodes** variable, linear and flat to terete, 4–10cm long to 3mm wide, leathery, grey-green, minutely hairy, 1 small gland at base. **Flowers** golden-yellow in spikes to 3cm long, singly or rarely in pairs on short stalks. **Pod** straight, flat, 2–4cm long to 1.5cm wide, margins prominently winged. Widely distributed in dry inland regions. Qld, NSW, SA, WA, NT. Winter, spring.

Acacia binervia | Coast Myall

Formerly *A. glaucescens*. Erect or spreading tree 5–15m high. **Phyllodes** sickle-shaped, 7–15cm long to 2cm wide, 2 or 3 prominent longitudinal veins, tip pointed, grey-green and covered with short dense hairs. **Flowers** bright yellow in spikes 2–6cm long, singly or up to 5 clustered in axil of phyllodes. **Pod** flat but raised over seeds, 6–8cm long to 5mm wide. Mainly coastal extending to tablelands and slopes, often in dry forest near streams. NSW. Winter, spring.

Acacia burrowii | Yarran

Erect slender tree 6–13m high. **Phyllodes** straight or slightly sickle-shaped, 4–10cm long to 1cm wide, leathery and sometimes glaucous, tip pointed. **Flowers** golden-yellow in spikes 2–3cm long, in axillary pairs. **Pod** linear, straight and flat, 5–8cm long, 2–4mm wide. Widespread in drier inland areas, especially in mallee. Qld, NSW. Winter, spring.

Acacia aneura

Acacia binervia

Acacia burrowi

Acacia doratoxylon | Currawang

Erect or spreading shrub or small tree 3–8m high. **Phyllodes** linear, straight or sickle-shaped, 7–20cm long and 2–7mm wide, grey-green, tip pointed. **Flowers** golden-yellow in spikes about 2cm long, in axillary groups of 2–5. **Pod** very narrow, slightly curved and flat, 6–10cm long to 3mm wide. Widespread on tablelands and western slopes, in woodland and mallee. NSW, Vic. Winter, spring.

Acacia floribunda | White Sally

Erect or spreading shrub or small tree 3–8m high. **Phyllodes** straight or slightly curved, 5–12cm long to 1cm wide, 2–4 longitudinal veins prominent, tip pointed, 1 gland near base. **Flowers** pale yellow in spikes to 5cm long, in axillary pairs. **Pod** narrow, flat but raised over seeds, to 12cm long. Widespread in forest and woodland, mainly coast but extending to tablelands. Qld, NSW, Vic. Winter, spring.

Acacia kempeana | Witchetty Bush

Erect spreading shrub or small tree 3–4m high. **Phyllodes** oblong, slightly curved, 5–10cm long to 1.5cm wide, grey-green, numerous faint longitudinal veins, tip rounded. **Flowers** golden-yellow in spikes usually to 3cm long. **Pod** oblong, flat, 3–7cm long to 1.5cm wide. Aborigines obtain witchetty grubs from the roots. Widespread in dry inland regions. Qld, SA, WA, NT. Winter, spring.

Acacia lasiocalyx |

Slender spreading shrub 3–5m high. **Phyllodes** linear, slightly curved, 15–25cm long to 4mm wide, dark green, tip softly pointed and curved. **Flowers** bright yellow in spikes to 4cm long, in axillary groups of 2–3. **Pod** linear, slightly curved, to 15cm long and 5mm wide. Near rocky outcrops in the southwest. WA. Winter, spring.

Acacia longifolia | Sydney Golden Wattle

Erect shrub or small spreading tree 2–8m high. **Phyllodes** straight variable, 6–20cm long and 4–20mm wide, 2 or 3 or more longitudinal veins, tip pointed, 1 gland near the base. **Flowers** golden-yellow in spikes 2–6cm long, singly or in pairs in axils. **Pod** terete, straight or curved, 5–12cm long to 6mm wide. Common from coast to the mountains in forest and woodland. NSW, Vic. Winter, spring.

Acacia doratoxylon

Acacia floribunda

Acacia kempeana

Acacia lasiocalyx

Acacia longifolia

Acacia mucronata | Narrow-leaved Wattle

Large erect shrub, rarely small tree, 2–8m high. **Phyllodes** narrow, fairly straight 4–20cm long to 1cm wide, 1–3 longitudinal veins, tip pointed. **Flowers** pale yellow, in spike 2–5cm long; individual flowers are well spaced along the spike. **Pod** rough, straight or curved 4–10cm long and 2–4mm wide. Coast to ranges on moderately moist soils in open forest often on granite outcrops. NSW, Vic, Tas. Winter, spring.

Acacia oxycedrus | Spike Wattle

Rigid erect shrub, sometimes small tree, 3–8m high; stems terete, densely hairy. **Phyllodes** flat and rigid, 2–4cm long to 5mm wide, tapering to very sharp point, 3– longitudinal veins prominent. **Flowers** lemon yellow in spikes to 3cm long, 1–3 in phyllode axils. **Pod** rough, terete, 4–10cm long to 4mm wide, hairy. Widespread in heath and open forest, usually on sandy soils. NSW, Vic, SA. Winter, spring.

Acacia sophorae | Coastal Wattle

Prostrate or dense spreading shrub to 3m high. **Phyllodes** straight, oblong to obovate 5–10cm long to 2.5cm wide, tip rounded ending in a very short point, 2–4 longitudinal veins prominent. **Flowers** yellow in spikes 2–3cm long, singly or in pairs in phyllode axils. **Pod** rough, terete, 6–10cm long and 2–4mm wide, often twisted. Widespread in coastal districts especially on sand dunes. Qld, NSW, Vic, Tas, SA. Winter, spring.

Acacia verticillata | Prickly Moses

Spreading prickly shrub 1–3m high; stems somewhat hairy. **Phyllodes** very narrow 1–2.5cm long and 1–2mm wide, in whorls around stems, tip sharply pointed. **Flowers** bright yellow in spikes 1–2cm long, singly or up to 3 in phyllode axils. **Pod** flat, almost straight 2–8cm long to 4mm wide, dark brown. Heath and open forest, often in moist sandy situations. NSW, Vic, Tas, SA. Winter, spring.

Acacia mucronata

Acacia oxycedrus

Acacia sophorae

Acacia verticillata

GROUP 2: WATTLES WITH GLOBULAR FLOWERHEADS AND PHYLLODES

Acacia acinacea | Gold-dust Wattle

Branched spreading shrub to 2m high; stems yellow-green sometimes with scattered hairs. **Phyllodes** variable in shape from circular to oval to oblong, 5–25mm long and 3–10mm wide, ending in a small straight or recurved point. **Flowers** golden-yellow in globular heads of 1–2 in phyllode axils, on slender stalks to 1.5cm long. **Pod** 3–7cm long to 4mm wide, twisted or spirally coiled. Drier inland regions in woodland. NSW, Vic, SA. Winter, spring.

Acacia adunca | Wallangarra Wattle

Dense spreading shrub to 3m high; stems terete and reddish when young. **Phyllodes** linear, 7–13cm long to 5mm wide, ending in sharp point or sometimes hooked tip. **Flowers** bright golden-yellow in globular heads on long axillary racemes. **Pod** slightly curved, to 8cm long and 1cm wide, glaucous. Open forest and shrubland often on granite outcrops. Qld, NSW. Winter, spring.

Acacia alata | Winged Wattle

Upright, sometimes straggly shrub with many stems 1–2m high. **Phyllodes** somewhat triangular, forming part of the flattened, zigzagging, hairy stems, tip sharply pointed. **Flowers** cream or bright yellow in globular heads, singly or in pairs from the axils on slender stalks 5–10mm long. **Pod** oblong, curved, 4–5cm long, hairy. Widespread in the southwest, often along rivers. WA. Winter, spring.

Acacia amblygona | Fan Wattle

Low spreading shrub or prostrate shrub to 1.5m high; stems densely hairy. **Phyllodes** ovate or lanceolate, 1–1.5cm long and 2–4mm wide, stiff, 2–3 longitudinal veins, tip sharply pointed. **Flowers** bright yellow in globular heads, singly in phyllode axils on stalks to 12mm long. **Pod** curved or coiled, to 3–16cm long and to 5mm wide. Open forest and heath. Qld, NSW. Winter, spring.

Acacia acinacea

Acacia adunca

Acacia alata

Acacia amblygona

Acacia argyrophylla | Silver Mulga

Rounded spreading shrub to 3m high; stems and young growth hairy. **Phyllodes** obovate to almost rounded, 2–4cm long to 1.5cm wide, grey-green and golden when young. **Flowers** golden-yellow in large globular heads, singly on stalks to 2cm long or on short racemes. **Pod** dark brown, 2–5cm long to 1.5cm wide, constricted between the few seeds. Low rainfall areas. SA. Winter, spring.

Acacia aspera | Rough Wattle

Erect or spreading shrub 1–2m high; stems resinous and hairy. **Phyllodes** linear–oblong, 1–4cm long, 2–4mm wide, with glandular hairs, tip a soft recurved point. **Flowers** golden-yellow in globular heads, singly on hairy stalks to 12mm long in phyllode axils. **Pod** curved or coiled, 2–7cm long to 5mm wide, densely hairy. Open forest and mallee. NSW, Vic. Winter, spring.

Acacia binervata | Two-veined Hickory

Erect tree to 12m high. **Phyllodes** lanceolate, 7–12cm long and 1–3cm wide, dark green, with 2–3 prominent longitudinal veins, tip pointed. **Flowers** pale yellow to almost white in globular heads, on short axillary racemes. **Pod** flat, straight and oblong, 7–14cm long to 1.5cm wide, glaucous. Widespread from coast to mountains in wet sclerophyll forest or margins of rainforest. Qld, NSW. Winter, spring.

Acacia boormanii | Snowy River Wattle

Erect bushy shrub 2–4m high. **Phyllodes** linear narrowing at base, 3–8cm long, 1–3mm wide, grey-green, tip with curved point. **Flowers** bright yellow in globular heads, or dense axillary racemes. **Pod** linear, straight or slightly curved, 4–10cm long, 4–6mm wide. Woodland often on banks of streams. NSW, Vic. Winter, spring.

Acacia brachybotrya | Grey Mulga

Spreading shrub 1–4m high; stems clothed with close silky hairs. **Phyllodes** obovate 1–4cm long to 1.5cm wide, tip rounded or sometimes with small point, usually hairy. **Flowers** bright yellow in globular heads, singly or in clusters or on very short racemes. **Pod** almost straight, 3–7cm long to 7mm wide, slightly constricted between the seeds. Widespread in dry inland areas, mainly in mallee. NSW, Vic, SA. Winter, spring.

Acacia buxifolia | Box-leaf Wattle

Erect shrub 1–3m high; stems angular often reddish. **Phyllodes** elliptic, 1–4cm long to 1cm wide, grey-green, midvein prominent, tip with small point. **Flowers** profuse, golden-yellow in globular heads, on short axillary racemes 3–5cm long. **Pod** flat, straight or slightly curved, 6–10cm long to 1cm wide, sometimes glaucous. Dry woodland and heath, often on rocky outcrops. Qld, NSW, Vic. Winter, spring.

Acacia argyrophylla

Acacia aspera

Acacia binervata

Acacia boormanii

Acacia brachybotrya

Acacia buxifolia

Acacia calamifolia | Wallowa

Erect to spreading shrub 2–4m high; stems slender, terete. **Phyllodes** linear, tapering to base, 4–12cm long, 1–5mm wide, tip with curved point, 1 gland near base. **Flowers** golden-yellow in globular heads, 1–4 in phyllode axils or on short racemes. **Pod** narrow, 8–20cm long to 6mm wide, constricted between seeds. Widespread in dry inland areas, mostly in woodland. NSW, Vic, SA. Winter, spring.

Acacia conferta |

Erect or spreading shrub 2–4m high, stems hairy. **Phyllodes** linear, to 1.5cm long and 4mm wide, crowded or in whorls, grey-green, glabrous or finely hairy, tip pointed. **Flowers** golden-yellow in globular heads, singly in phyllode axils on hairy stalks to 12mm long. **Pod** flat, almost straight, 4–7cm long to 2cm wide, sometimes glaucous. Mainly in semi-arid regions in open forest and woodland. Qld, NSW. Winter, spring.

Acacia cultriformis | Knife-leaf Wattle

Erect or spreading glaucous shrub 2–4m high. **Phyllodes** oval to almost triangular 1–3cm long to 1.5cm wide, midvein prominent, tip pointed, bluish-green. **Flowers** bright yellow in globular or ovoid heads, on axillary racemes extending well beyond the phyllodes. **Pod** flat and thin-textured, 5–7cm long, 4–7mm wide, glaucous. Mainly on western slopes and plains, in woodland and mallee. Qld, NSW. Winter, spring.

Acacia dictyophleba |

Erect slender shrub 1–4m high, stems ribbed and sticky. **Phyllodes** oblanceolate 2–6cm long, 5–10mm wide, with 2–3 longitudinal veins and prominent lateral veins, tip rounded with small point. **Flowers** golden-yellow in globular heads, 1–2 on sticky stalks to 2cm long in phyllode axils. **Pod** oblong, flat, 5–9cm long to 1.5cm wide, sticky when young. Widespread in central Australia, often in sandy areas in open woodland. Qld, SA, WA, NT. Autumn, winter.

Acacia extensa | Wiry Wattle

Slender erect shrub 1–3m high; stems angular and often almost winged. **Phyllodes** very narrow, stiff and flattened, 8–20cm, midrib prominent, tip ending in small recurved point. **Flowers** bright yellow in globular heads, usually solitary or in small clusters on stalks to 1cm long along the stems. **Pod** oblong, 8–10cm long to 5mm wide, constricted between seeds. Common in jarrah forest in the southwest. WA. Winter, spring.

Acacia calamifolia

Acacia conferta

Acacia cultriformis

Acacia dictyophleba

Acacia extensa

Acacia fimbriata | Fringed Wattle

Erect bushy shrub or small tree 5–8m high, often with pendulous branches. **Phyllodes** linear, 2–5cm long and 2–5mm wide, dark green, margins fringed with fine hairs, tip pointed. **Flowers** bright yellow in globular heads, on slender axillary racemes extending beyond the phyllodes. **Pod** flat, straight, 5–8cm long, 6–8mm wide. Chiefly coastal, but also farther inland in dry forest and woodland. Qld, NSW. Winter, spring.

Acacia glaucoptera | Clay Wattle

Multi-branched spreading shrub to 1.5m high; stems flattened and wavy. **Phyllodes** triangular and wing-like, continuous along the stems, about 2.5cm long, narrowing into sharp point, blue-green. **Flowers** bright yellow in globular heads, singly on stalks to 5mm long, arising from nodes on the phyllodes. **Pod** narrow, curved and twisted, 4–5cm long to 4mm wide. Widespread in the southwest, often on heath or in mallee shrubland. WA. Winter, spring.

Acacia gunnii | Ploughshare Wattle

Spreading shrub 1–2m high; stems smooth or densely hairy. **Phyllodes** somewhat triangular, 4–10mm long, 2–5mm wide, often hairy, prominent vein near lower margin, tip sharply pointed. **Flowers** pale yellow to white in globular heads, singly on stalks to 1cm long. **Pod** flat, 2–4cm long and 3–6mm wide, constricted between seeds. Widespread, mostly slightly inland, in open forest. Qld, NSW, Vic, Tas, SA. Winter, spring.

Acacia hakeoides | Hakea Wattle

Multi-branched spreading shrub 2–5m high. **Phyllodes** oblong but broader toward tip, 4–14cm long, 3–12mm wide, midvein prominent, tip rounded; 1 or 2 glands present on upper margin. **Flowers** bright yellow in globular heads, on extended axillary racemes 2–8cm long. **Pod** flat, 7–12cm long, 4–7mm wide, constricted between seeds, dark brown. Widespread and common inland in woodland and mallee. Qld, NSW, Vic, SA, WA. Winter, spring.

Acacia harpophylla | Brigalow

Erect densely crowned tree 5–20m high. **Phyllodes** lanceolate and curved, 10–20cm long, 7–20mm wide, blue-green, 3–5 prominent longitudinal veins, tip pointed, 1 raised gland at base. **Flowers** yellow in globular heads, in axillary clusters or on short racemes. **Pod** curved and flat, 5–12cm long to 1cm wide, slightly constricted between seeds. Widespread in semi-arid regions, sometimes forming dense thickets. Qld, NSW. Winter, spring.

Acacia havilandiorum | Haviland's Wattle

Erect and spreading shrub, 1–4m high. **Phyllodes** terete, slightly curved, 3–9cm long and 1mm wide, tip finely pointed, 1 or 2 glands present on margin near the centre. **Flowers** bright yellow, profuse, in globular heads, 1–3 per axil. **Pod** curved, 4–9cm long, 2–3mm wide, slightly constricted between seeds. Widespread in semi-arid regions, usually in mallee and woodland. NSW, Vic, SA. Winter, spring.

Acacia fimbriata

Acacia glaucoptera

Acacia gunnii

Acacia hakeoides

Acacia harpophylla

Acacia havlandiorum

Acacia hemignosta

Tall shrub or small bushy tree 3–8m high with drooping branches. **Phyllodes** broades toward tip, 7–10cm long, 1–2.5cm wide, curved, grey-green, usually 3 prominent longitudina veins, tip rounded. **Flowers** yellow in globular heads, singly but most often on axillar racemes 5–12cm long. **Pod** straight, oblong, 5–9cm long to 1.5cm wide, light brown Widespread across northern Australia, mostly in open woodland. Qld, WA, NT. Winter.

Acacia ixiophylla

Erect shrub 1–5m high; stems resinous and often hairy. **Phyllodes** oblong–lanceolate 2–4.5cm long, 3–8mm wide, 3 or more prominent longitudinal veins, tip rounded. **Flower** golden-yellow to white in globular heads, on short axillary racemes. **Pod** curved, slende 3–7cm long, 2–3mm wide, brown, resinous. Widespread in semi-arid regions in open fores and woodland. Qld, NSW, WA. Winter, spring.

Acacia juncifolia | Rush-leaved Wattle

Erect shrub 1–2.5m high; stems terete and dark brown. **Phyllodes** terete or slightl flattened, 7–20cm long to 1mm wide, tip with short curved point. **Flowers** deep yellow i globular heads, singly or in pairs in axils, on stalks to 1cm long. **Pod** straight, flat, 7–10cm lon to 4mm wide, slightly constricted between seeds. Widespread from coast to slightly inlan in open forest and woodland. Qld, NSW. Winter, spring.

Acacia leprosa | Cinnamon Wattle

Erect shrub or small tree, 1.5–6m high; branchlets often weeping. **Phyllodes** variable 4–12cm long, 4–20mm wide, 1 prominent central vein, tip with small point, sticky whei young. **Flowers** bright to pale yellow in globular heads, 1–4 per axil, on hairy stalks t 1.5cm long. **Pod** narrow, straight and flat, 4–8cm long, 2–4mm wide. Slightly inland in ope forest and woodland. NSW, Vic. Spring.

Acacia ligulata | Umbrella Bush

Bushy spreading shrub, 2–4m high. **Phyllodes** linear–oblong, 4–10cm long, 2–10mn wide, grey-green, 1 prominent central vein or up to 3 longitudinal veins, tip rounded with smal point. **Flowers** golden-yellow to orange in globular heads on short axillary racemes. **Pod** fla and straight, 3–8cm long, 4–10mm wide, constricted between seeds, often woody. Widesprea in dry inland regions, often in mulga and saltbush areas. NSW, Vic, SA, WA, NT. Winter, spring

Acacia linearifolia | Stringybark Wattle

Tall shrub or small tree 3–6m high. **Phyllodes** linear, 8–15cm long to 2mm wide midvein prominent, raised gland near centre of upper margin, tip with small hooked point **Flowers** bright yellow in globular heads on long axillary racemes. **Pod** straight and flat 5–10cm long, 5–7mm wide. Widespread in central and southern areas in open forest and woodland. NSW. Spring.

Acacia hemignosta

Acacia ixiophylla

Acacia juncifolia

Acacia leprosa

Acacia ligulata

Acacia linearifolia

Acacia linifolia | Flax Wattle

Erect slender shrub 2–4m high; stems slender and often arching. **Phyllodes** linear, 2–4cm long, 1–2mm wide, tip mostly pointed. **Flowers** light cream in globular heads, on slender axillary racemes. **Pod** oblong, straight and flat, 5–10cm long, 8–15mm wide, not constricted between seeds. Mainly coastal and slightly inland in open forest on sandstone NSW. Summer, autumn.

Acacia melanoxylon | Blackwood

Tall tree 8–30m high. **Phyllodes** broad–lanceolate, 5–15cm long, to 3cm wide, dull green, 3 or more prominent longitudinal veins, lateral veins visible, tip rounded with small point. **Flowers** pale yellow to almost white in globular heads, on short racemes. **Pod** curved or coiled, 4–12cm long to 1cm wide. Widespread from coast to ranges, often common at higher altitudes in wet forest and rainforest margins. Qld, NSW, Vic, Tas, SA. Winter, spring.

Acacia myrtifolia | Myrtle Wattle

Erect shrub 1–3m high, stems angular and often reddish. **Phyllodes** lanceolate, thick, 2–6cm long, 5–30mm wide, midvein prominent, margins thickened, tip with blunt point, gland below centre on upper margin. **Flowers** pale yellow to white in globular heads, 3–8 on short axillary racemes. **Pod** curved, 4–11cm long, 3–5mm wide, woody. Widespread from coast to ranges in open forest and woodland. Qld, NSW, Vic, Tas, SA, WA. Winter, spring.

Acacia paradoxa | Kangaroo Thorn

Formerly *A. armata*. Erect shrub 2–4m high; stems angular and often hairy, sometimes arching. **Phyllodes** oblong to lanceolate, 1–3cm long, 3–7mm wide, upper margin wavy, tip pointed; spine-like stipules present. **Flowers** golden-yellow in globular heads, 1 or rarely 2 per axil on stalks to 2cm long. **Pod** straight and flat, 2–7cm long, 3–5mm wide, hairy. Widespread from coast to inland, in open forest and woodland. Qld, NSW, Vic, Tas, SA, WA. Winter, spring.

Acacia pendula | Weeping Myall

Erect tree 5–12m high, with weeping branches. **Phyllodes** linear–lanceolate, curved 5–14cm long, 4–10mm wide, 1–3 longitudinal veins, silvery-grey and glaucous. **Flowers** golden-yellow in globular heads, on short axillary racemes. **Pod** flat, 3–8cm long to 2cm wide, margins winged. Widespread in inland districts on flood plains. Qld, NSW, Vic. Summer, autumn.

Acacia perangusta |

Large shrub or small tree 5–8m high. **Phyllodes** linear, 4–10cm long to 1mm wide, dark green and glabrous, tip pointed. **Flowers** pale to bright yellow in globular heads, on long axillary racemes. **Pod** flat and straight, 5–7cm long to 5mm wide, constricted between seeds. Mainly along the banks of streams in sheltered forests. Qld. Winter, spring.

Acacia linifolia

Acacia melanoxylon

Acacia myrtifolia

Acacia paradoxa

Acacia pendula

Acacia perangusta

Acacia podalyriifolia | Queensland Silver Wattle

Large shrub to small tree 3–5m high; stems glaucous and hairy. **Phyllodes** broadly ovate, 1–3cm long, 1–2.5cm wide, silvery-grey and glabrous, midvein prominent, tip with fine point; 1 or 2 raised glands may be present along margin. **Flowers** golden-yellow in globular heads on slender axillary racemes to 10cm long. **Pod** flat, 5–12cm long, 1–2cm wide, glaucous. Mainly coastal, also nearby ranges. NSW, Qld. Winter, spring.

Acacia pravifolia | Coil-pod Wattle

Erect rigid shrub 1–2m high; stems usually covered with downward-pointing hairs. **Phyllodes** somewhat triangular, 3–14mm long, 3–8mm wide, hairy, 2–4 longitudinal veins, upper margin rounded, tip sharply pointed. **Flowers** golden-yellow in globular heads, singly in axils. **Pod** narrow, 3.5cm long to 5mm wide, strongly twisted or coiled. Semi-arid regions, mostly in woodland. Qld, NSW, SA. Winter, spring.

Acacia pravissima | Ovens Wattle

Shrub or small tree 3–8m high; stems angular, sometimes weeping. **Phyllodes** roughly triangular, 5–16mm long to 13mm wide, 2 main veins, tip pointed; raised gland near base. **Flowers** yellow in globular heads, on axillary racemes to 10cm long. **Pod** flat, straight or curved, 3–8cm long to 7mm wide, brown. Mountainous areas near streams. NSW, Vic. Winter, spring.

Acacia prominens | Gosford Wattle

Erect tall shrub or tree 4–18m high. **Phyllodes** narrow lanceolate, 3–5cm long to 12mm wide, blue-green, midvein prominent, tip pointed or rounded with a small mucro (stiff point); conspicuous gland on margin just below centre. **Flowers** pale yellow in globular heads, in dense axillary racemes to 8cm long. **Pod** straight and flat, 5–8cm long, 1–2cm wide. Confined to central and north coast, mainly in wet forest. NSW. Winter, spring.

Acacia pycnantha | Golden Wattle

Erect shrub to small tree 3–8m high. **Phyllodes** variable, lanceolate, curved, 6–20cm long, 1–5cm wide, dark green, thick and leathery, midvein prominent, lateral veins conspicuous, tip pointed or rounded; gland near base. **Flowers** golden-yellow in globular heads, on axillary racemes to 15cm long. **Pod** straight and flat, 5–15cm long to 8mm wide, leathery. Australia's national floral emblem. Widespread in dry forest and heath, sometimes on stony ground. NSW, Vic, SA. Winter, spring.

Acacia rigens | Needle Wattle

Spreading shrub 1–4m high; stems resinous and minutely hairy. **Phyllodes** almost terete, 3–13cm long, 1–4mm wide, grey-green, tip sharply pointed; gland near base. **Flowers** golden-yellow in globular heads, 1–4 per axil. **Pod** curved or twisted, 4–10cm long, 2–8mm wide, slightly constricted between seeds. Widespread in arid and semi-arid regions, mainly in mallee and woodland. Qld, NSW, Vic, SA, WA. Winter, spring.

Acacia podalyriifolia

Acacia pravifolia

Acacia pravissima

Acacia prominens

Acacia pycnantha

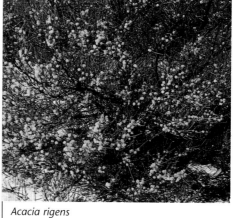

Acacia rigens

Acacia rupicola | Rock Wattle

Erect and spreading shrub 1–2m high; stems sticky. **Phyllodes** narrow lanceolate 1–2cm long to 2mm wide, rigid, broadest near base, tip sharply pointed; small gland near base. **Flowers** yellow in globular heads, singly in axils. **Pod** linear, curved, 5–8cm long to 5mm wide. Widespread from coast to ranges. Vic, SA. Winter, spring.

Acacia saligna | Golden Wreath Wattle

Shrub or small spreading tree 3–8m high; stems often weeping. **Phyllodes** variable, slightly curved, 8–30cm long to 1–5cm wide, midvein prominent, tip tapering to point. **Flowers** bright yellow in globular heads, profuse on axillary racemes to 5cm long. **Pod** linear, 5–15cm long, 4–6mm wide, slightly constricted between seeds. Widespread in the southwest. WA. Winter, spring.

Acacia sclerophylla | Hard-leaf Wattle

Small spreading shrub 1–2m high; stems sticky. **Phyllodes** narrow–oblong, broadest at tip, 1–4cm long, 1–4mm wide, rigid, several longitudinal veins, tip sharply pointed. **Flowers** golden-yellow in globular heads, 1–2 per axil. **Pod** linear, twisted or coiled, 3–6cm long to 3mm wide. Widespread in dry inland regions, often in mallee. NSW, Vic, SA, WA. Winter, spring.

Acacia siculiformis | Dagger Wattle

Erect shrub 1–3m high; stems terete. **Phyllodes** linear–lanceolate, rigid and spreading, 1–3cm long to 3mm wide, sometimes slightly sticky, midvein prominent, tip sharply pointed. **Flowers** yellow in globular heads, 1 or 2 per axil on very short stalks. **Pod** straight, 2–5cm long to 6mm wide, resinous. Dry forest and woodland, often in rocky places in moist mountainous situations. NSW, Vic, Tas. Spring.

Acacia spathulifolia |

Erect bushy shrub 1–3m high; branches spreading. **Phyllodes** spoon-shaped, 1–2cm long to 4mm wide, fleshy, tip rounded with small blunt point. **Flowers** bright yellow in globular heads, singly or in pairs in axils on stalks to 1cm long. **Pod** linear–oblong, to 3.5cm long and 5mm wide, slightly hairy. Mainly on coastal limestone, from the Carnarvon Region south to Jurien Bay, in heath. WA. Spring.

Acacia spinescens | Spiny Wattle

Erect rigid shrub to 1.5m high; stems ribbed, ending in spines. **Phyllodes** usually absent, when present, narrow to 2.5cm long and 2mm wide, tip with curved point. **Flowers** golden-yellow in globular heads, singly, on short stalks or sessile, along the stem. **Pod** linear, curved and twisted, 2–3cm long to 3mm wide, constricted between seeds. Dry regions on sandy soil. Vic, SA. Winter, spring.

Acacia rupicola

Acacia saligna

Acacia sclerophylla

Acacia siculiformis

Acacia spathulifolia

Acacia spinescens

Acacia spondylophylla

Spreading, aromatic shrub to 1.5m high; stems resinous. **Phyllodes** linear, sticky, 1–2cm long, in whorls of 8–14, margins recurved, tip pointed. **Flowers** golden-yellow in globular heads, singly on stalks to 2.5cm long. **Pod** oblong, twisted, 3–4cm long to 8mm wide, sticky. Widespread in dry inland regions often on shallow soils in rocky situations. Qld, WA, NT. Winter, spring.

Acacia stricta | Hop Wattle

Erect shrub or small tree 2–5m high; stems angular and ribbed. **Phyllodes** narrow–oblong, 4–14cm long to 1.5cm wide, dull green, thin textured and slightly twisted, midvein prominent, tip rounded with short mucro. **Flowers** yellow in globular heads, 2–4 per axil on hairy stalks to 8mm long. **Pod** thin, flat and straight, 4–10cm long to 5mm wide, light brown. Widespread and common from coast to mountains in open forest, especially on dry hillsides. Qld, NSW, Vic, Tas, SA. Winter, spring.

Acacia suaveolens | Sweet Wattle

Erect shrub to 2.5m high; stems angular, new growth pinkish. **Phyllodes** narrow, 5–15cm long to 1cm wide, blue-green, midvein prominent, tip rounded with small point. **Flowers** pale yellow to white in globular heads, on short racemes of 5–10 flowers; unopened raceme enclosed in brownish deciduous bracts. **Pod** oblong, flat, 2–5cm long to 1.5cm wide, glaucous. Widespread from coast to ranges in heath, open forest and woodland on sandy soils. Qld, NSW, Vic, Tas, SA. Autumn, winter, early spring.

Acacia sulcata

Spreading dense shrub to 1.5m high. **Phyllodes** almost terete, 1–2cm long, dark green, furrowed, tip pointed. **Flowers** deep yellow in globular heads, 1–2 per axil. **Pod** oblong, to 1–2cm long and 5mm wide, light brown. Mainly inland on sandplains. WA. Winter, spring.

Acacia tetragonophylla | Dead Finish

Multi-branched spreading shrub 1–4m high. **Phyllodes** linear, 1–4cm long to 1mm wide, often in whorls or clusters, tip sharply pointed. **Flowers** golden-yellow in globular heads, 2–5 per axil, on stalks to 1.5cm long. **Pod** linear, strongly curved or twisted, 6–10cm long to 8mm wide, much constricted between seeds, dark brown. Widespread in dry inland areas in mulga scrub and woodland. Qld, NSW, SA, WA, NT. Winter, spring.

Acacia spondylophylla

Acacia stricta

Acacia suaveolens

Acacia sulcata

Acacia tetragonophylla

Acacia tindaleae | Golden-top Wattle

Erect dense shrub 1–2m high; stems hairy. **Phyllodes** crowded, linear, 6–12mm long, 1–2mm wide, grey-green, hairy, tip rounded with small point. **Flowers** golden-yellow in globular heads, singly on hairy stalks to 13mm long. **Pod** straight and flat, 3–7cm long to 1cm wide, brown. Widespread on slopes and plains, common in Pilliga Scrub. Qld, NSW. Winter, spring.

Acacia uncinata | Gold-dust Wattle

Erect or spreading shrub 1–3m high; branches sometimes weeping. **Phyllodes** ovate to almost round, 1–2cm long to 1.5cm wide, sometimes hairy, midvein prominent, margins often wavy, tip pointed. **Flowers** bright yellow in globular heads, singly on hairy stalks to 2cm long. **Pod** oblong, 4–8cm long to 3cm wide. Coastal and farther inland in open forest, often in rocky situations. Qld, NSW. Spring, summer.

Acacia verniciflua | Varnish Wattle

Variable shrub or small tree 1–5m high; stems resinous and pendulous. **Phyllodes** narrow–lanceolate, 3–14cm long to 3mm wide, 2 prominent longitudinal veins, tip pointed, resinous. **Flowers** golden-yellow in globular heads, 2 or 3 per axil on sparsely hairy stalks to 1cm long. **Pod** narrow, straight or curved, 4–10cm long, 2–6mm wide, sticky. Widespread, mainly in dry forest and woodland on ranges and plains. NSW, Vic, Tas, SA. Winter, spring.

Acacia vestita | Hairy Wattle

Spreading shrub 1–5m high; stems pendulous, hairy. **Phyllodes** ovate, 1–2cm long to 1cm wide, grey-green, softly hairy, midvein prominent, tip with soft hooked point. **Flowers** golden-yellow in globular heads, on slender axillary racemes. **Pod** oblong, straight, 3–9cm long to 1.5cm wide, glaucous. Mainly slopes and tablelands in open forest. NSW. Spring.

Acacia tindaleae

Acacia uncinata

Acacia verniciflua

Acacia vestita

GROUP 3: WATTLES THAT RETAIN BIPINNATE LEAVES WHEN MATURE

Acacia baileyana | Cootamundra Wattle

Spreading tree 3–6m high. **Leaves** bipinnate with 2–6 pairs of pinnae and 12–24 pairs of leaflets; each leaflet blue-green, linear to oblong, to 9mm long. **Flowers** golden-yellow in globular heads, profuse, on dense axillary racemes to 10cm long. **Pod** flat, 4–10cm long to 12mm wide, often glaucous. Endemic to West Wyalong district, but widely naturalised in eastern States. NSW. Winter, early spring.

Acacia cardiophylla | Wyalong Wattle

Bushy shrub 1–3m high; stems terete, hairy when young. **Leaves** bipinnate with 8–15 pairs of pinnae and 8–12 pairs of leaflets; each leaflet ovate, to 2mm long, incurved, hairy. **Flowers** golden-yellow in globular heads, profuse on simple or branched axillary racemes. **Pod** straight and flat, 3–9cm long to 6mm wide, dark brown, hairy. Western slopes and plains, mainly in mallee. NSW. Winter, spring.

Acacia dealbata | Silver Wattle

Erect tree 10–20m high; stems silvery-white and felty. **Leaves** bipinnate with 10–20 pairs pinnae, raised glands at base of each pair, 20–50 pairs of leaflets; each leaflet linear, crowded, about 5mm long with short grey hairs. **Flowers** bright yellow in globular heads on dense racemes or panicles. **Pod** straight and flat, 5–10cm long to 1cm wide, grey-green to purplish. Widespread from coast to mountain forests. NSW, Vic, Tas. Winter, spring.

Acacia decurrens | Black Wattle

Erect tree 5–15m high; branches and stems with wing-like ridges. **Leaves** bipinnate with 5–12 pairs of pinnae and 20–35 pairs of widely spaced leaflets; each leaflet dark green, linear, 6–14mm long, less than 1mm wide. Glands present at base of each pair of pinnae. **Flowers** golden-yellow in globular heads on dense axillary racemes to 10cm long. **Pod** linear, straight, 5–10cm long to 8mm wide. Open forest and woodland from coast to ranges; naturalised in all eastern States. NSW. Winter, spring.

Acacia drummondii | Drummond's Wattle

Variable shrub 50cm–2m high. **Leaves** bipinnate with 1–3 pairs of pinnae and 1–3 pairs of leaflets; each leaflet green or blue-green, flat or recurved, to 1cm long. **Flowers** golden-yellow in cylindrical spikes, singly on hairy stalks to 2cm long. **Pod** oblong, 1–4cm long to 8mm wide, margins thickened, tip pointed. Southwest forests. WA. Winter, spring.

Acacia farnesiana | Mimosa Bush

Spreading shrub or small tree, 3–6m high. **Leaves** bipinnate, 3–7 pairs of pinnae and 8–20 pairs of leaflets; leaflet linear, to 9mm long; stipules thorny, to 2.5cm long, in pairs in leaf axils. **Flowers** golden in globular heads, 1–3 per axil, on stalks, 2cm long. **Pod** terete, 4–6 by 1cm wide, dark brown. Widespread in northern Australia. Qld, NSW, SA, WA, NT. Winter, spring.

Acacia baileyana

Acacia cardiophylla

Acacia dealbata

Acacia decurrens

Acacia drummondii

Acacia farnesiana

Acacia leucoclada

Erect tree 4–15m high; bark rough and blackish. **Leaves** glaucous, bipinnate with 6–18 pairs of pinnae and 17–40 pairs of leaflets; each leaflet linear, 2–5mm long. Glands numerous, scattered along central stalk. **Flowers** bright yellow in globular heads, on axillary racemes to 12cm long. **Pod** straight and flat, 4–12cm long to 1cm wide, reddish-brown. Dry forest from coast to inland slopes and plains. Qld, NSW. Winter, spring.

Acacia mearnsii | Black Wattle

Erect spreading tree 7–10m high; bark black. **Leaves** bipinnate with 8–25 pairs of pinnae and 20–70 pairs of crowded leaflets, each leaflet linear, to 4mm long, hairy on undersurface. Glands numerous, scattered along central stalk. **Flowers** pale yellow in globular heads on axillary racemes to 12cm long. **Pod** terete, 5–15cm long to 1cm wide, constricted between seeds. Widespread and common in open forest on hillsides. NSW, Vic, Tas, SA. Spring.

Acacia polybotrya | Western Silver Wattle

Tall spreading shrub 2–5m high. **Leaves** bipinnate with 2–6 pairs of pinnae and 7–12 pairs of leaflets; each leaflet oblong, blue-green and hairy, to 1cm long and 2mm wide; 1 gland often present between lowest pair of pinnae. **Flowers** bright yellow in globular heads on axillary racemes to 12cm long. **Pod** linear, about 7cm long to 8mm wide, constricted between seeds. Inland districts in open forest. NSW, Qld. Winter, spring.

Acacia pubescens

Spreading shrub 1–3m high, stems pendulous and hairy. **Leaves** bipinnate with 3–6 pairs of pinnae and 12–20 pairs of crowded leaflets, each leaflet bright green, oblong, to 3mm long and 1mm wide. **Flowers** bright yellow in globular heads on slender racemes to 6cm long. **Pod** straight and flat, 3–7cm long to 1cm wide, margins thickened. Mainly coastal in open forest and woodland; endangered and uncommon. NSW. Winter, spring.

Acacia spectabilis | Mudgee Wattle

Erect shrub or small tree 2–6m high; stems often drooping, densely hairy. **Leaves** bipinnate 2–6 pairs of pinnae and 4–8 pairs of leaflets; each leaflet blue-green, oblong to ovate, to 1cm long and 4mm wide, tip rounded. **Flowers** golden-yellow in globular heads on long racemes or panicles to 15cm long. **Pod** 5–10cm long to 1.5cm wide, glaucous. Mainly slopes and plains in open forest. NSW, Qld. Winter, spring.

Acacia terminalis | Sunshine Wattle

Shrub or small tree 1–6m high; stems usually angular and reddish. **Leaves** bipinnate with 2–6 pairs of pinnae and 8–20 pairs of leaflets, each leaflet oblong, 1–2cm long and 2–5mm wide, dark green above and paler below. **Flowers** pale yellow in globular heads widely spaced on racemes to 8cm long. **Pod** 3–10cm long to 1.5cm wide, margins thickened. Coastal to farther inland in open forest on sandstone. NSW, Vic, Tas. Autumn, winter.

Acacia leucoclada

Acacia mearnsii

Acacia polybotrya

Acacia pubescens

Acacia spectabilis

Acacia terminalis

MYOPORACEAE | Boobialla family

A small family of shrubs or trees found mainly in Australia and the western Pacific, but extending to eastern Asia, New Guinea and New Zealand. Worldwide there are 7 genera and about 240 species with 5 genera and about 230 species occurring in Australia. Leaves, stems and floral parts are often sticky or resinous. Leaves simple and usually alternate. Flowers irregular or almost regular (*Myoporum*), mostly bisexual, tubular, usually 5-lobed, sometimes 2-lipped (*Eremophila*). Stamens usually 5 (sometimes 4) enclosed or exserted. Ovary superior. Fruit dry or drupe-like.

Eremophila abietina | Spotted Poverty Bush

Sticky shrub 1–2m high; stems rough. **Leaves** linear, crowded, to 2cm long and 1mm wide, curved, tip pointed. **Flowers** tubular, to 2.5cm long, white to pale mauve with purple spots, hairy, on long curved stalks; calyx is persistent and enlarges around the fruit. Laverton district in Great Victoria Desert. WA. Winter, early spring.

Eremophila alternifolia | Narrow-leaved Fuchsia Bush

Erect sticky shrub 2–3m high. **Leaves** linear to terete, 2–5cm long to 1mm wide, smooth, tip pointed and curved. **Flowers** tubular, to 3cm long, deep pinky red (rarely white or yellow), interior spotted, on curved stalks to 3cm long, stamens exserted; calyx lobes broad and overlapping. Dry inland districts on shallow soils on hills and ranges. NSW, SA, WA, NT. Winter, spring.

Eremophila bignoniiflora | Bignonia Emubush

Erect shrub to small tree 3–7m high; stems glabrous and resinous, often drooping. **Leaves** linear–lanceolate, 7–20cm long to 1.5cm wide, pale green, glabrous, tip tapering to point. **Flowers** tubular, to 3cm long, cream tinged pinkish-brown, spotted pink or brown and hairy inside, on sticky stalks to 2.5cm long. Widespread in dry inland districts on plains subject to periodic flooding. Qld, NSW, Vic, SA, WA, NT. Winter, spring.

Eremophila bowmanii | Silver Turkeybush

Erect or spreading shrub to 2m high; stems covered with whitish-grey hairs. **Leaves** variable from linear, ovate to obovate or circular, 1–5cm long to 1.5cm wide, densely covered with hairs, margins revolute. **Flowers** tubular, to 3cm long, lilac (rarely white) on hairy stalks to 2.5cm long; calyx lobes densely hairy. Inland districts in mulga and mallee scrubland. Qld, NSW. Winter, spring.

Eremophila abietina

Eremophila alternifolia

Eremophila bignoniiflora

Eremophila bowmanii

Eremophila calorhabdos | Red Rod

Erect shrub to 2m high; stems slender, densely hairy. **Leaves** ovate–oblong, to 2.5cm long and 1cm wide, concave, margins toothed near tip. **Flowers** tubular, to 3cm long, pink or red, lobes pointed and reflexed, on short stalks in upper leaf axils forming a spike; calyx lobes small, glabrous. Woodland in semi-arid regions in southwest. WA. Spring.

Eremophila compacta |

Bushy shrub to 1.5m high. **Leaves** linear–oblong to oblanceolate, to 1cm long and 5mm wide, silvery-grey, glandular and covered in short grey hairs. **Flowers** tubular, to 2cm long, pale pink or mauve on short hairy stalks; calyx lobes darker pink and hairy. Austin District, usually on stony situations. WA. Winter, spring.

Eremophila christophori |

Erect shrub 1–2m high. **Leaves** crowded, elliptic, 1–3cm long to 1cm wide, hairy or glabrous, tip pointed. **Flowers** tubular with pointed lobes, to 2cm long, blue or mauve, exterior hairy, on very short stalks and crowded in upper leaf axils forming a leafy spike. MacDonnell Ranges in central Australia. NT. Winter, spring.

Eremophila debilis | Amulla

Formerly *Myoporum debile*. Prostrate shrub to 1m across. **Leaves** lanceolate, 2–12cm long to 2cm wide, margins with few scattered teeth toward base, tip pointed. **Flowers** bell-shaped, about 1cm long, white to pale mauve, unspotted, stamens enclosed; 1–2 per leaf axil. **Fruit** ovoid, fleshy, to 1cm long, reddish. Widespread coast, tablelands, slopes and plains in open forest. Qld, NSW. Spring, summer.

Eremophila decipiens | Slender Fuchsia

Spreading shrub to 1m high; stems often sticky. **Leaves** linear to lanceolate, 2–4cm long to 1cm wide, slightly hairy when young, tip pointed. **Flowers** tubular, about 2.5cm long, red, glabrous, on slender curved stalks; calyx lobes pointed. **Fruit** ovoid, fleshy to 8mm long. Semi-arid and arid regions; conspicuous on Nullarbor Plain. WA, SA. Winter, spring.

Eremophila drummondii |

Erect shrub 1–2.5m high; stems sticky. **Leaves** narrow–linear or terete, 2–6cm long to 1mm wide, sticky, tip pointed. **Flowers** tubular, about 2cm long, blue or purple, 1–2 per axil on slender curved stalks; calyx lobes pointed. Semi-arid districts in southwest in sand heath or woodland. WA. Winter, spring.

Eremophila calorhabdos

Eremophila compacta

Eremophila christophori

Eremophila debilis

Eremophila decipiens

Eremophila drummondii

Eremophila gibsonii | Gibson's Desert Fuchsia

Erect sticky shrub 1–2m high; stems glabrous and shiny. **Leaves** linear, 2–7cm long to 2mm wide, sticky, margins slightly toothed, tip pointed and hooked. **Flowers** tubular, about 1.5cm long, pink, blue or white, exterior hairy, 1–2 per axil; calyx lobes green, enlarge after flowering. **Fruit** ovoid, to 6mm long, ribbed and sticky. Sand dunes in central Australia. SA, WA, NT. Winter, spring.

Eremophila gilesii | Desert Fuchsia

Small spreading shrub to 1m high; stems hairy and sticky. **Leaves** linear to linear–oblanceolate, 2–6cm long, 1–3mm wide, grey to green, margins entire or slightly toothed, tip pointed, hairy. **Flowers** tubular, to 3cm long, blue, lilac or purple, exterior densely hairy, lobes pointed, 1–2 per axil on curved stalks to 3cm long; calyx lobes pointed. Widespread in arid central Australia, usually in association with mulga. Qld, NSW, SA, WA, NT. Winter, spring.

Eremophila glabra | Tar Bush

Prostrate to erect shrub to 2m high; stems often covered with dense white hairs. **Leaves** lanceolate to oblanceolate, 1–6cm long to 2cm wide, glabrous to densely hairy, margins usually entire, tip pointed. **Flowers** tubular, 2–3cm long, yellow, orange, pink or red, exterior glabrous or covered with glandular hairs, lobes pointed, stamens exserted. **Fruit** ovoid, to 1cm long. Widespread in arid and semi-arid regions. Qld, NSW, Vic, SA, WA, NT. Winter, spring, summer.

Eremophila latrobei | Crimson Turkeybush

Erect shrub 2–3m high; stems warty, finely hairy. **Leaves** linear to terete, 2–9cm long to 5mm wide, glabrous or hairy, often warty, margins entire and revolute. **Flowers** tubular, 2–3cm long, red to purplish-red, exterior covered with glandular hairs, lobes pointed, stamens exserted. **Fruit** conical, to 1cm long. Widespread in arid regions on sandplains in mulga, rocky ridges and hills. Qld, NSW, SA, WA, NT. Winter, spring.

Eremophila gibsonii

Eremophila gilesii

Eremophila glabra

Eremophila latrobei

Eremophila longifolia | Berrigan

Erect shrub or small tree, 2–8m high; branches drooping, warty and hairy. **Leaves** linear–lanceolate, 3–20cm long to 12mm wide, dull green, glabrous or sparsely hairy, margins entire, tip pointed and hooked. **Flowers** tubular, to 3cm long, dull red, exterior hairy, stamens exserted; 1–3 per axil. **Fruit** ovoid, about 1cm long. Widespread in inland districts in a variety of habitats. Qld, NSW, Vic, SA, WA, NT. Winter, spring.

Eremophila macdonnellii |

Small spreading shrub to about 1m high; stems sparsely to densely hairy. **Leaves** linear to narrow–ovate, to 2.5cm long and to 6mm wide, sessile, green and glabrous or grey and hairy, tip pointed. **Flowers** tubular, to 3.5cm long, deep purple, exterior glabrous, solitary on curved stalks to 3cm long. **Fruit** globular, fleshy to 1.5cm across. Arid regions in central Australia. Qld, SA, NT. Winter, spring.

Eremophila maculata | Spotted Fuchsia

Erect multi-branched shrub to 3m high; stems hairy. **Leaves** linear to oblanceolate, to 4cm long and 1cm wide, mostly glabrous, margins entire, tip pointed. **Flowers** tubular, to 3.5cm long, yellow, orange or red often with spotted interior, exterior glabrous, lobes pointed, stamens exserted; on curved stalks to 2.5cm long. **Fruit** globular, to 2cm long. Widespread in inland districts; mostly on heavy clay soils subject to periodic flooding. Qld, NSW, Vic, SA, WA, NT. Winter, spring.

Eremophila maculata var. brevifolia |

Erect shrub to 2m high; stems softly hairy. **Leaves** obovate to almost circular, to 2.5cm long, glabrous, margins thickened. **Flowers** tubular, to 4cm long, red, on curved reddish stalks to 3cm long. Arid regions, mainly in low woodland. WA, NT. Winter, spring.

Eremophila neglecta |

Sticky open shrub to 2.5m high; stems with short hairs. **Leaves** lanceolate, 3–5cm long to 8mm wide, sticky and greyish-green or shiny and mid-green, margins entire, tip pointed. **Flowers** tubular, 2–3cm long, dull red, exterior minutely hairy, on hairy stalks to 2cm long; calyx enlarged after flowering. **Fruit** to 7mm long, angular and beaked. Arid regions in central Australia. SA, NT. Autumn, winter.

Eremophila nivea |

Erect silvery-grey shrub to 1.5m high; stems covered in dense white hairs. **Leaves** linear–lanceolate, to 1.5cm long, pale grey, hairy, margins recurved, tip pointed. **Flowers** profuse, tubular, to 2cm long, lilac, in upper leaf axils forming showy spikes. **Fruit** ovoid, about 7mm long. Irwin district, mainly on sandy soils. WA. Winter, spring.

Eremophila longifolia

Eremophila macdonnellii

Eremophila maculata

Eremophila maculata var. *brevifolia*

Eremophila neglecta

Eremophila nivea

Eremophila oldfieldii

Erect shrub 2–4m high; stems sparsely hairy. **Leaves** variable, lanceolate to narrow–linear, to 12cm long and 1cm wide, glabrous, margins entire, tip pointed. **Flowers** tubular, to 3.5cm long, red, exterior glabrous, on stalks to 1cm long; calyx lobes pointed, green. **Fruit** about 4mm long. Arid districts in southwest; mainly on red soils. WA. Winter, spring.

Eremophila ovata

Small shrub to 1m high; stems densely hairy. **Leaves** ovate to almost circular, to 3.5cm long and 2cm wide, densely hairy, margins entire, tip slightly pointed. **Flowers** tubular, to 2.5cm long, lilac, exterior hairy, sessile; calyx lobes pointed and hairy. **Fruit** to 8mm across, hairy. Central Australia, mainly on ranges. NT. Winter, spring.

Eremophila pachyphylla

Erect shrub to 3m high. **Leaves** narrow–elliptic, to 2.5cm long and 4mm wide, margins entire, tip pointed and hooked. **Flowers** tubular, about 2cm long, pale mauve-pink, exterior glabrous, 1–3 per axil; calyx dark mauve. **Fruit** to 1cm long, hairy. Woodland in semi-arid regions of southwest. WA. Winter, spring.

Eremophila polyclada   Flowering Lignum

Spreading shrub to 3m high; stems glabrous and rigid. **Leaves** linear, 2–8cm long to 3mm wide, margins entire, tip rounded or pointed. **Flowers** tubular, to 3.5cm long, white often tinged lilac, interior conspicuously spotted and hairy, exterior glabrous, stamens enclosed; usually solitary. **Fruit** almost cylindrical to 1.5cm long. Dry inland regions usually in low-lying situations subject to flooding. Qld, NSW, Vic, SA. Spring and autumn.

Eremophila oldfieldii

Eremophila ovata

Eremophila pachyphylla

Eremophila polyclada

Eremophila purpurascens

Erect shrub to 1.5m high; stems rigid and warty. **Leaves** spoon-shaped to 1.5cm long and to about 5mm wide, leathery, glabrous but warty, margins entire, tip mostly rounded. **Flowers** tubular, to 2.5cm long, light reddish-purple, hairy, interior spotted, stamens exserted; calyx lobes enlarged; on slender curved stalks. **Fruit** about 4mm long. Around Norseman on granite hills. WA. Winter, spring.

Eremophila racemosa

Erect shrub to 2m high; stems glabrous. **Leaves** narrow–oblanceolate, 2–5cm long to 8mm wide, margins entire, tip slightly pointed. **Flowers** tubular, to 2.5cm long, change colour from initially yellow, then orange to pink, magenta to red, stamens exserted; solitary, on slender curved stalks. **Fruit** rounded, to 1.5cm across. North of Ravensthorpe in the southwest. WA. Spring.

Eremophila santalina

Erect shrub 2–6m high; stems glabrous and drooping. **Leaves** lanceolate, 3–8cm long to 8mm wide, tip tapering to a point. **Flowers** tubular, to 2cm long, white, exterior glabrous, solitary or rarely in pairs, on slender stalks about 12mm long. **Fruit** ovoid, succulent to 1cm across. Flinders Range. SA. Winter, spring.

Eremophila scoparia | Silver Emubush

Erect broom-like shrub to 3m high; stems and leaves covered with silvery scales. **Leaves** linear to terete, 1–3cm long and to 2mm wide, margins entire, tip pointed and hooked. **Flowers** tubular, to 2.5cm long, lilac to white, exterior scaly, stamens enclosed; 1–2 per axil on short stalks. **Fruit** conical, to 5mm long. Widespread in southern inland regions, usually in woodland. NSW, Vic, SA, WA. Winter, spring.

Eremophila spectabilis | Showy Eremophila

Erect shrub 1–2m high; stems sticky. **Leaves** linear–lanceolate, to 7cm long and 3mm wide, slightly sticky and hairy, margins entire or faintly toothed, tip pointed. **Flowers** tubular, to 3.5cm long, mauve or purple, exterior glabrous, stamens enclosed; on slender curved stalks to 2cm long. **Fruit** narrow, about 1cm long. Meekatharra district, usually in mulga scrubland. WA. Winter.

Eremophila viscida | Varnish Bush

Erect then spreading shrub 2–5m high; stems and leaves sticky. **Leaves** lanceolate, 5–10cm long to 1cm wide, turned inward, margins entire, tip pointed. **Flowers** tubular, about 2cm long, pale pink to reddish, interior spotted, exterior hairy, stamens exserted; calyx enlarged after flowering. **Fruit** ovoid, about 7mm long. Widespread in semi-arid regions of the southwest, usually in woodland. WA. Spring, summer.

Eremophila purpurascens

Eremophila racemosa

Eremophila santalina

Eremophila scoparia

Eremophila spectabilis

Eremophila viscida

Myoporum bateae

Spreading shrub to 4m high; branches warty. **Leaves** linear–elliptic, 5–15cm long to about 1cm wide, glandular, margins finely toothed, tip pointed. **Flowers** bell-shaped, about 6mm across, white or pale mauve, 3–10 per axil on stalks to 3mm long; stamens 4. **Fruit** ovoid, to 3mm long. South coast, mostly in moist situations in dry forest. NSW. Spring, summer.

Myoporum floribundum | Slender Myoporum

Shrub to 3m high; stems somewhat pendulous. **Leaves** linear to terete, 2–10cm long to 3mm wide, pendent, dark green, margins entire, tip finely pointed. **Flowers** small somewhat bell-shaped, about 7mm across, white, 6–8 per axil on short stalks, profuse; stamens 4. **Fruit** oblong to 3mm long. Forest, often along creek banks. NSW, Vic. Spring, summer.

Myoporum insulare | Boobialla

Tall shrub or small tree to 6m high; stems warty. **Leaves** lanceolate to obovate, 3–10cm long to 2cm wide, fleshy, margins entire or slightly toothed toward tip, glabrous. **Flowers** somewhat bell-shaped, to 1cm across, white with purple spots, 3–8 per axil on stalks to 1cm long. **Fruit** globular, to 1cm long, greenish-purple. Common on or near the coast, usually on sand. NSW, Vic, Tas, SA, WA. Spring.

Myoporum montanum | Western Boobialla

Erect shrub or small tree to 8m high; stems sticky and sometimes warty. **Leaves** elliptic to lanceolate, 3–14cm long, 2–4cm wide, margins entire, tip pointed, glabrous. **Flowers** bell-shaped, to 8mm across, white, spotted purple, 1–7 per axil on stalks to 1.5cm long; stamens 4. **Fruit** almost globular, to 8mm across, reddish-purple. Widespread in semi-arid inland regions, mainly in open forest and woodland. Qld, NSW, Vic, SA, WA, NT. Winter, spring.

Myoporum parvifolium | Creeping Boobialla

Prostrate shrub with spreading stems to 3m across. **Leaves** linear to oblanceolate, 1–6cm long to 8mm wide, margins entire or slightly toothed, tip pointed or blunt, glabrous. **Flowers** about 1cm across, white, spotted purple, with 5 spreading lobes and hairy interior. **Fruit** globular, to 7mm across, whitish-brown. Mainly coastal in saline situations. NSW, Vic, SA. Spring, summer.

Myoporum platycarpum | Sugarwood

Tall shrub or small tree to 10m high; bark dark grey and deeply fissured; stems somewhat warty. **Leaves** linear–lanceolate, 2–9cm long and 3–12mm wide, deep green, margins sparsely toothed, tip pointed, glabrous. **Flowers** bell-shaped, to 7mm across, white (rarely pink) spotted purple and hairy inside, 2–12 per axil on stalks about 5mm long. **Fruit** ovate, to 6mm long. Semi-arid regions, chiefly in woodland and open forest. Qld, NSW, Vic, SA, WA. Winter, spring.

Myoporum bateae

Myoporum floribundum

Myoporum insulare

Myoporum montanum

Myoporum parvifolium

Myoporum platycarpum

MYRTACEAE | Myrtle family

A large family of about 140 genera and 300 species widely distributed throughout tropical America, islands of the Pacific and Australia, with fewer representatives in Europe, South Africa and Asia. Australia has about 70 genera and 1400 species occurring in all States. They are mostly shrubs and trees. Leaves, usually opposite, are undivided and often dotted with oil-glands. Flowers regular, usually with showy stamens, which may be free or fused into groups or bundles as in *Callistemon* and *Melaleuca*. Petals 4 or 5 free, or united with calyx to form a lid (operculum) covering the flower in bud (*Eucalyptus* and *Corymbia*). In some genera, such as *Thryptomene*, *Micromyrtus* and *Leptospermum*, the stamens are few and the 5 petals are prominent. The fruit is usually a capsule with small seeds, or a fleshy berry, or more rarely a drupe.

Acmena smithii | Lilly Pilly

Erect shrub or tree 8–20m or more high; bark grey-brown, slightly scaly. **Leaves** narrow–lanceolate to broad–ovate, 3–10cm long and 1–5cm wide, tip elongated with narrow rounded point, glossy green, oil glands conspicuous. **Flowers** creamy-white with 4 tiny circular petals and numerous stamens about 3mm long, in terminal panicles. **Fruit** globular berry, to 2cm across, white, pink or purple. Widespread in rainforest from coast to mountains. Qld, NSW, Vic. Spring, summer.

Actinodium cunninghamii | Swamp Daisy

Small shrub to 1m high; stems wiry and erect. **Leaves** very small, linear–terete, about 5mm long, overlapping along the stem, aromatic. **Flowers** heads daisy-like, to 3cm across, composed of white outer flowers that are sterile and smaller red inner ones that are fertile. Low-lying, moist sandy areas in the southwest. WA. Spring, summer.

Agonis flexuosa | Willow Myrtle

Spreading single-trunked tree 8–15m high; stems slender and often pendulous. **Leaves** linear to linear–lanceolate, 5–15cm long to 1.5cm wide, tip pointed, strongly aromatic when crushed. **Flowers** open-petalled, about 1cm across, white, crowded in axillary clusters along stems. **Capsule** globular, about 5mm across. Common in coastal woodland and karri forest in southwest. WA. Spring, summer.

Agonis juniperina | Juniper Myrtle

Tall shrub or small tree 5–13m high. **Leaves** crowded, narrow, to 1cm long, rigid and turned upward, tip pointed, aromatic. **Flowers** very small, white with brown centre, grouped in axillary rounded heads toward the ends of branches. **Capsule** a fused cluster, sessile. Karri forest and along creeks and swampy situations in southwest. WA. Autumn, winter, spring.

Acmena smithii

Actinodium cunninghamii

Agonis flexuosa

Agonis juniperina

Angophora floribunda | Rough-barked Apple

Spreading tree to 30m high; bark grey-brown and fibrous; branches often twisted **Leaves** opposite, lanceolate, 8–12cm long, 2–3cm wide, dull green, veins spreading, tip pointed. **Flowers** about 2cm across, with 5 broad-based white petals and numerous creamy-white stamens in several rings, in dense terminal clusters. **Capsule** thin-walled, ribbed, abou 1cm across. Open forest and woodland, mainly on the coast and tablelands. Qld, NSW, Vic Spring, summer.

Angophora hispida | Dwarf Apple

Straggly shrub or small tree 3–7m high; stems covered with stiff, reddish hairs. **Leave** ovate to oblong, 5–10cm long, to 5cm wide, grey-green, heart-shaped at base, tip rounded **Flowers** about 2cm across, with 5 small white petals surrounded by several rings of showy creamy stamens, in dense terminal clusters. **Capsule** thin-walled, ribbed, about 1.5cm across Central coast on sandstone. NSW. Spring, summer.

Astartea fascicularis |

Spreading open shrub 2–3m high; stems arching. **Leaves** narrow–linear or semi-terete to 6mm long, arranged in clusters along the stems, aromatic. **Flowers** flat, about 1cm across with 5 rounded white or pale pink petals, often tinged deep pink at the base, massed along stems. **Capsule** flattened, 3-celled. Widespread in southwest. WA. Autumn, winter, spring.

Astartea heteranthera |

Small shrub to 50cm high; stems wiry and spreading. **Leaves** club-shaped to semi-terete, 3–7mm long, fleshy, clustered on short side branches. **Flowers** flat, about 1cm across with 5 rounded white petals, pink in bud, on slender stems longer than the leaves. **Capsule** 3-celled. Southern coastal districts and farther inland. WA. Winter, spring.

Backhousia citriodora | Lemon Ironwood

Erect tree 3–20m high; stems and young shoots softly hairy. **Leaves** narrow–elliptic 5–12cm long to 2.5cm wide, lateral veins prominent, tip tapering to a blunt point; strongly lemon-scented when crushed. **Flowers** creamy-white, with 5 petals alternating with 5 large sepals, stamens numerous. **Capsule** thin-walled with persistent sepals. Coastal rainforest Qld. Summer, autumn.

Backhousia myrtifolia | Grey Myrtle

Tall shrub or small tree 3–10m high; stems with spreading hairs. **Leaves** ovate to elliptic, 3–7cm long to 2.5cm wide, hairy when young, becoming glabrous with age, lateral veins prominent, tip tapering to fine point. **Flowers** yellowish-green with 5 small petals 5 prominent sepals and numerous stamens, arranged in small terminal clusters. **Capsule** dry enclosed within the enlarged sepals. Widespread from coast to ranges in rainforest, often along streams. Qld, NSW. Summer.

Angophora floribunda

Angophora hispida

Astartea fascicularis

Astartea heteranthera

Backhousia citriodora

Backhousia myrtifolia

Baeckea astarteoides

Small shrub to 1m high; stems slender and arching. **Leaves** linear to semi-terete, about 5mm long, mostly in clusters. **Flowers** flat, about 5mm across, with 5 rounded pink petals, solitary on stalks to 8mm long in leaf axils. **Capsule** 2–3 celled, woody. Southern coastal districts. WA. Spring, summer.

Baeckea crassifolia | Desert Baeckea

Small shrub to 75cm high. **Leaves** slightly spreading, narrow–obovate to oblong, 1–3mm long, tip rounded. **Flowers** 5–7mm across, with 5 rounded pink petals, solitary on stalks to 2mm long in leaf axils. **Capsule** 3-celled, to 2mm long. Drier areas, mostly on mallee sandplains. NSW, Vic, SA, WA. Winter, spring.

Baeckea densifolia

Bushy shrub to 1m high; stems slender and arching. **Leaves** linear to terete, 4–7mm long and 1mm wide, tip with minute recurved point. **Flowers** 5–7mm across, with 5 rounded white petals, solitary on short stalks in the leaf axils. **Capsule** about 2mm across. Open forest and heath from coast to ranges. Qld, NSW. Spring, summer.

Baeckea gunniana | Alpine Baeckea

Prostrate or erect shrub to 1m high. **Leaves** crowded and fleshy, obovate to oblong, 2–4mm long, less than 1mm wide, concave. **Flowers** 4–5mm across, with 5 rounded white petals, solitary on very short stalks in leaf axils. **Capsule** to 2mm across. Mainly heathland at high altitudes, usually in moist situations. NSW, Vic, Tas. Summer.

Baeckea astarteoides

Baeckea crassifolia

Baeckea densifolia

Baeckea gunniana

Baeckea ramosissima | Rosy Baeckea

Low, spreading shrub to 60cm high. **Leaves** linear, 4–7mm long to 2mm wide, tip mostly pointed. **Flowers** to 1cm across, with 5 rounded rosy-pink petals, solitary on slender reddish stalks in the leaf axils. **Capsule** to 5mm across. Mainly coastal in heath, woodland and open forest. NSW, Vic, Tas, SA. Winter, spring, summer.

Baeckea virgata | Tall Baeckea

Erect shrub 1–4m high; stems spreading and sometimes pendulous at the tips. **Leaves** to oblanceolate, 1–2.5cm long, 2–6mm wide, midvein prominent. **Flowers** to 8mm across, with 5 rounded white petals, 3–7 together in umbel-like clusters. **Capsule** to 3mm across. Widespread in coastal districts, mainly in heath and open forest. Qld, NSW, Vic. Spring, summer.

Beaufortia decussata | Gravel Bottlebrush

Erect shrub 1–2m high. **Leaves** broadly ovate, about 1cm long, with numerous veins, concave, arranged in opposite pairs at right angles. **Flowers** deep red with prominent stamens, in oblong spikes to 10cm long and 4cm in diameter. **Capsule** 3-celled, woody, retained on branches. Heath and open forest, on rocky soil, in the southwest. WA.

Beaufortia schaueri | Pink Bottlebrush

Small branched shrub to 1m high. **Leaves** narrow–linear, 2–6mm long, crowded, tip pointed. **Flowers** pink or lilac, in rounded heads about 2cm diameter, at the ends of short lateral branches. **Capsules** persistent, fused together around the stems. Common in sandy heaths and rocky hillsides in southern coastal areas. WA. Winter, spring.

Beaufortia sparsa | Swamp Bottlebrush

Open, spreading shrub 1–3m high. **Leaves** obovate to ovate–lanceolate, to 1.2cm long and 5mm wide, with numerous veins, crowded, tip rounded. **Flowers** reddish-orange, in spikes to 7cm long and wide; stamens drooping. **Capsules** fused together around the older stems. Mainly in swampy situations along the southern coast. WA. Summer, autumn.

Beaufortia squarrosa | Sand Bottlebrush

Erect spreading shrub 1–2m high. **Leaves** obovate to ovate, about 5mm long and 3mm wide, sessile, crowded, reflexed, in opposite pairs. **Flowers** bright red (or sometimes orange-yellow), in tufted spikes about 3cm long and wide. **Capsules** woody and persistent, in a single row. Sand plains and heaths on the west coast. WA. Spring, summer, autumn.

Baeckea ramosissima

Baeckea virgata

Beaufortia decussata

Beaufortia schaueri

Beaufortia sparsa

Beaufortia squarrosa

Callistemon citrinus | Red Bottlebrush

Erect shrub or small tree 2–6m high. **Leaves** elliptic to oblanceolate, 3–7cm long, 5–8mm wide, midrib prominent, tip with short point, oil glands often noticeable. **Flowers** deep red (sometimes white or pinkish), in spikes 6–10cm long and 6cm in diameter. **Capsule** globular, to 7cm diameter, with flattened top. Widespread and common in coastal districts, usually in swampy situations. Qld, NSW. Spring, summer.

Callistemon comboynensis | Cliff Bottlebrush

Shrub 1–2m high; branches often straggly; new growth pinkish and silky. **Leaves** narrow–oblanceolate, 5–9cm long to 2cm wide, often twisted, oil glands numerous and conspicuous. **Flowers** bright red, in spikes 6–7cm long, and to 6cm diameter. **Capsule** globular, to 6mm across, with broad opening. Coastal ranges in rocky situations. Qld, NSW. Summer, autumn.

Callistemon formosus |

Tall shrub to 5m high; bark dark brown and hard; branches pendulous. **Leaves** narrow–elliptic, 5–8cm long to 1cm wide, tip pointed. **Flowers** pale yellow to cream, in spikes 3–8cm long to 3.5cm across. **Capsule** globular, to 6mm diameter. Confined to the Kingaroy district, in exposed rocky situations. Qld. Winter, spring.

Callistemon glaucus | Albany Bottlebrush

Formerly *C. speciosus*. Erect shrub 1–2m high. **Leaves** lanceolate, 6–12cm long to 2cm wide, dull green or grey, margins thickened, veins prominent, tip ending in hard point. **Flowers** deep red, in densely packed spikes to 12cm long and 7cm across. **Capsule** globular, about 1cm diameter. Common in swampy situations in the Albany district. WA. Spring, summer.

Callistemon montanus | Mountain Bottlebrush

Erect shrub or small tree 2–4m high; new growth silky-hairy. **Leaves** narrow–oblanceolate, 5–10cm long to 1cm wide, veins prominent, tip pointed; silky-hairy and often pinkish when young. **Flowers** crimson, in spikes 3–5cm long to 6cm across. **Capsule** cup-shaped, about 8mm diameter. Coastal ranges near cliffs. Qld, NSW. Spring.

Callistemon pachyphyllus | Wallum Bottlebrush

Spreading open shrub to 1.5m high. **Leaves** narrow–oblanceolate, 4–9cm long to 1cm wide, dull green, thick-textured, tip with small point. **Flowers** bright red (occasionally green, pictured), in spikes 6–10cm long to 6cm across. **Capsule** globular, to 6mm diameter. Coastal heath known as Wallum, usually in moist situations. Qld, NSW. Spring, summer.

Callistemon citrinus

Callistemon comboynensis

Callistemon formosus

Callistemon glaucus

Callistemon montanus

Callistemon pachyphyllus

Callistemon pallidus | Lemon Bottlebrush

Erect shrub 3–6m high; young growth silky-hairy. **Leaves** narrow–elliptic to oblanceolate, 3–7cm long to 1.5cm wide, tapering to both ends, tip pointed, oil glands conspicuous. **Flowers** cream to greenish-yellow, in spikes 3–7cm long and 3.5–5cm across. **Capsule** globular, about 6mm diameter. Widespread on ranges, mainly in moist rocky situations and near streams. Qld, NSW, Vic. Spring, summer.

Callistemon pinifolius | Pine-leaved Bottlebrush

Erect or spreading shrub to 1m high. **Leaves** linear to terete, 4–8cm long to about 1mm wide, channelled above, tip sharply pointed. **Flowers** bright green (occasionally red), in spikes 5–7cm long and about 5cm wide. **Capsule** globular, about 7mm diameter. Mainly coastal, in damp situations in open forest and woodland. NSW. Spring, summer.

Callistemon pityoides | Alpine Bottlebrush

Compact shrub 1–3m high; young growth silvery-grey. **Leaves** linear to terete, 1–3cm long and 1–2mm wide, tip sharply pointed. **Flowers** yellow or cream, in spikes 3–4cm long to 2cm wide. **Capsule** globular, about 5mm diameter. Widespread on tablelands, often in boggy conditions. Qld, NSW, Vic. Spring, summer.

Callistemon polandii | Gold-tipped Bottlebrush

Tall open shrub to 4m high; young growth silvery-pink and silky. **Leaves** ovate–lanceolate, 8–15cm long and 2–5cm wide, lateral veins prominent, light green, tip pointed, oil glands conspicuous. **Flowers** deep red with golden anthers, in spikes 6–10cm long to 5cm wide. **Capsule** globular, about 7mm diameter. Exposed mountain slopes, among rock crevices. Qld. Winter.

Callistemon pallidus

Callistemon pinifolius

Callistemon pityoides

Callistemon polandii

Callistemon rigidus | Stiff Bottlebrush

Erect rigid shrub 2–3m high; young growth silky-hairy. **Leaves** linear to narrow–oblanceolate, 5–7cm long to 4mm wide, stiff, margins thickened, tip pointed, oil glands prominent on lower surface. **Flowers** red, in spikes 7–10cm long and about 6cm wide. **Capsule** globular, about 7mm diameter. Coastal areas in damp heath and shrublands. NSW. Spring, summer.

Callistemon rugulosus | Scarlet Bottlebrush

Spreading, much-branched shrub to 4m high. **Leaves** oblanceolate to narrow–elliptic 3–8cm long and about 5mm wide, margins thickened, tip sharply pointed, oil glands prominent. **Flowers** red with yellow anthers, in spikes to 10cm long and 5cm wide. **Capsule** globular, about 1cm diameter. Semi-arid regions in southern Australia, usually on sandy low lying areas. Vic, SA. Spring, summer, autumn.

Callistemon salignus | Willow Bottlebrush

Tall shrub or small bushy tree 5–10m high; bark papery; branches somewhat pendulous; young growth bright pink. **Leaves** narrow–elliptic, 6–9m long to 1.5cm wide, tapering to both ends, tip pointed, veins and oil glands distinct. **Flowers** mostly creamy-white (occasionally pink or red), in spikes 4–5cm long to 3.5cm wide. **Capsule** globular, about 5mm diameter. Widespread, mainly coastal along the banks of freshwater streams and on alluvial flats. Qld, NSW. Spring, summer.

Callistemon sieberi | River Bottlebrush

Shrub or small tree 2–5m high; branches weeping; young growth pink and silky. **Leaves** narrow–oblanceolate, 2–6cm long to 5mm wide, greyish-green, tip pointed. **Flowers** yellow, in short spikes 3–5cm long to 2.5cm wide. **Capsule** globular, about 5mm diameter. Widespread in damp places, usually along creek banks. Qld, NSW, Vic. Spring, summer.

Callistemon subulatus |

Small spreading shrub 1–2m high; branches arching. **Leaves** linear to semi-terete 2–5cm long and about 3mm wide, tip with pungent point. **Flowers** red, in spikes 4–8cm long and to 5cm wide, sometimes in clusters at branch ends. **Capsule**, about 5mm diameter, top flattened. Coast and tablelands, along rivers and streams. NSW, Vic. Spring, summer.

Callistemon viminalis | Weeping Bottlebrush

Tall shrub or small tree to 10m high; branches usually drooping; young growth silky. **Leaves** linear to narrow–elliptic, 3–7cm long and 3–7mm wide, tip pointed, oil glands prominent. **Flowers** bright red, in spikes 5–10cm long, 3–6cm wide. **Capsule** cup-shaped, about 6mm diameter, with wide opening. Coastal and farther inland, along freshwater rivers and streams. Qld, NSW. Spring, summer.

Callistemon rigidus

Callistemon rugulosus

Callistemon salignus

Callistemon sieberi

Callistemon subulatus

Callistemon viminalis

Callistemon viridiflorus | Green Bottlebrush

Erect and spreading shrub to 3m high. **Leaves** elliptical, about 3cm long an 1cm wide, often twisted, tip pointed. **Flowers** pale yellowish-green, in spikes 6–8cm long an to 4cm wide. **Capsule** globular, about 8mm diameter, warty. Damp situations mostly o hillsides. Tas. Spring, summer.

Calothamnus quadrifidus | Common Netbush

Spreading shrub to 2.5m high and across. **Leaves** linear terete, to 3cm long, brigh green, tip pointed or blunt. **Flowers** bright red, in 1-sided spikes along older stems; stamens i bundles in 4 of equal length about 3cm long; calyx glabrous. **Capsule** 4–6mm diameter. Wide spread in the southwest, mainly in sandy soils in heath and woodland. WA. Spring, summer.

Calothamnus rupestris | Cliff Netbush

Spreading shrub to 2m high. **Leaves** linear terete, 2–5cm long, crowded, tip pungent pointed. **Flowers** deep pink to red, in 1-sided or cylindrical spikes on older stems; stamen in bundles in 4 of equal length to 4cm long; calyx tube and lobes hairy. **Capsule** abou 2cm long, with pointed tips. Granite outcrops on the Darling Range, east of Perth. WA Winter, spring.

Calothamnus validus | Barrens Clawflower

Erect shrub to 1m high. **Leaves** terete, 2–3cm long, rigid, thick, tip slightly pungen **Flowers** bright red, in small clusters on old wood; stamens in bundles in 4 of equal length t 3cm long; calyx tube about 1cm long, minutely pubescent. **Capsule** almost globular, to 1.5cn long. Endemic to quartzite hills of the Barren Ranges. WA. Spring, summer.

Callistemon viridiflorus

Calothamnus quadrifidus

Calothamnus rupestris

Calothamnus validus

Calytrix alpestris | Snow Myrtle

Shrub 1–2m high; branches sometimes arching. **Leaves** aromatic, linear, about 5mm long, hairy and crowded at right angles to the stem. **Flowers** star-like, white or pale pink, about 1.5cm across, often pink in bud, in small clusters in upper leaf axils; calyx lobes do not develop hair-like bristles. Widespread, often in damp areas. Vic. Spring, summer.

Calytrix exstipulata | Turkey Bush

Erect bushy shrub 1–4m high; stems short, numerous. **Leaves** 3-sided, scale-like, about 2mm long, crowded and overlapping on stems. **Flowers** star-like, deep pink to purple, about 2.5cm across, profuse in clusters in upper leaf axils; calyx lobes extend into long hair-like bristles. Widespread in tropical regions across Northern Australia, often in open woodland and shrubland. Qld, WA, NT. Autumn, winter.

Calytrix sullivani |

Erect bushy shrub to 3m high. **Leaves** linear, about 1cm long, crowded, tip pointed. **Flowers** star-like, white, about 1.5cm across, in dense clusters in upper leaf axils; calyx lobes extend into long hair-like bristles. Endemic to the Grampians, often in rocky situations. Vic. Winter, spring.

Calytrix tetragona | Fringe Myrtle

Erect or spreading shrub 1–2m high; stems slender and often arching. **Leaves** linear to oblong, to 1cm long and 1mm wide, aromatic, margins often finely fringed. **Flowers** star-like, about 1.5cm across, white to pink, in clusters in upper leaf axils; calyx lobes extend into long hair-like bristles. Widespread in heath and open forest. Qld, NSW, Vic, Tas, SA, WA. Winter, spring.

Chamelaucium ciliatum |

Erect bushy shrub to 1m high. **Leaves** linear–lanceolate, about 1cm long, crowded, tip rounded. **Flowers** with 5 rounded petals, white or pale pink, about 1cm across, aging to a deep pink, in clusters in upper leaf axils; calyx lobes fringed. Widely distributed in the southwest, mainly in sand heath. WA. Spring.

Chamelaucium drummondii |

Small shrub to about 1m high. **Leaves** linear, 6–8mm long, margins fringed with long hairs, tip rounded. **Flowers** white to pink, about 5mm across, aging to red, in terminal heads of up to 10 per cluster; petals and calyx lobes minutely fringed. Widespread in the south, mainly in sand heath. WA. Winter, spring.

Calytrix alpestris

Calytrix exstipulata

Calytrix sullivani

Calytrix tetragona

Chamelaucium ciliatum

Chamelaucium drummondii

Chamelaucium forrestii | Walpole Wax

Formerly *C. sp.* (Walpole). Dense shrub 2–3m high. **Leaves** semi-terete, about 2cm long, opposite, channelled above, tip pointed. **Flowers** white with purplish centre, about 1.5cm across, in loose clusters in upper leaf axils; young buds enclosed in reddish-brown bracteoles; calyx lobe pink-tipped. Walpole area west of Albany. WA. Spring.

Chamelaucium uncinatum | Geraldton Wax

Erect shrub 2–5m high; branches numerous and slender. **Leaves** aromatic, linear to semi-terete, to 3cm long, glabrous, tip with hooked point. **Flowers** waxy, open-petalled white, pink or purple, to 2.5cm across, in small terminal clusters. Sandplains north of Perth to around Kalbarri. WA. Winter, spring.

Darwinia citriodora | Lemon-scented Myrtle

Dense, aromatic shrub to 1.5m high. **Leaves** mostly opposite, ovate–lanceolate, to 1.5cm long, mostly opposite, blue-green sometimes with reddish tints, margins recurved. **Flowers** orange, with prominent styles, 4–6 per head, surrounded by 4 orange and green outer leaf-like bracts. Widespread in southwest, often on granite outcrops. WA. Winter, spring.

Darwinia fascicularis |

Spreading, aromatic shrub to 2m high. **Leaves** light green, almost terete, 1–1.5cm long, crowded toward branch ends, opposite or in whorls. **Flowers** creamy-white, aging to red, with prominent styles, in terminal clusters of 4–20 per head. Central coast and nearby ranges, in heath and open forest. NSW. Winter, spring.

Chamelaucium forrestii

Chamelaucium uncinatum

Darwinia citriodora

Darwinia fascicularis

Darwinia lejostyla

Dense, aromatic shrub to 1m high. **Leaves** linear, to 1.5cm long, crowded. **Flowers** 8–10 per head, enclosed by large, deep pink and greenish bracts forming a terminal pendent bell-shaped inflorescence to 4cm long. Stirling and Barren Ranges, in the southwest WA. Winter, spring.

Darwinia macrostegia | Mondurup Bell

Erect shrub 1–2m high. **Leaves** sessile, elliptic–oblong, 1–2cm long, sessile, margins recurved, tip rounded. **Flowers** 6–8 per head, enclosed by creamy-white inner, petal-like bracts streaked with red, arranged in a terminal pendent bell-shaped inflorescence to 6cm long. Stirling and Porongurup Ranges in the southwest. WA. Autumn, spring.

Darwinia meeboldii | Cranbrook Bell

Erect shrub 2–3m high. **Leaves** linear, to 1cm long, bright green and fleshy, held erect on stems. **Flowers** 7–8 per head, enclosed by long white inner bracts with red tips and shorter green outer bracts, arranged in a terminal pendent bell-shaped inflorescence to 3cm long. Stirling Ranges in the southwest. WA. Spring.

Darwinia oldfieldii

Shrub to 1m high; stems numerous, short. **Leaves** oblong, 2–6mm long, glandular, margins fringed and usually recurved. **Flowers** deep red, 10–12 per head, with long exserted styles and short bracts. Murchison River district on sandplains. WA. Winter, spring.

Darwinia oxylepis

Erect dense shrub to 1.5m high; stems numerous, short. **Leaves** linear to semi-terete, to 1cm long, crowded, usually recurved. **Flowers** 10–12 per head, enclosed by red inner bracts and shorter green and red outer bracts, arranged in a terminal pendent bell-shaped inflorescence to 3cm long. Stirling Range in the southwest. WA. Spring.

Darwinia taxifolia

Erect or spreading shrub to 1m high. **Leaves** semi terete, to 1.2cm long, opposite, grey-green. **Flowers** deep red, 2–4 per head, with long exserted styles, enclosed by deep pink bracts, arranged in an axillary erect inflorescence to 1.5cm long. Central and southern tablelands. NSW. Spring, summer.

Darwinia lejostyla

Darwinia macrostegia

Darwinia meeboldii

Darwinia oldfieldii

Darwinia oxylepis

Darwinia taxifolia

Eremaea beaufortioides | Round-leaved Eremaea

Dense shrub to 1.5m high; stems short and numerous, hairy. **Leaves** ovate to elliptical, to 5mm long and 3mm wide, 3–5 longitudinal veins, recurved, margins hairy. **Flowers** orange, with numerous showy stamens, 2–5 per terminal head. **Capsule** barrel-shaped, about 1cm long. Sand heath and open woodland north of Perth. WA. Spring.

Eremaea brevifolia |

Spreading shrub to 60cm high; stems short and numerous. **Leaves** broadly obovate, 5–7mm long to 5mm wide, hairy. **Flowers** bright orange, to 1cm across, singly at branch ends; calyx tube and lobes silky-hairy. **Capsule** cup-shaped, to 1.5cm across, hairy. Sand heath north of Perth. WA. Winter, spring.

Eucalyptus amplifolia | Cabbage Gum

Tree to 25m high; bark smooth grey, bluish or white, deciduous. **Leaves** lanceolate, 10–18cm long, 2–4cm wide, dull green both surfaces. Buds elongated. **Flowers** white, about 2cm across, 10–20 per axillary umbel. **Capsule** ovoid to globular, 4–6mm long to 8mm across, valves exserted. Coast and tablelands. NSW. Winter, spring.

Eucalyptus caesia | Gungurru

Mallee or small tree 6–10m high; bark reddish-brown, deciduous in longitudinally curling strips revealing green bark beneath. Stems, buds and capsules powdery white. **Leaves** lanceolate, 8–20cm long, 2–4cm wide, grey-blue. Buds spindle-shaped. **Flowers** red, to 5cm across, pendent, usually in 3s. **Capsule** urn-shaped, to 3cm long, valves enclosed. Southern wheatbelt region, on or near granite outcrops. WA. Winter, spring.

Eremaea beaufortioides

Eremaea brevifolia

Eucalyptus amplifolia

Eucalyptus caesia

Eucalyptus calycogona | Gooseberry Mallee

Mallee or small tree 3–6m high; bark smooth, grey, deciduous in ribbons. **Leaves** narrow–lanceolate, 6–10cm long to 1.5cm wide, glossy, pale green on both surfaces. Bud club-shaped. **Flowers** cream (or pink), about 2cm across, 7 per axillary umbel. **Capsule** urn-shaped, to 1.5cm long, 4-angled, valves enclosed. Widespread in semi-arid regions of southern Australia. NSW, Vic, SA, WA. Winter, spring.

Eucalyptus costata | Ridge-fruited Mallee

Mallee 4–6m high; bark smooth, grey-brown, deciduous in ribbons. **Leaves** lanceolate, 6–11cm long to 2.5cm wide, grey-green, thick and semi-glossy. Buds ribbed with conical cap. **Flowers** creamy, about 2cm across, 3–7 per axillary umbel. **Capsule** urn-shaped usually ribbed, to 1.4cm long. Semi-arid regions in mallee shrubland. NSW, Vic, SA. Spring.

Eucalyptus curtisii | Plunkett Mallee

Mallee or small tree 2–6m high; bark greyish, deciduous in thin strips. **Leaves** lanceolate, 8–14cm long to 2.5cm wide, shiny above, paler below. Buds club-shaped. **Flowers** white, about 2cm across, profuse in large terminal panicles. **Capsule** ovoid, to 1cm long, valves enclosed. Around Brisbane and farther inland, in low, open forest. Qld. Winter, spring.

Eucalyptus diversifolia | Soap Mallee

Mallee or small tree 3–8m high; bark smooth, greyish or light brown, deciduous in long strips. **Leaves** lanceolate, to 12cm long and about 2cm wide, grey-green. Buds conical. **Flowers** cream, about 1.5cm across, 3–11 in axillary umbels. **Capsule** hemispherical, to 1.5cm across, valves at rim level. Coastal and slightly inland, mainly on calcareous soils. Vic, SA, WA. Spring, summer.

Eucalyptus dumosa | White Mallee

Mallee (rarely small tree) 2–10m high; bark grey, persistent at base, then deciduous in long strips. **Leaves** lanceolate, 7–10cm long and 2cm wide, grey-green on both surfaces, tip pointed. Buds cylindrical, yellow-green to reddish. **Flowers** white, about 1.5cm across, 7 per axillary umbel. **Capsule** cup-shaped, to 1cm long, valves at rim level or slightly exserted. Widespread in semi-arid regions, usually in mallee communities. NSW, Vic, SA. Winter, spring.

Eucalyptus dwyeri | Dwyer's Red Gum

Mallee or small tree 5–15m high; bark smooth, cream to grey, deciduous in small flakes. **Leaves** narrow–lanceolate, 8–15cm long to 2.5cm wide, dull green on both surfaces. Buds ovoid, often red. **Flowers** cream, about 2cm across, 3–7 per axillary umbel. **Capsule** bell-shaped, to 7mm across, valves exserted. Central-western districts, mainly in mallee communities. NSW, Vic. Winter, spring.

Eucalyptus calycogona

Eucalyptus costata

Eucalyptus curtisii

Eucalyptus diversifolia

Eucalyptus dumosa

Eucalyptus dwyeri

Eucalyptus ficifolia | Red-flowering Gum

Also now called *Corymbia ficifolia* by some botanists. Small tree to about 12m high with dense, rounded crown; bark grey-brown, persistent. **Leaves** broad–lanceolate, 6–14cm long to 5cm wide, dark green above, paler below. Buds club-shaped. **Flowers** various shades of red (also cream), about 4cm across, 3–7 per terminal umbel. **Capsule** urn-shaped, to 3.5cm long, valves enclosed. Restricted to small area west of Albany. WA. Summer, autumn.

Eucalyptus flocktoniae | Merrit

Mallee or slender tree to 12m high; bark smooth, light grey, deciduous, exposing fresh reddish-brown bark. **Leaves** lanceolate, 8–12cm long, 1cm wide, dark green and shiny with prominent oil glands. Buds with long beaked cap. **Flowers** cream or pale yellow, to 2cm across, up to 11 per axillary umbel. **Capsule** pendulous, urn-shaped, to 1cm long, valves slightly exserted. Semi-arid regions of the southwest. Also in the Eyre Peninsula. SA, WA. Spring, summer.

Eucalyptus forrestiana | Fuchsia Gum

Mallee or small tree to 5m high; bark smooth, grey, deciduous in long strips. **Leaves** lanceolate to lanceolate–oblong, 6–9cm long to 2cm wide, thick, deep green, glandular. Buds 4-sided, bright red. **Flowers** yellow, to 2cm across, usually solitary (rarely 3) on pendulous stalks. **Capsule** pear-shaped, 4-sided, 3–5cm long, valves deeply enclosed. Restricted to small area inland between Ravensthorpe and Esperance. WA. Summer, autumn.

Eucalyptus goniantha | Jerdacuttup Mallee

Mallee shrub or small tree 3–6m high; bark smooth, grey, deciduous in strips. **Leaves** lanceolate–ovate, 6–12cm long, 2–3cm wide, thick. Buds creamy, ovoid, pendent. **Flowers** cream or lemon-yellow, about 2cm across, 3–7 in axillary umbels. **Capsule** pear-shaped, to 1.5cm long, ribbed, valves pointed and exserted. Southern coastal districts, often in sandy heath. WA. Winter, spring.

Eucalyptus ficifolia

Eucalyptus flocktoniae

Eucalyptus forrestiana

Eucalyptus goniantha

Eucalyptus grossa | Coarse-leaved Mallee

Mallee shrub or small, straggly tree 3–6m high; bark rough and grey on trunk, upper branches smooth and reddish. **Leaves** lanceolate to ovate, to 13cm long, 3–5cm wide, thick, midrib yellow, lateral veins distinct. Buds bullet-shaped, reddish. **Flowers** stalkless, yellow or yellow-green, to 4cm across, in axillary umbels of up to 7. **Capsule** cylindrical, to 2cm long, valves deeply enclosed. Mainly semi-arid regions in the south. WA. Winter, spring.

Eucalyptus lansdowneana | Crimson Mallee

Mallee or small tree 3–10m high; bark rough at base, smooth above and deciduous. **Leaves** lanceolate, 8–13cm long, 1–2cm wide, glossy. Buds cylindrical. **Flowers** crimson or pink, about 1.5cm across, 3–6 per umbel. **Capsule** barrel-shaped, to 1.2cm long, valves enclosed. Eyre Peninsula, Kangaroo Island northward to Gawler Ranges. SA. Winter, spring.

Eucalyptus lehmannii | Lehmann's Mallee

Mallee or small tree with broad crown, 4–8m high; bark smooth, greyish-brown, often rough near base. **Leaves** elliptic to lanceolate, 5–7cm long, 1–2cm wide. Buds cylindrical, 4–5cm long, up to 20, and fused at the base. **Flowers** green or yellow-green, united in a globular head to 12cm across. **Capsule** fused into a globular woody head, about 8cm diameter, valves pointed and exserted. Mainly southern coastal areas from Albany, eastward to around Esperance. WA. Winter, spring.

Eucalyptus leucoxylon | Yellow Gum

Tree 5–30m high; bark smooth, cream or bluish-grey, deciduous, often rough near base. **Leaves** lanceolate, 7–18cm long to 3.5cm wide, grey-green, veins distinct. Buds ovoid, to 1.5cm long, on slender stalks. **Flowers** cream, pink, red or yellow, to 3cm across, in umbels of 3. **Capsule** barrel-shaped, to 1.2cm long, valves enclosed. Widespread and variable in a variety of habitats and locations. NSW, Vic, SA. Winter, spring.

Eucalyptus macrocarpa | Mottlecah

Sprawling mallee shrub 1–4m high; bark smooth, grey; stems, new bark and buds powdery grey. **Leaves** broadly ovate, 8–12cm long, 5–8cm wide, silvery-grey, thick-textured, stalkless. Buds rounded, to 6cm long, cap pointed. **Flowers** deep pink to red, about 10cm across, solitary on thick, short stalks. **Capsule** top-shaped or hemispherical, to 9cm wide, valves triangular and exserted. Open sandy heath in wheatbelt districts of the southwest. WA. Spring.

Eucalyptus melliodora | Yellow Box

Tree to 30m high; bark persistent, fibrous on trunk and lower branches, upper branches smooth, deciduous in long ribbons. **Leaves** narrow–lanceolate or lanceolate, 6–14cm long to 2cm wide, grey-green, veins distinct. Buds club-shaped to ovoid. **Flowers** creamy, to 1.5cm across, in umbels of up to 7. **Capsule** globular, to 7mm across, valves enclosed. Widespread and fairly common in woodland, mainly inland of the ranges. Qld, NSW, Vic. Spring, summer.

Eucalyptus grossa

Eucalyptus lansdowneana

Eucalyptus lehmannii

Eucalyptus leucoxylon

Eucalyptus macrocarpa

Eucalyptus melliodora

Eucalyptus orbifolia | Round-leaved Mallee

Mallee shrub to 3m high; bark smooth, reddish-brown, deciduous in curling longitudinal strips, exposing fresh green bark. **Leaves** rounded, 3–7cm long, grey-green, tip indented. Buds powdery grey with pinkish conical cap. **Flowers** pale yellow, to 2.5cm across, in umbels of up to 7. **Capsule** bell-shaped, to 2cm wide, powdery grey, valves exserted. Confined to Goldfields in Coolgardie district, usually on or near granite outcrops. WA. Winter, spring.

Eucalyptus pachyphylla | Red-budded Mallee

Mallee shrub 2–5m high; bark smooth and grey, deciduous in long strips, stems red. **Leaves** ovate–lanceolate, 3–15cm long to 5cm wide, thick. Buds red, to 3.5cm long, distinctly ribbed. **Flowers** pale yellow, to 4cm across, in umbels of up to 3. **Capsule** hemispherical, about 2.5cm wide, disc raised, valves exserted. Central Australia in red sands. Qld, SA, NT. Winter, spring.

Eucalyptus preissiana | Bell-fruited Mallee

Straggling mallee shrub 2–5m high; bark grey, deciduous. **Leaves** ovate, 7–12cm long, 3–5cm wide, grey-green, thick. Buds reddish, pear-shaped, to 2cm long. **Flowers** bright yellow, to 5cm across, 3 per umbel on flattened stalk to 2.5cm long. **Capsule** bell-shaped, to 2.5cm long and 3cm wide, valves enclosed. Coastal or slightly inland in southern districts. WA. Winter, spring.

Eucalyptus pyriformis | Pear-fruited Mallee

Mallee shrub 2–5m high; bark smooth, grey and deciduous in strips. **Leaves** lanceolate to ovate–lanceolate, 6–8cm long, 1.5–3cm wide, grey-green, thick-textured. Buds grey to red, to 3.5cm long, ribbed. **Flowers** yellow, pink or red, to 10cm across, up to 3 per umbel on thick stalks, often pendulous. **Capsule** top-shaped, to 6.5cm across, triangular valves at rim level or exserted. Sandy heath in wheatbelt region, north to the Murchison River. WA. Winter, spring.

Eucalyptus orbifolia

Eucalyptus pachyphylla

Eucalyptus preissiana

Eucalyptus pyriformis

Eucalyptus rhodantha | Rose Mallee

Sprawling mallee shrub 2–3m high; bark smooth, grey-brown; stems powdery grey. **Leaves** rounded–heart-shaped, 6–8cm long and wide, glaucous to powdery grey, thick-textured, tip pointed. Buds conical, to 5cm long. **Flowers** red (rarely cream), to 7.5cm across, solitary on grey pendent stalk to 2cm long. **Capsule** broadly top-shaped, to 5.5cm across, with 2 faint ribs, valves exserted. Rare, sandplains from Hill River to New Norcia. WA. Spring, summer, autumn.

Eucalyptus setosa | Rough-leaved Bloodwood

Also called *Corymbia setosa* by some botanists. Mallee or crooked small tree 3–8m high; bark grey, tessellated, persistent on the trunk and branches. **Leaves** stalkless and opposite, ovate–lanceolate, 5–14cm long, 3–7cm wide, rough or hairy. Buds ovoid, to 1cm long, hairy. **Flowers** white, pink or red, to 3.5cm across, 3–7 per umbel, stalks hairy. **Capsule** urn-shaped to 3.5cm long, roughly hairy, valves enclosed. Widespread in northern Australia, extending into central Australia. Qld, WA, NT. Spring, summer.

Eucalyptus shirleyi | Shirley's Ironbark

Small, open tree to 10m high; bark dark grey, persistent on trunk and branches. **Leaves** stalkless and opposite, broadly ovate to almost rounded, 5–8cm long and wide, silvery-grey and glaucous. Buds ovoid, to 1cm long. **Flowers** creamy, to 2cm across, 3–7 per umbel on flattened stalks to 2cm long. **Capsule** ovoid to cylindrical, to 1cm long, valves enclosed. Slightly inland between Cook and Bowen, where locally common on ridges. Qld. Spring, autumn.

Eucalyptus sideroxylon | Red Ironbark

Tree to 30m high; bark dark brown deeply furrowed, persistent on trunk and branches. **Leaves** broad–lanceolate, 6–14cm long to 2cm wide, dull green. Buds ovoid, to 1.2cm long, pendent. **Flowers** cream, pink or red, to 2cm across, 7 per umbel, on slender stalks to 2cm long. **Capsule** barrel-shaped, to 1cm long, valves enclosed. Widespread in open forest and woodland. Qld, NSW, Vic. Winter, spring.

Eucalyptus socialis | Red Mallee

Mallee shrub or small tree to 6m high; bark smooth grey, deciduous in long strips, persistent on lower trunk; stems reddish. **Leaves** lanceolate, 6–10cm long to 2cm wide, grey-green, thick. Buds ovoid, to 1.4cm long, cap elongated. **Flowers** creamy, to 2cm across, 7–13 per umbel on flattened stalks to 2cm long. **Capsule** globular, to 1cm long, valves exserted. Widespread in dry inland regions, mainly in mallee woodland. NSW, Vic, SA, NT. Winter, spring.

Eucalyptus tetragona | Tallerack

Straggly mallee shrub or small tree 2–8m high; bark smooth, greyish-white, deciduous; stems mealy white. **Leaves** opposite, oval, 7–15cm long, 3–7cm wide, thick, pale grey-green. Buds club-shaped, to 1cm long, 4-angled. **Flowers** creamy, to 3cm across, in umbels of 3. **Capsule** urn-shaped, to 2cm long, grey, valves enclosed. Widespread in heath near the coast, mainly in the south. WA. Spring, summer.

Eucalyptus rhodantha

Eucalyptus setosa

Eucalyptus shirleyi

Eucalyptus sideroxylon

Eucalyptus socialis

Eucalyptus tetragona

Eucalyptus tetraptera | Four-winged Mallee

Straggly mallee shrub 2–3m high; bark smooth, grey; stems angular. **Leaves** broad–lanceolate, to 18cm long and 7cm wide, bright green, leathery. Buds bright red, to 5.5cm long, with 4 distinct wings. **Flowers** pink or red, to 3.5cm across, solitary on broad twisted stalk that curves downward. **Capsule** 4-sided, about 5cm long, valves enclosed. Widespread on the southern coast and slightly inland, mainly in heathland. WA. Spring.

Eucalyptus torquata | Coral Gum

Tree to 12m high with dense crown; bark dark grey and rough on trunk and lower branches, smooth above. **Leaves** lanceolate, 9–12cm long to 2cm wide, grey-green, oil glands distinct. Buds reddish, to 2.5cm long, cap elongated with ribbed base. **Flowers** pink or red to 3.5cm across, 7 per umbel on thin, pendent stalks to 2.5cm long. **Capsule** cylindrical, to 1.5cm long, ribbed with expanded base, valve tips at rim level. Common in the Coolgardie district, usually on hillsides. WA. Spring, summer.

Eucalyptus woodwardii | Lemon-flowered Gum

Tree to 15m high; bark whitish-grey, smooth; stems powdery white. **Leaves** lanceolate, 10–15cm long, 2–4cm wide, pale green or glaucous. Buds globular, to 2cm long, cap beaked. **Flowers** bright lemon-yellow, to 5cm across, up to 7 per umbel, on short stalks to 1cm long. **Capsule** bell-shaped, to 1.5cm long and wide, valve tips below or at rim level. Confined to a small area east of Kalgoorlie. WA. Winter, spring.

Homoranthus darwinioides |

Spreading, aromatic shrub to 1.5m high. **Leaves** linear to terete, to 5mm long and 1mm wide, grey-green, tip pointed. **Flowers** cream to pink, about 7mm long, in pendent pairs; each flower enclosed in 2 bracteoles before shedding; style to 1.2cm long, protrudes well beyond the flower, tipped with ring of hairs. Dry forest and woodland on sandstone between Putty and Dubbo. NSW. Spring.

Eucalyptus tetraptera

Eucalyptus torquata

Eucalyptus woodwardii

Homoranthus darwinioides

Homoranthus flavescens

Spreading, aromatic shrub to about 50cm high; branches horizontal to 1m across. **Leaves** linear to semi-terete, to 1cm long and 1.5mm wide, tip finely pointed. **Flowers** yellow, tubular, about 7mm long, in clusters toward ends of branches; style to 8mm long, protrudes beyond petals. Heath and dry forest on northern tablelands and western slopes and plains. Qld, NSW. Spring, summer.

Homoranthus virgatus

Small erect shrub to 1m high. **Leaves** linear to terete, to 1cm long and 1mm wide, grey-green, tip finely pointed. **Flowers** pale green or yellow, about 5mm long, in clusters toward ends of branches; style protrudes beyond petals. Coastal heath or dry forest. Qld, NSW. Spring, summer.

Hypocalymma angustifolium | White Myrtle

Erect, many-stemmed shrub to 1m high; stems 4-sided. **Leaves** opposite, narrow–linear to semi-terete, 1–3cm long, to 1mm wide, tip pointed. **Flowers** white, often with pinkish tinge, about 8mm across, sessile, in axillary clusters around the stem. Mostly coastal in southwest, also inland. WA. Winter, spring.

Hypocalymma linifolium

Small shrub 30–60cm high; stems erect. **Leaves** opposite, narrow–oblong or elliptical, 1–2cm long, to 3mm wide, sessile, tip rounded or pointed. **Flowers** yellow to white, about 1cm across, sessile, in axillary clusters around the stem. Sandplains north of Perth. WA. Winter, spring.

Hypocalymma robustum | Swan River Myrtle

Small erect shrub to 1m high; stems twiggy. **Leaves** opposite, linear–lanceolate, to 2.5cm long and to 2mm wide, tip finely pointed. **Flowers** fragrant, pink, to 1cm across, sessile, in axillary clusters around the stem. Common in woodland and jarrah forest, from near Perth to Albany. WA. Winter, spring.

Kunzea affinis

Erect compact shrub to 1m high; stems many, twiggy. **Leaves** terete, to 6mm long, dark green, thick, tip rounded. **Flowers** bright pink, open-petalled, to 1cm across, 1–3 per terminal cluster; stamens, with yellow anthers, same length as petals. Mainly heath, coastal districts in the south. WA. Winter, spring.

Homoranthus flavescens

Homoranthus virgatus

Hypocalymma angustifolium

Hypocalymma linifolium

Hypocalymma robustum

Kunzea affinis

Kunzea ambigua | Tick Bush

Large spreading shrub to 4m high. **Leaves** narrow–linear, to 1cm long and about 1.5mm wide, dark green, aromatic, tip pointed. **Flowers** white (rarely pink), about 1.5cm across, sessile, in upper leaf axils; stamens white, longer than the petals. Mainly on or near the coast in heath and open forest. NSW, Vic, Tas. Spring, summer.

Kunzea baxteri | Crimson Kunzea

Spreading, many-stemmed shrub 1–2m high. **Leaves** linear–oblong, 1.5cm long to 3mm wide, often edged with white silky hairs. **Flowers** deep red, about 2.5cm across, sessile, in dense cylindrical spikes to 10cm long; stamens are prominent part of the flower. On granite outcrops from Esperance to Israelite Bay. WA. Spring.

Kunzea bracteolata | Stiff Kunzea

Erect shrub to 1.5m high. **Leaves** elliptic, 4–8mm long to about 2mm wide, tip pointed, finely hairy when young, tip pointed. **Flowers** cream, about 1cm across, sessile in terminal, head-like clusters; stamens cream, longer than the petals. On granite hills on northern tablelands to around Stanthorpe. Qld, NSW. Spring, summer.

Kunzea capitata | Heath Kunzea

Erect, many-stemmed shrub to 1.5m high; stems usually hairy. **Leaves** oblanceolate to obovate, to 1cm long and 4.5mm wide, tip rounded and recurved; 3 main veins visible. **Flowers** pink to purple (rarely white), about 1.2cm across, in terminal head-like clusters; stamens longer than the petals. Widespread from coast to ranges in heath and dry forest. NSW. Winter, spring.

Kunzea ericoides | Burgan

Tall shrub or small tree 4–5m high. **Leaves** narrow–elliptic to oblanceolate, to 2.5cm long and 4.5mm wide, dark green, tip pointed. **Flowers** white, about 1.2cm across, shortly stalked in upper leaf axils; petals are prominent and only some stamens longer than petals. Widespread in heath and open forest, often at higher elevations near streams. Qld, NSW, Vic, SA. Spring, summer.

Kunzea jucunda |

Multi-branched shrub to 2m high. **Leaves** obovate–elliptical to almost round, about 3mm long, glabrous, tip rounded. **Flowers** mauve, about 1cm across, sessile, in small terminal clusters; stamens shorter than petals. Mainly from Stirling Range to Ravensthorpe in the southwest, usually in sand heath. WA. Winter, spring.

Kunzea ambigua

Kunzea baxteri

Kunzea bracteolata

Kunzea capitata

Kunzea ericoides

Kunzea jucunda

Kunzea muelleri | Yellow Kunzea

Prostrate, spreading to erect shrub to 1m high; stems hairy. **Leaves** linear to terete 3–8mm long and less than 1mm wide, grey-green, hairy, tip pointed. **Flowers** yellow, about 1cm across, sessile in small terminal clusters; stamens longer than petals. Heath in alpine and sub-alpine regions. NSW, Vic. Summer.

Kunzea obovata |

Dense shrub to 3m high; stems hairy. **Leaves** obovate, to 1cm long and 1.5mm wide, tip pointed and recurved. **Flowers** pink, about 1cm across, sessile in small terminal heads, stamens much longer than petals. Open forest on granite soils in New England Tablelands and Darling Downs district. Qld, NSW. Spring.

Kunzea pulchella | Granite Kunzea

Dense shrub, 2–3m high; branches spreading or arching. **Leaves** obovate, to 1cm long, grey-green, silky-hairy, tip pointed or blunt. **Flowers** bright red, about 3cm across, in short terminal spikes; stamens much longer than petals. Semi-arid regions in the southwest, occurring only on granite outcrops. WA. Spring, summer.

Leptospermum epacridoideum |

Erect shrub to 2m high. **Leaves** elliptic to almost round, 2–3mm long and 2mm wide, sessile, dark green, glandular on lower surface, margins incurved, tip rounded. **Flowers** open-petalled, white (sometimes pink), about 1cm across, solitary, terminal on short side branches. **Capsule** domed, about 8mm across, persistent. Coastal, in moist, sandy situations in heath and open forest. NSW. Autumn.

Kunzea muelleri

Kunzea obovata

Kunzea pulchella

Leptospermum epacridoideum

Leptospermum erubescens

Spreading multi-branched shrub to 2m high. **Leaves** obovate, to 6mm long and 4mm wide, grey-green and silky-hairy, tip rounded. **Flowers** open-petalled, white or pink, to 1cm across, 1–2 at branch ends. **Capsule** 5-celled, about 5mm across, hairy, deciduous. Semi-arid, inland areas of the southwest, in heath and woodland. WA. Winter, spring.

Leptospermum juniperinum | Prickly Teatree

Erect shrub 2–3m high. **Leaves** narrow–elliptical to narrow–lanceolate, to 1.5cm long and 2mm wide, slightly incurved, tip sharply pointed. **Flowers** open-petalled, white, to 1cm across, usually solitary. **Capsule** 5-celled, to 7mm across, persistent. Mainly coastal, in heath and swampy situations. Qld, NSW. Spring, summer.

Leptospermum laevigatum | Coast Teatree

Tall dense shrub 3–6m high. **Leaves** narrow–obovate, 1–3cm long to 8mm wide, grey-green, tip rounded with very small point. **Flowers** open-petalled, white, to 2cm across, usually in pairs. **Capsule** 6-celled to 11-celled, to 8mm across, deciduous. Widespread, coastal heath on sand dunes and on cliffs. NSW, Vic, Tas, SA; introduced Qld, WA. Winter, spring.

Leptospermum lanigerum | Woolly Teatree

Erect shrub or small tree 2–5m high; stems and young growth densely hairy. **Leaves** oblong to narrow–oblanceolate, to 1.5cm long and 2–4mm wide, dark green to grey-green, hairy especially on lower surface, tip pointed. **Flowers** open-petalled, white (sometimes with pink tinge), to 1.5cm across, solitary; calyx tube densely hairy. **Capsule** 5-celled, to 12mm across, persistent. Widespread from coast to mountains, in damp or swampy situations and along watercourses. NSW, Vic, Tas, SA. Spring, summer.

Leptospermum liversidgei | Olive Teatree

Erect shrub to 4m high. **Leaves** narrow–obovate, 5–7mm long to 2mm wide, lemon-scented, bright green and glabrous, tip pointed or blunt, recurved. **Flowers** open-petalled, white or pink, about 1.2cm across, solitary. **Capsule** 5-celled, to 1cm across, persistent. Coastal heath in swampy situations. Qld, NSW. Spring, summer.

Leptospermum macrocarpum |

Erect shrub to 2m high; new growth often reddish. **Leaves** broad–elliptic to obovate, 1–2cm long to 1cm wide, tip pointed. **Flowers** open-petalled, white, lemon-yellow, pink or red, to 3cm across, solitary on short branches. **Capsule** usually 5-celled, to 2cm across, persistent. Mainly Blue Mountains on sandstone or rocky sites. NSW. Spring, summer.

Leptospermum erubescens

Leptospermum juniperinum

Leptospermum laevigatum

Leptospermum lanigerum

Leptospermum liversidgei

Leptospermum macrocarpum

Leptospermum myrsinoides | Heath Teatree

Erect or spreading shrub 1–3m high. **Leaves** obovate to oblanceolate, to 1cm long and 3mm wide, margins incurved, tip pointed. **Flowers** open-petalled, white (sometimes pink), to 1.5cm across, usually solitary, terminal on short branches. **Capsule** 4–5-celled, to 6mm across, deciduous. Widespread, common in inland mallee communities and coastal heath, often in sandy swampy sites. NSW, Vic, SA. Spring.

Leptospermum obovatum | River Teatree

Erect shrub 2–3m high. **Leaves** obovate to narrow–oblanceolate, to 2cm long and 2–8mm wide, glabrous, margins incurved, tip pointed or indented. **Flowers** open-petalled, white, to 1.2cm across, profuse, solitary or in pairs. **Capsule** 5-celled, to 8mm across, persistent. Mainly on tablelands, but also farther inland, often beside streams. NSW, Vic. Spring, summer.

Leptospermum petersonii | Lemon-scented Teatree

Erect shrub or small tree to 5m high; bark flaky and persistent. **Leaves** narrow–lanceolate, to 4cm long and to 5mm wide, lemon-scented, glabrous, tip pointed or indented. **Flowers** open-petalled, white, to 1.5cm across, usually solitary. **Capsule** 5-celled, to 6mm across, persistent. Near rainforest or wet forest, along creeks and on rocky escarpments. Qld, NSW. Summer.

Leptospermum polygalifolium | Tantoon

Formerly *L. flavescens*. Shrub or tree 1–5m high. **Leaves** oblanceolate to linear–elliptic, 1–2cm long to 3mm wide, aromatic, glabrous, margins recurved, tip pointed. **Flowers** open-petalled, white or greenish, to 1.5cm across, profuse, solitary. **Capsule** usually 5-celled, to 1cm across, persistent. Extremely variable; widespread, usually in heath and open forest, often in damp sandy soils. Qld, NSW. Spring, summer.

Leptospermum myrsinoides

Leptospermum obovatum

Leptospermum petersonii

Leptospermum polygalifolium

Leptospermum rotundifolium | Round-leaf Teatree

Erect shrub 2–3m high; young stems reddish and hairy. **Leaves** almost round, 4–7mm long and wide, dark green, tip sometimes pointed and recurved. **Flowers** open-petalled, pale pink or pink (sometimes white), to 3cm across, solitary, terminal on short stems. **Capsule** 5-celled, to 1.2cm across, persistent. Central and south coast and tablelands, in heath and open forest, often on sandstone. NSW. Spring.

Leptospermum scoparium | Manuka

Erect shrub to 2m high; stems silky when young. **Leaves** broad–lanceolate, to 2cm long, 2–6mm wide, margins incurved, tip sharply pointed. **Flowers** open-petalled, white (rarely pink), to 3cm across, profuse, solitary, terminal on short stems. **Capsule** 5-celled, to 1cm across, persistent. Heath and woodland, often in rocky sites or along streams. NSW, Vic, Tas. Spring, summer.

Leptospermum sericeum | Silver Teatree

Spreading shrub 1–3m high. **Leaves** obovate, 1–2cm long to 1cm wide, silvery-grey and silky, tip rounded with short point. **Flowers** open-petalled, pale pink, to 2.5cm across, often profuse, usually solitary; calyx tube hairy. **Capsule** 4–6-celled, about 5mm across, deciduous. Around Esperance and nearby islands, often in rock crevices. WA. Spring.

Leptospermum spectabile |

Erect shrub to 3m high; stems hairy when young. **Leaves** narrow–elliptic, to 3.5cm long, 3–5mm wide, mostly glabrous, tip pointed and stiff. **Flowers** open-petalled, dark red, to 2cm across, solitary, terminal on short stems. **Capsule** 4-celled or 5-celled, to 1.2cm across, persistent. Confined to banks of the Colo River in central coast district. NSW. Spring.

Leptospermum squarrosum | Peach-blossom Teatree

Open shrub 1–4m high. **Leaves** broad–elliptic to ovate–lanceolate, 5–15mm long, 2–5mm wide, dark green, margins incurved, tip sharply pointed. **Flowers** open-petalled, white or pink, to 2cm across, solitary, on short stems along older stems. **Capsule** 5-celled, to 1.2cm across, persistent. Coast and tablelands on sandstone soils in heath and open forest. NSW. Autumn.

Melaleuca acuminata | Mallee Honey-myrtle

Shrub 2–4m high; bark rough and scaly. **Leaves** narrow–lanceolate to ovate, to 1cm long, 2–4mm wide, in opposite pairs, tip pointed. **Flowers** creamy, in lateral clusters of 3–6 flowers, on short stalks, usually along older wood. **Capsule** globular, about 4mm across. In mallee woodland, usually as understorey plant. NSW, Vic, SA, WA. Spring.

Leptospermum rotundifolium

Leptospermum scoparium

Leptospermum sericeum

Leptospermum spectabile

Leptospermum squarrosum

Melaleuca acuminata

Melaleuca alternifolia

Tall shrub or small tree to 7m high; bark papery. **Leaves** linear–lanceolate, 1–3cm long to 1mm wide, tip pointed. **Flowers** white, in loose spikes 3–5cm long, mostly terminal. **Capsule** cup-shaped, to 3mm across. A valuable oil-producing species. Along creeks and rivers, north from Grafton district. Qld, NSW. Spring.

Melaleuca armillaris | Bracelet Honey-myrtle

Shrub or small tree 5–8m high; bark firm and greyish. **Leaves** linear, to 2.5cm long and 1mm wide, tip pointed and recurved. **Flowers** white (rarely pink), in cylindrical heads 3–7cm long to 2.5cm wide. **Capsule** cylindrical, about 5mm across. Coast and nearby ranges, widespread in heath. NSW, Vic, Tas. Spring, summer.

Melaleuca calothamnoides

Multi-branched shrub to 3m high. **Leaves** linear–terete to 2cm long and about 1cm wide, tip rounded. **Flowers** green and pale orange or red, in squat cylindrical spikes to 5cm long and 4cm across, on short lateral shoots from old wood. **Capsule** urn-shaped, about 4mm across, in crowded clusters. Sandy heath in the Murchison River district. WA. Spring.

Melaleuca capitata

Spreading shrub to 2m high; bark scaly. **Leaves** narrow–elliptic, 1–2.5cm long to 2mm wide, tip pointed. **Flowers** pale yellow, in dense terminal heads about 2.5cm diameter. **Capsule** urn-shaped, to 7mm across, in rounded clusters. Southern coast and tablelands, in heath or dry forest. NSW. Summer.

Melaleuca conothamnoides

Spreading shrub to 1.5m high and across. **Leaves** oblong–lanceolate, to 4cm long and 1cm wide, thick, grey-green, tip rounded with short point. **Flowers** mauve-purple with golden anthers, in dense terminal heads to 3cm diameter. **Capsule** globular, about 6mm across, in rounded clusters. Wheatbelt district on sandheath. WA. Spring.

Melaleuca alternifolia

Melaleuca armillaris

Melaleuca calothamnoides

Melaleuca capitata

Melaleuca conothamnoides

Melaleuca depressa

Multi-branched, spreading shrub to 1.5m high. **Leaves** oblong–elliptic or oblanceolate, to 1cm long and 3mm wide, thick, oil dots prominent, tip rounded. **Flowers** pale yellow, in rounded heads to 2cm diameter, in upper leaf axils. **Capsule** urn-shaped, to 4mm across. Northern wheatbelt district. WA. Spring.

Melaleuca elliptica | Granite Honey-myrtle

Erect shrub 2–4m high; bark slightly papery and grey. **Leaves** elliptic, to 1.5cm long and 1cm wide, thick, tip usually rounded. **Flowers** red, in cylindrical spikes to 8cm long and 5cm across, on older stems. **Capsule** rounded, to 8mm across, crowded around old wood. Granite outcrops in southern districts. WA. Spring, summer.

Melaleuca filifolia | Wiry Honey-myrtle

Formerly *M. nematophylla*. Erect shrub to 2.5m high. **Leaves** terete, 4–10cm long to 15mm wide, slightly curved, tip pointed. **Flowers** mauve-purple with golden anthers, in rounded terminal heads about 5cm diameter. **Capsule** cup-shaped, about 8mm across, in rounded clusters. Northern sand plains. WA. Spring.

Melaleuca fulgens | Scarlet Honey-myrtle

Erect shrub 1–3m high. **Leaves** linear–lanceolate, to 3cm long and 4mm wide, margins incurved, tip pointed. **Flowers** red (sometimes orange or deep pink), in spikes 3–5cm long and 4cm diameter, on older stems. **Capsule** urn-shaped, to 1cm across. Widespread in wheatbelt districts, often associated with granite outcrops. WA. Spring, summer.

Melaleuca gibbosa | Slender Honey-myrtle

Open shrub to 2m high. **Leaves** ovate to obovate, 2–6mm long to 4mm wide, sessile in opposite pairs, tip rounded and recurved. **Flowers** mauve-pink, in short spikes about 2cm long, on short lateral stems. **Capsule** cylindrical, to 5mm across, slightly embedded in stems. Widespread in heath in moist situations. Vic, Tas, SA. Spring, summer.

Melaleuca globifera

Shrub to small tree 1–6m high; bark papery. **Leaves** elliptical to obovate, 3–6cm long and to 2cm wide, thick, 5–7 prominent longitudinal veins, tip rounded or pointed. **Flowers** pale yellow, in terminal rounded heads to 3.5cm diameter. **Capsule** rounded, to 4mm across, in tight clusters. Southern coastal districts, on granite cliffs. WA. Spring, summer.

Melaleuca depressa

Melaleuca elliptica

Melaleuca filifolia

Melaleuca fulgens

Melaleuca gibbosa

Melaleuca globifera

Melaleuca glomerata | Inland Paperbark

Multi-branched shrub or small tree 2–7m high; bark papery. **Leaves** linear–oblanceolate, 2–5cm long to 2mm wide, tip pointed, hairy when young. **Flowers** yellow, in small globular heads, about 1.5cm across. **Capsule** barrel-shaped, about 2mm across, in tight globular clusters. Widespread in inland districts, often along dry watercourses. NSW, SA, WA, NT. Spring, summer.

Melaleuca hamulosa |

Erect dense shrub 2–4m high. **Leaves** semi-terete to terete, to 1.5cm long and 1mm wide, tip pointed and recurved. **Flowers** white (sometimes mauve), in dense cylindrical spikes 3–5cm long, about 1.5cm across. **Capsule** globular, about 3mm across, in spike-like clusters. Widespread in wheatbelt districts and southern coast. WA. Spring, summer.

Melaleuca holosericea |

Bushy shrub to 2m high. **Leaves** linear or somewhat terete, 1–2cm long to 2mm wide, usually curved, grey-green, silky-hairy when young, tip rounded. **Flowers** pink to purple, in semi-globular heads to 2cm across. **Capsule** globular, about 4mm across, in small rounded clusters. Widespread in wheatbelt districts and southern coast. WA. Spring, summer.

Melaleuca hypericifolia | Hillock Bush

Spreading shrub 2–6m high; bark somewhat papery. **Leaves** lanceolate to oblong, 1–4cm long to 1cm wide, in opposite pairs, tip rounded or pointed. **Flowers** dull red, in cylindrical spikes 3–5cm long to 4cm wide, on lateral shoots from older wood. **Capsule** urn-shaped, to 1cm across, with pointed lobes. Coastal districts usually, on sandy soils in damp situations. NSW. Spring, summer.

Melaleuca glomerata

Melaleuca hamulosa

Melaleuca holosericea

Melaleuca hypericifolia

Melaleuca incana | Grey Honey-myrtle

Weeping shrub or small tree 1–5m high. **Leaves** linear to narrow–ovate, 1–2cm long and to 2mm wide, grey-green, often softly hairy, oil glands prominent, tip pointed. **Flowers** creamy-yellow, in axillary spikes to 5cm long; male in terminal spikes and more rounded. **Capsule** bell-shaped, to 6mm across. Mainly coastal in Darling district, often in swamps. WA. Spring, summer.

Melaleuca lateritia | Robin Redbreast Bush

Multi-stemmed, open shrub to 2m high. **Leaves** linear, 1–2cm long to 2mm wide, flat or concave, tip pointed. **Flowers** orange-red, in spikes 5–8cm long to 6cm wide, on short lateral stems from old wood. **Capsule** cup-shaped, to 8mm across, in clusters or spikes. South-western coastal districts, often in damp situations. WA. Spring, summer.

Melaleuca laxiflora |

Spreading shrub 1–2m high. **Leaves** narrow–obovate, 1–3cm long to 4mm wide, grey-green, tip pointed. **Flowers** mauve-pink, in spikes 1–3cm long on short lateral stems. **Capsule** almost globular, to 4mm across. Widespread in southwest, slightly inland in mallee or heath. WA. Spring, summer.

Melaleuca linariifolia | Narrow-leaved Paperbark

Tall shrub or small spreading tree to 10m high; bark papery. **Leaves** linear to narrow–elliptic, 2–4.5cm long to 3mm wide, tip pointed. **Flowers** white, in spikes to 4cm long, usually terminal. **Capsule** cylindrical, to 4mm across. Widespread on coast and ranges, mostly in swampy situations. Qld, NSW. Spring, summer.

Melaleuca megacephala |

Erect bushy shrub to 3m high; stems hairy. **Leaves** obovate, to 2.5cm long and 1cm wide, 3-nerved, tip rounded or slightly pointed. **Flowers** pale yellow, in terminal globular heads about 4cm diameter. **Capsule** cylindrical, about 5mm across, in rounded clusters. Murchison River district in heath. WA. Winter, spring.

Melaleuca nesophila | Showy Honey-myrtle

Bushy shrub to 2m high, sometimes taller; bark papery. **Leaves** obovate to oblong, 1–4cm long to 1cm wide, leathery, tip rounded, sometimes with small point. **Flowers** mauve-purple, in terminal globular heads to 3cm across. **Capsule** to 2mm across, in fused cluster. Southern coast on sand. WA. Winter, spring.

Melaleuca incana

Melaleuca lateritia

Melaleuca laxiflora

Melaleuca linariifolia

Melaleuca megacephala

Melaleuca nesophila

Melaleuca nodosa

Erect shrub 1–4m high; bark papery. **Leaves** linear or terete, 1–4cm long to 3mm wide, rigid, tip sharply pointed. **Flowers** pale yellow, in terminal and axillary globular heads to 1.5cm diameter. **Capsule** to 3mm across, in fused cluster. Widespread in coastal districts, often in heath. Qld, NSW. Spring, summer.

Melaleuca pulchella | Claw Flower

Spreading shrub to 2m high. **Leaves** oblong to obovate, to 5mm long and 3mm wide. **Flowers** mauve-pink with large, incurved claw-like stamens, about 1.5cm across, borne singly or in opposite pairs. **Capsule** urn-shaped, about 6mm across, singly or in opposite pairs. Southern sandplains and heath. WA. Spring, summer.

Melaleuca quinquenervia | Broad-leaved Paperbark

Erect tree 10–15m high; bark papery. **Leaves** lanceolate to oblanceolate, 3–7cm long to 2.5cm wide, leathery, 3–5 veins prominent, tip pointed to blunt. **Flowers** white or cream, in dense terminal or axillary spikes 3–6cm long. **Capsule** cup-shaped, to 5mm across. Widespread in coastal districts, mostly in swampy situations. Qld, NSW. Autumn, winter.

Melaleuca radula | Graceful Honey-myrtle

Spreading shrub 1–2m high. **Leaves** linear to narrow–elliptic, 2–5cm long to 4mm wide, glandular, incurved, tip pointed. **Flowers** pink to purple, in spikes 2–5cm long, on short lateral stems from older wood. **Capsule** globular, to 1cm across. Widespread in coastal and wheatbelt districts, sometimes associated with granite outcrops. WA. Winter, spring.

Melaleuca nodosa

Melaleuca pulchella

Melaleuca quinquenervia

Melaleuca radula

Melaleuca scabra | Rough Honey-myrtle

Small spreading shrub 1–2m high. **Leaves** linear or linear–terete, to 1cm long, oil dots raised and prominent, tip rounded or pointed. **Flowers** deep pink or purple, in globular terminal heads about 1cm across. **Capsule** about 3mm wide, in rounded clusters. Widespread in southwest, in heath and woodland. WA. Spring, summer.

Melaleuca spathulata

Shrub to 1m high; stems short and often twisted. **Leaves** obovate to spathulate, less than 1cm long and 5mm wide, dull green, tip rounded. **Flowers** mauve-purple, in globular terminal heads, 1–2cm across. **Capsule** tiny, in tight rounded clusters, about 8mm long. Southwest corner, coastal and slightly inland, in heath and shrubland. WA. Spring.

Melaleuca spicigera

Open, spreading shrub to 1.5m high; branches sometimes arching. **Leaves** ovate to broad–ovate, to 1.5cm long and 6mm wide, prominently veined, glandular dotted, tip pointed. **Flowers** pink or mauve, in short spikes to 2cm long, on lateral stems from older wood. **Capsule** urn-shaped, about 4mm across. Southern wheatbelt district in mallee and heath communities. WA. Spring.

Melaleuca squarrosa | Scented Paperbark

Shrub or small tree to 12m high; bark papery. **Leaves** ovate to broad–ovate, to 1.5mm long and 7mm wide, stiff, dark green, opposite at right angles, prominently veined, tip pointed. **Flowers** cream, in terminal cylindrical heads to 5cm long and 1.5cm wide. **Capsule** cup-shaped, about 4mm across, crowded along stem. Widely distributed in the southeast, in heath and open forest, in damp places. NSW, Vic, Tas, SA. Spring, summer.

Melaleuca styphelioides | Prickly Paperbark

Shrub or tree to 20m high; bark papery. **Leaves** ovate, to 2cm long and 6mm wide, sessile, bright green, slightly twisted, tip sharply pointed. **Flowers** white, profuse, in terminal cylindrical heads to 3cm long and 1.5cm wide. **Capsule** ovoid, to 3mm across. Widespread along coast, along stream banks or near swamps. Qld, NSW. Spring, summer.

Melaleuca tamarascina

Shrub or small tree to 6m high; bark spongy and papery. **Leaves** ovate, 3–5mm long and 1mm wide, sessile and appressed to the stems, concave, tip pointed. **Flowers** white (sometimes pale mauve), in loose spikes 1–2.5cm long. **Capsule** globular, to 4mm across. Central-inland in open forest on poorly drained sites. Qld. Winter, spring.

Melaleuca scabra

Melaleuca spathulata

Melaleuca spicigera

Melaleuca squarrosa

Melaleuca styphelioides

Melaleuca tamarascina

Melaleuca thymifolia | Thyme Honey-myrtle

Spreading shrub to 1m high and across; bark corky. **Leaves** narrow–elliptic, to 1.5cm long and 1–3mm wide, stiff, tip pointed. **Flowers** pink or mauve (rarely white), stamens claw-like and curled inward, in irregular clusters about 3cm across on older wood. **Capsule** cup-shaped, about 5mm across, with pointed lobes. Widespread from coast to mountains, in open forest or heath, in damp places. Qld, NSW. Winter, spring.

Melaleuca trichostachya |

Tree to 10m high; bark papery. **Leaves** linear to linear–lanceolate, 1–3cm long and 1–3mm wide, flat, tip pointed. **Flowers** white, in loose spikes to 4cm long. **Capsule** top-shaped, to 4mm across, valves exserted from wide opening. Widespread in inland regions, often along watercourses. Qld, NSW, SA, NT. Spring, summer.

Melaleuca uncinata | Broombush

Erect multi-stemmed shrub to 3m high; bark papery. **Leaves** terete or semi-terete, 2–6cm long and 1mm wide, tip pointed and strongly recurved. **Flowers** pale yellow, in globular heads about 1.5cm across, either axillary or terminal. **Capsule** almost globular, to 3mm across, in tight rounded clusters. Widespread in dry inland regions of southern Australia, often forming dense stands. Qld, NSW, Vic, SA, WA, NT. Winter, spring.

Melaleuca undulata | Hidden Honey-myrtle

Erect multi-stemmed shrub to 2.5m high. **Leaves** lanceolate to ovate–lanceolate to 1.5cm long and about 3mm wide, sessile, twisted, prominently veined, tip pointed. **Flowers** scented, white, in clusters about 2cm across, on old wood. **Capsule** cup-shaped, about 5mm across. Widespread in southwest, in woodland, mallee and heath. WA. Winter, spring.

Melaleuca thymifolia

Melaleuca trichostachya

Melaleuca uncinata

Melaleuca undulata

Melaleuca viminea

Large bushy shrub or small tree to 7m high; bark fibrous. **Leaves** linear, to 2cm long and 1–2mm wide, tip pointed and recurved. **Flowers** white or cream, in spikes 2–4cm long, on short branches. **Capsule** cup-shaped, about 4mm across, in loose spikes. Widespread in southwest, usually along watercourses and in damp places. WA. Winter, spring.

Melaleuca violacea

Spreading shrub to 1.5m high; branches layered and often horizontal. **Leaves** ovate–cordate, 6–15mm long, 2–6mm wide, sessile, tip pointed. **Flowers** mauve to purple, with incurved stamens, in irregular clusters on older wood. **Capsule** about 7mm across, with star-like lobes. Southern coastal districts in heath. WA. Spring, summer.

Melaleuca wilsonii | Wilson's Honey-myrtle

Shrub 1–3m high; branches spreading or arching. **Leaves** linear–lanceolate, to 1.5cm long and 2mm wide, sessile, in opposite pairs, glandular, tip pointed. **Flowers** deep pink or mauve, in dense spike-like clusters on older wood. **Capsule** bell-shaped, about 5mm across, in spikes. Semi-arid regions. Vic, SA. Winter, spring.

Micromyrtus ciliata | Fringed Heath-myrtle

Low spreading to erect shrub to 1m high. **Leaves** linear to oblong, 1–4mm long and about 1mm wide, sessile, in opposite pairs at right angles, margins minutely fringed. **Flowers** cup-shaped, white to pink, aging to deep pink, petals 5, singly in upper leaf axils, profuse. **Fruit** a nut. Widespread in heath, open forest and mallee. NSW, Vic, SA. Spring, summer.

Pileanthus peduncularis | Coppercups

Spreading, multi-stemmed shrub to 1.5m high. **Leaves** linear to semi-terete, 2–4mm long and about 2mm wide, thick, tip rounded. **Flowers** orange to red, about 1.5cm across on slender stalks; petals 5, prominently fringed. **Fruit** a capsule. Widespread on northern sand plains to north of Carnarvon on red sand. WA. Spring.

Scholtzia laxiflora

Shrub 1–2m high; stems slender and often arching. **Leaves** obovate, 2–4mm long, narrowing toward the base, tip rounded. **Flowers** small, pink, 5-petalled, 2–5 per umbel on fine stalks. Northern sandplains and heath. WA. Winter, spring.

Melaleuca viminea

Melaleuca violacea

Melaleuca wilsonii

Micromyrtus ciliata

Pileanthus peduncularis

Scholtzia laxiflora

Thryptomene baeckeacea |

Dense much-branched shrub 1–2m high. **Leaves** obovate to oblong, to 2mm long, incurved, tip rounded. **Flowers** deep pink or mauve (rarely white), 5-petalled, on slender stalks in upper leaf axils. Murchison River area. WA. Winter, spring.

Thryptomene calycina | Grampians Heath-myrtle

Spreading much-branched shrub to 2.5m high; branches often arching. **Leaves** oblanceolate, 8–12mm long, aromatic, tip rounded. **Flowers** white with a golden centre, aging to pink, 5-petalled, profuse in axillary clusters; white or pink calyx prominent. Endemic to the Grampians. Vic. Winter, spring.

Thryptomene maisonneuvii | Desert Heath-myrtle

Spreading shrub to 1.5m high. **Leaves** obovate, to 2mm long and 1mm wide, sessile and closely packed, thick, tip rounded. **Flowers** white to pink, small, about 2mm across, 5-petalled, almost sessile in upper leaf axils. Arid inland areas, often on sand dunes. SA, WA, NT. Winter, spring.

Thryptomene racemulosa |

Small erect shrub to 1m high. **Leaves** obovate, 2–3mm long, sessile and closely packed, thick, tip rounded. **Flowers** pink, about 5mm across, 5-petalled, almost sessile in upper leaf axils; calyx lobes fringed. Northern sandplains and heath. WA. Winter, spring.

Thryptomene baeckeacea

Thryptomene calycina

Thryptomene maisonneuvii

Thryptomene racemulosa

Thryptomene saxicola | Rock Thryptomene

Erect shrub to 1.5m high; branches arching. **Leaves** obovate, 4–8mm long, sessile and closely packed. **Flowers** white or pale pink, about 4mm across, 5-petalled, on short stalks in upper leaf axils. Southern coastal districts, among granite outcrops. WA. Winter, spring.

Verticordia chrysantha |

Small erect shrub to 80cm high. **Leaves** variable, linear or semi-terete toward base, to 1cm long, upper ones oblong to obovate, tip pointed. **Flowers** yellow, in loose clusters; petals deeply lobed; calyx lobes densely fringed. Southern sandplains. WA. Spring, summer.

Verticordia grandiflora | Claw Featherflower

Erect shrub to 70cm high. Lower **leaves** linear, upper ones oblong, 5–15mm long. **Flowers** yellow, to 1.5cm across, in loose clusters turning reddish-brown on maturity; petals deeply lobed; calyx lobes densely fringed; stamens claw-like. Widespread on heath in south-west. WA. Winter, spring.

Verticordia grandis | Scarlet Featherflower

Open, straggly shrub to 2m high. **Leaves** rounded, 8–15mm across, opposite. **Flowers** bright red, to 2.5cm across, in leafy spikes; petals toothed; calyx lobes densely fringed; style conspicuous, to 2.5cm long. Irwin district on sand heath. WA. Spring, summer.

Thryptomene saxicola

Verticordia chrysantha

Verticordia grandiflora

Verticordia grandis

Verticordia helichrysantha

Small bushy shrub to 50cm high. **Leaves** linear to semi-terete, grey-green, crowded on small side shoots. **Flowers** pale yellow, about 1cm across; petals hairy; calyx lobes fringed; style conspicuous to 2.5cm long. Eyre district near coast. WA. Spring.

Verticordia huegelii | Variegated Featherflower

Erect spreading shrub to 80cm high. **Leaves** linear–terete, 3–6mm long, crowded on small side shoots. **Flowers** white aging to deep pink, about 1.5cm across; petals rounded and fringed; calyx lobes fringed; style with broad stigma. Among granite outcrops in southwest. WA. Spring.

Verticordia lindleyi

Small shrub 30–60cm high. **Leaves** obovate, to 5mm long, shortly hairy, on short stalks. **Flowers** pale pink, to 1.5cm across, in leafy spikes; petals toothed; calyx lobes fringed; style curved. Northern wheatbelt district. WA. Spring, summer.

Verticordia ovalifolia

Erect sparsely branched shrub to 80cm high. **Leaves** elliptic to obovate, 4–6mm long, grey-green, tip rounded. **Flowers** creamy-white with pinkish tinge, to 2cm across, in small terminal heads; petals divided into 5 or 6 fringed lobes; calyx lobes with long plumes; style with bearded tip. Sand plains north of Perth. WA. Spring.

Verticordia pennigera

Small shrub to 60cm high. **Leaves** 3-sided, to 4mm long, crowded on short side shoots, margins fringed with small hairs. **Flowers** pink, on short stalks in leafy spikes; petals toothed; calyx lobes fringed. Widespread in southwest. WA. Spring, summer.

Verticordia helichrysantha

Verticordia huegelii

Verticordia lindleyi

Verticordia ovalifolia

Verticordia pennigera

Verticordia picta | Painted Featherflower

Small shrub to about 1m high. **Leaves** linear, to 1cm long. **Flowers** pink to purple, to 12mm across, profuse in loose clusters; petals rounded and larger than the fringed calyx lobes. From Lake King north to Murchison River district, on sand heath. WA. Spring.

Verticordia plumosa | Plumed Featherflower

Erect bushy shrub to 1m high. **Leaves** linear to semi-terete, to 1cm long, grey-green, crowded. **Flowers** pink, about 7mm across, forming dense heads; petals rounded; calyx lobes shortly fringed; style with bearded tip. Southern regions, on granite outcrops. WA. Spring, summer.

Verticordia staminosa | Wongan Featherflower

Spreading branched shrub to 70cm high. **Leaves** linear–terete, 7–14mm long. **Flowers** greenish-yellow aging to rusty red, about 1cm across; petals lobed; calyx lobes fringed; stamens red, exceeding the petals. Near Wongan Hills, on granite outcrops. WA. Winter.

Verticordia verticillata |

Shrub or small tree 2–4m high. **Leaves** linear, 3-sided, to 2cm long and 1mm wide, in whorls of 3 or 4. **Flowers** white, about 1.5cm across; petals irregularly toothed; calyx lobes fringed; style exserted to 12mm long. Tropical north, often in rocky places. WA, NT. Winter, spring.

Verticordia picta

Verticordia plumosa

Verticordia staminosa

Verticordia verticillata

ORCHIDACEAE | Orchid Family

A very large cosmopolitan family of monocotyledons comprising about 730 genera and more than 30,000 species found in all parts of the world, but most abundant in the tropics. Australia has about 100 genera and more than 1200 species. They are terrestrial, lithophytic, epiphytic or saprophytic (rarely subterranean) perennial herbs. Terrestrials, lithophytes and saprophytes have fleshy rhizomes or tubers; epiphytes and saprophytes have creeping stems or rhizomes, and often develop thickened storage organs (pseudobulbs). Leaves usually alternate or radical, sometimes reduced to scales. Flowers usually bisexual, irregular with a complex structure. Sepals 3, petals 3; the front petal usually differs considerably from the others and is known as the labellum. Stamens highly modified, fused with style into a single central structure (column). Pollen united into waxy masses (pollinia) and concealed by an anther cap. Ovary inferior, 1-chambered. Fruit a capsule. Seeds minute, numerous. The orchid family is the largest family of flowering plants in the world. Leaves are not illustrated in this family as they are too similar for identification purposes.

GROUP 1: TERRESTRIAL AND SAPROPHYTIC ORCHIDS

Caladenia eminens | Common White Spider Orchid

Erect clump-forming perennial herb to 80cm high. **Leaf** linear–lanceolate, to 25cm long and 2cm wide, very hairy and spotted red at base. **Flowers** spider-like, white (sometimes with green or pink markings), to 20cm across. Sepals and petals with very long, fine tail-like tips covered with reddish glandular hairs. **Labellum** undivided, ovate, flat in middle part, then recurved, margins toothed; central calli in 4–8 rows. Widespread and common in southwest in heath, woodland and open forest. WA. Spring.

Caladenia flava | Cowslip Orchid

Erect perennial herb to 30cm high; often in colonies. **Leaf** lanceolate, to 25cm long and 1cm wide, hairy on lower surface. **Flowers** yellow with red and sometimes white markings, 3–5cm across; up to 4 produced on one wiry stem to 30cm high. **Labellum** heart-shaped with 2 or 3 pairs of calli. Widespread and common in southwest, in sandy soils. WA. Winter, spring.

Caladenia huegelii | King Spider Orchid

Erect perennial herb to 55cm high. **Leaf** lanceolate, to 24cm long and 1.5cm wide, hairy. **Flowers** spider-like white or cream with reddish markings, to 8cm across. Dorsal sepal erect and almost as long as lateral sepals. Sepals and petals with tail-like tips covered with hairs. **Labellum** white at base, maroon above, about 2.5cm across, including the lateral fringes; midlobe with 4 or more rows of calli. Common on coastal plain between Perth and Albany usually in winter-wet situations. WA. Spring.

Caladenia eminens

Caladenia flava

Caladenia huegelii

Caladenia latifolia | Pink fairies

Erect perennial herb to 40cm high. **Leaf** lanceolate to 20cm long and 3cm wide, hairy. **Flowers** pink, about 3cm across; up to 4 on hairy wiry stem. Sepals and petals pointed. **Labellum** 3-lobed, midlobe fringed with hairy calli and a semi-circle of yellow calli near the base. Widespread and common in coastal areas. Vic, SA, WA. Spring.

Caladenia pusilla | Tiny Caladenia

Small perennial herb less than 10cm high. **Leaf** narrow–linear, to 6cm long and 1.5mm wide. **Flowers** fan-shaped, pale pink to deep pink, about 1.5cm across. Sepals and petals with pointed or rounded lobes; dorsal sepal incurved. **Labellum** 3-lobed, recurved narrow midlobe with 2 rows of yellowish calli. Widespread in heath and open forest, in sandy soils. NSW, Vic, Tas. Spring.

Caladenia reptans | Little Pink Fairy Orchid

Small perennial herb to 20cm high. **Leaf** to 5cm long and 8mm wide, sparsely hairy on both surfaces and reddish below. **Flowers** bright pink, about 3cm across. Sepals and petals spreading and relatively broad. **Labellum** small, with prominent midlobe and narrow lateral lobes with red stripes. Widespread in southwest, in open forest. WA. Spring.

Calanthe triplicata | Christmas Orchid

Erect tuft-forming perennial herb. **Leaves** ovate to lanceolate, to 80cm long, ribbed, up to 10 per pesudobulb. **Flowers** white, to 3cm across, with up to 40 crowded at top of erect stem to 1.5m long. Sepals and petals widely spreading. **Labellum** distinctly 4-lobed. Rainforest or in moist shady places, often in dense colonies. Qld, NSW. Spring, summer.

Caleana major | Flying Duck Orchid

Small erect herb to 40cm high. **Leaf** narrow–lanceolate, to 10cm long and 8mm wide, reddish. **Flowers** dark reddish-brown, often with greenish sepals and petals, upside down and resembling a duck in flight; 1–5 per erect flowering stem to 40cm high. The **labellum**, which is attached to a sensitive claw, forms the duck's head. Widespread and common in heath, woodland and open forest, in sandy soils. Qld, NSW, Vic, Tas, SA. Winter, spring.

Calochilus robertsonii | Purplish Bearded Orchid

Erect perennial herb to 45cm high. **Leaf** linear, to 40cm long, channelled. **Flowers** pale green with maroon veins, about 3cm across, with up to 9 per flowering stem to 45cm high. The showy ovate **labellum** is densely covered with long, purplish hairs becoming shorter and gland-like near the base. Widespread and quite common from coast to inland slopes, in woodland and open forest. Qld, NSW, Vic, Tas, SA, WA. Spring.

Caladenia latifolia

Caladenia pusilla

Caladenia reptans

Calanthe triplicata

Caleana major

Calochilus robertsonii

Dipodium punctatum | Hyacinth Orchid

Leafless saprophytic herb to 1m high when in flower; roots fleshy. **Flowers** pale pink to deep pink with conspicuous darker spots, about 2cm across, with up to 60 flowers per flowering stem. Sepals and petals are free, spreading and similar. **Labellum** 3-lobed with small lateral lobes and a pubescent mid-lobe. Widespread and common from coast to ranges, in woodland and dry open forest. Qld, NSW, Vic. Summer.

Diuris abbreviata | Lemon Doubletail

Erect tuft-forming perennial herb to 45cm high. **Leaves** linear, to 35cm long, 2–3 per plant. **Flowers** light yellow, with small brown blotches on labellum and at base of dorsal sepal, about 3cm across, with up to 9 per flowering stem. Dorsal sepal narrow–elliptic, slightly reflexed; lateral sepals linear and weakly crossed. Petals elliptic and tilted sideways. **Labellum** 3-lobed with small spreading lateral lobes and much larger rounded midlobe with 2 ridges. Widespread on coast, tablelands and slightly farther inland, in heath, woodland and open forest. Qld, NSW. Spring.

Diuris corymbosa | Wallflower Orchid

Erect tufted perennial herb to 35cm high; often forming dense colonies. **Leaves** linear, to 20cm long, 2–3 per plant. **Flowers** yellow, blotched or suffused with brown and purple, about 3cm across, with up to 5 per flowering stem. Dorsal sepal almost semicircular with small tip; lateral sepals longer than petals, pointed downward and sometimes crossed. Petals broadly ovate or oblong. **Labellum** 3-lobed with lateral lobes strongly spreading. Widespread in heath, woodland and open forest. NSW, Vic, Tas, SA, WA. Spring.

Diuris maculata | Leopard Orchid

Erect perennial herb to 40cm high. **Leaves** linear, to 30cm long, 2–3 per plant. **Flowers** yellow with dark brown blotches and spots, about 2.5cm across, with up to 10 per flowering stem. Dorsal sepal ovate to broad–ovate; lateral sepals linear, greenish-brown, usually strongly crossed. Petals ovate to circular. **Labellum** 3-lobed with lateral lobes strongly spreading and midlobe with prominent raised ridge. Widespread and common in heath and open forest. NSW, Vic, Tas, SA. Winter, spring.

Elythranthera brunonis | Purple Enamel Orchid

Erect perennial herb to 30cm high. **Leaf** narrow–lanceolate, to 8cm long and 6mm wide, glandular hairy on both surfaces. **Flowers** purple and glossy on inside, about 3cm across, 1–3 per wiry stem to 30cm high. **Labellum** linear with white lip and two long black calli. Column hooded concealing the anther and stigma. Widespread and common in southwest, in a variety of habitats. WA. Spring.

Dipodium punctatum

Diuris abbreviata

Diuris corymbosa

Elythranthera brunonis

Diuris maculata

Glossodia major | Waxlip Orchid

Erect perennial herb to 30cm high. **Leaf** lanceolate, to 1cm long and 2cm wide, hairy. **Flowers** mauve or purple becoming white near the base, about 4.5cm across, usually solitary. **Labellum** ovate, white with a 2-lobed thickening at base, mauve at tapered tip. Common and widespread in heath and open forest, often in colonies. Qld, NSW, Vic, Tas, SA. Spring.

Prasophyllum alpinum | Alpine Leek Orchid

Erect perennial herb to 35cm high. **Leaf** tubular and hollow, to 30cm long, partly enclosing flowering stem. **Flowers** fragrant, green or yellowish-green sometimes with reddish-brown stripes, about 12mm across, up to 25 arranged on spike to 10cm long. Dorsal sepal lanceolate, concave; lateral sepals joined for at least half their length. **Labellum** bent back near the middle, the thick callus extending almost to the tip. Subalpine and alpine regions in herbfields, grassland and woodland. NSW, Vic, Tas. Summer.

Prasophyllum suttonii | Mauve Leek Orchid

Perennial herb to 30cm high. **Leaf** tubular and hollow, to 20cm long, partly enclosing base of flowering stem. **Flowers** white and purple, about 13mm across, up to 35 arranged on spike to 11cm long. Dorsal sepal ovate, curving upward. **Labellum** oblong to ovate, white with wavy margins, recurved near the middle, the callus extending to just beyond the bend. Subalpine and alpine regions, in moist situations in herbfields. NSW, Vic, Tas. Summer.

Pterostylis acuminata | Sharp Greenhood

Erect perennial herb to 25cm high. **Leaves** elliptic, to 4.5cm long and 2cm wide, in a basal rosette. **Flowers** white with green stripes, solitary on flowering stem to 25cm high. Hood formed by middle sepal and 2 upper petals slightly bent forward, tip pointed. Lateral sepals swept slightly backward. **Labellum** lanceolate, curved for half its length, protruding strongly between lateral sepals. Mostly coastal districts, in heath and open forest. Qld, NSW. Autumn.

Pterostylis curta | Blunt Greenhood

Erect perennial herb to 30cm high. **Leaves** elliptic, to 10cm long and 3cm wide, in basal rosettes. **Flowers** white with green stripes and brownish tints, solitary on flowering stem to 30cm high. Hood formed by middle sepal and 2 upper petals, erect then slightly curved. Lateral sepals point upward and backward, rarely rising above hood. **Labellum** protruding with twisted tip. Common from coast to inland in moist situations. Qld, NSW, Vic, Tas, SA. Winter, spring.

Pterostylis nutans | Nodding Greenhood

Erect perennial herb to 30cm high. **Leaves** elliptic with wavy margins, to 4cm long and 1.5cm wide, in basal rosette. **Flowers** white with green stripes, on flowering stem to 30cm long. Hood formed by middle sepal and 2 lower petals is bent downward, the tip often recurved. Lateral sepals point forward. **Labellum** ovate, strongly curved downward with a bristly upper surface. Widespread and common on coast, ranges and farther inland, in heath, wet and dry sclerophyll forests. Qld, NSW, Vic, Tas, SA. Winter, spring.

Glossodia major

Prasophyllum alpinum

Prasophyllum suttonii

Pterostylis acuminata

Pterostylis curta

Pterostylis nutans

Pterostylis recurva | Jug Orchid

Erect perennial herb to 40cm high. Stem **leaves** narrow–ovate, to 6cm long. **Flowers** 1–3, white with prominent green or brownish stripes. Hood formed by middle sepal and 2 lower petals held erect. Lateral sepals with long tips erect and almost level with the top of the hood. **Labellum** tapers to a linear point. Widespread in southwest, in woodland and forest, usually in sheltered situations. WA. Winter, spring.

Thelymitra ixioides | Spotted Sun Orchid

Erect perennial herb to 60cm high. **Leaf** linear, channelled, to 20cm long. **Flowers** blue or pink, about 3cm across, usually spotted on upper 3 segments, in raceme of up to 9 flowers. Petals and sepals similar. Column erect with prominent wings bearing 2 lateral arms terminating in a tuft of hairs. Unspotted forms are identified by flower colour and column shape. Widespread and common from the coast, ranges to farther inland, in heath woodland and open forest. Qld, NSW, Vic, Tas, SA. Winter, spring.

Thelymitra nuda | Plain Sun Orchid

Robust perennial herb to 60cm high. **Leaf** linear to lanceolate, channelled, to 30cm long. **Flowers** fragrant, pale blue, light mauve to white, about 3cm across, in raceme of up to 20 flowers. Petals and sepals similar. Column erect with inflated midlobe, usually notched at the yellowish tip; column arms bearing white hair tufts on the upper side. Widespread and abundant on coast, ranges and farther inland, in heath, woodland, mallee and open forest. Qld, NSW, Vic, Tas, SA, WA. Winter, spring.

Thelymitra villosa | Custard Orchid

Robust perennial herb to 50cm high. **Leaf** broad, to 6cm long and 3.5cm wide, shortly hairy. **Flowers** yellow, dotted reddish-brown, about 3.5cm across, in raceme of up to 15 flowers. Petals and sepals similar. Column erect with brown, inflated midlobe; column arms bearing forward-pointing tufts of orange hairs. Widespread in coastal areas of southwest, usually in sand plains. WA. Spring.

GROUP 2: EPIPHYTIC AND LITHOPHYTIC ORCHIDS

Cymbidium suave | Snake Orchid

Erect epiphytic orchid forming large clumps on hollow logs and tree trunks. Pseudobulbs absent. **Leaves** linear, to 60cm long and 2cm wide. **Flowers** deep yellow or greenish, sometimes tinged with red, about 2.5cm across, in raceme of up to 70 flowers, on pendulous stem to 30cm long. **Labellum** 3-lobed with purplish-brown blotch near the base. Mainly coastal areas in woodland and open forest. Qld, NSW. Spring.

Pterostylis recurva

Thelymitra ixioides

Thelymitra nuda

Cymbidium suave

Thelymitra villosa

Dendrobium x delicatum

Lithophytic orchid forming large clumps. Pseudobulbs slender, to 50cm long, broadest at base. **Leaves** narrow–ovate, to 18cm long and 3.5cm wide, up to 6 near the apex of pseudobulb. **Flowers** waxy white to pink, sometimes suffused darker pink, to 2.5cm across, in racemes of up to 30 flowers on stem to 40cm long. **Labellum** 3-lobed with pink or purple markings, lateral lobes pointing forward. A natural hybrid between *D. kingianum* and *D. tarberi*. Coast and tablelands, on boulders and cliff faces. Qld, NSW. Winter, spring.

Dendrobium falcorostrum | Beech Orchid

Erect or spreading epiphytic orchid forming large clumps, mainly on Antarctic Beech (*Nothofagus moorei*) trees but also some other trees. Pseudobulb cylindrical to 50cm long, and widening at base. **Leaves** elliptic, to 15cm long and 3cm wide, with up to 6 near apex of pseudobulb. **Flowers** fragrant, waxy white, to 3.5cm across, opening widely. Sepals and petals similar. **Labellum** 3-lobed with purple and yellow markings, midlobe curving upward to a prominent point. Restricted to cool temperate rainforest. Qld, NSW. Spring.

Dendrobium gracilicaule

Erect or spreading epiphytic orchid. Pseudobulbs linear–cylindrical, to 60cm long. **Leaves** elliptic, to 12cm long and 4cm wide, thin and leathery, up to 6 near apex of pseudo-bulb. **Flowers** bell-like and drooping, dull yellow suffused with red on the outside, about 1.5cm across, up to 30 flowers in pendulous raceme to about 12cm long. **Labellum** 3-lobed with broad midlobe. Coast and nearby ranges, in open forest and rainforest. Qld, NSW. Winter, spring.

Dendrobium kingianum | Pink Rock Orchid

Lithophytic orchid forming large clumps. Pseudobulbs cylindrical, to 30cm long, widening at base. **Leaves** narrow–elliptic, to 10cm long and 2cm wide, up to 7 near apex of pseudobulb. **Flowers** pink (also white, red and purple) with darker markings, opening widely, up to 15 flowers in racemes to 15cm long. **Labellum** 3-lobed with darker stripes or blotches. Coast and tablelands in woodland and open forest, mainly on rocks, boulders and cliff faces. Qld, NSW. Winter, spring.

Dendrobium linguiforme | Tongue Orchid

Spreading epiphytic or lithophytic orchid. Stems thick, branching. **Leaves** elliptic, to 4cm long and 1.5cm wide, fleshy, grooved. **Flowers** white or cream, about 1cm across, up to 20 flowers in racemes to 15cm long. Sepals and petals slender and pointed. **Labellum** 3-lobed, midlobe narrow, recurved with ruffled margins. Coast, tablelands and western slopes, in open forest, on rocks or tree trunks. Qld, NSW. Spring.

Dendrobium x delicatum

Dendrobium falcorostrum

Dendrobium gracilicaule

Dendrobium kingianum

Dendrobium linguiforme

Dendrobium monophyllum | Lily-of-the-Valley Orchid

Spreading epiphytic or lithophytic orchid. Pseudobulb ovoid, to 10cm long and 3cm wide. **Leaf**, usually solitary, oblong to 12cm long and 3cm wide near apex of pseudobulb. **Flowers** pendulous and bell-like, waxy yellow, about 8mm across, with up to 20 flowers on arching stem to 18cm long. **Labellum** 3-lobed, prominent and curved. Coast and nearby ranges, in open forest and rainforest. Qld, NSW. Winter, spring.

Dendrobium ruppianum | Oak Orchid

Robust clump-forming epiphytic orchid. Pseudobulb cylindrical, to 50cm long, narrow at both ends. **Leaves** ovate, to 15cm long and 6cm wide, up to 7 near apex of pseudobulb. **Flowers** fragrant, creamy-white, to 2.5cm across, numerous in raceme up to 40cm long. Sepals and petals slender and pointed. **Labellum** 3-lobed, with transverse purple stripes. Common in the north, in open forest and rainforest. Qld. Winter, spring.

Dendrobium schoeninum | Pencil Orchid

Spreading or semi-erect epiphytic or lithophytic orchid. Stems branching. **Leaves** terete, to 16cm long and 12mm wide, deeply grooved. **Flowers** white, pale green or mauve with red or purple stripes toward base, about 3cm across. Sepals and petals narrow and pointed. **Labellum** 3-lobed, white with purple markings, strongly curved, margins ruffled. Common, mainly in rainforest and along stream banks, on *Casuarina* species and rocks. Qld, NSW. Spring.

Dendrobium speciosum | King Orchid

Large clump-forming lithophytic or epiphytic orchid. Pseudobulbs to 40cm long and 6cm wide, often swollen at the base then tapering toward tip. **Leaves** elliptic, to 25cm long and 8cm wide, with up to 5 near apex of pseudobulb. **Flowers** fragrant, creamy-white or yellow, about 3.5cm across, with up to 110 flowers per raceme to 70cm long. Petal and petals linear–oblong and pointed. **Labellum** 3-lobed with 3 purple spots. Widespread and common, mainly coastal and generally on rocks. Qld, NSW, Vic. Winter, spring.

Dendrobium striolatum | Streaked Rock Orchid

Spreading lithophytic orchid. Stems short and branching. **Leaves** terete, to 12cm long and 3mm wide, thick and fleshy. **Flowers** creamy-yellow or greenish with brown lines on outer surface. Sepals and petals oblong and pointed. **Labellum** 3-lobed, white and unmarked, strongly curved, margins of midlobe ruffled. Widespread and common in the southeast, usually in open forest and rainforest on boulders and cliff faces. NSW, Vic, Tas. Spring.

Sarcochilus falcatus | Orange Blossom Orchid

Epiphytic orchid with creeping aerial roots. **Leaves** oblong–lanceolate, to 16cm long and 2cm wide, curved. **Flowers** perfumed, white, to 3.5cm across, with up to 12 flowers on flowering stem to 13cm long. Petals and sepals broad and spreading and nearly equal in size. **Labellum** 3-lobed, lateral lobes usually yellow and marked with dark red lines. Widespread on coastal ranges and tablelands, often in rainforest on tree trunks. Qld, NSW, Vic. Winter, spring.

Dendrobium monophyllum

Dendrobium ruppianum

Dendrobium schoeninum

Dendrobium speciosum

Dendrobium striolatum

Sarcochilus falcatus

PHORMIACEAE

Large Southern Hemisphere family of about 8 genera. Australia has about 4 genera and 20 species, the most widespread and best known genus being *Dianella* (about 15 species). They are mostly rhizomatous perennial herbs with fibrous roots. Leaves usually linear with flattened leaf bases, numerous along the stems or concentrated at the base of the plant, arranged in 2 opposite rows. Flowers bisexual, regular or slightly irregular, borne in a terminal branched panicle or cyme. Floral segments 6, free, sometimes twisting after flowering. Stamens 6, free or rarely fused at the base; filaments sometimes hairy or swollen. Ovary superior, 3-celled. Fruit a berry with numerous black seeds. In some classifications the family is included with the broadly defined Liliaceae. Leaves are not illustrated in this family as they are too similar for identification purposes.

Dianella caerulea | Paroo Lily

Clump-forming perennial herb to 50cm high. **Leaves** linear, to 60cm long and 1–2cm wide, sheathing and closed at the base (often splitting with age) and folded tightly just above the sheath, then flat for most of their length, often with rough margins. **Flowers** blue, with spreading segments and 6 hairless yellow stamens with thickened filaments, on panicle to 30cm long. **Berry** blue-purple. Widespread from coast to ranges, in heath and open forest, in sandy soils. Qld, NSW, Vic. Spring, summer.

Dianella revoluta | Spreading Flax Lily

Clump-forming perennial herb to 90cm high. **Leaves** linear, 20–40cm long to 1cm wide, sheathing at the base, with revolute margins for most of their length. **Flowers** dark blue, with spreading segments and 6 yellow stamens with brown or black anthers, on large loose panicle 50–90cm long. **Berry** blue. Widespread from coast to ranges, in open forest on sandy soils. All States, except NT. Spring, summer.

Dianella tasmanica | Tasman Flax Lily

Clump-forming perennial herb to 1.5m high. **Leaves** linear, to 80cm long and 1–3cm wide, folded along midrib near the sheathing base, margins rough with small teeth. **Flowers** blue with spreading segments and 6 yellow stamens with yellow anthers, on loose and branched panicles to 1.5m long. **Berry** blue-purple. Widespread and common, especially in wetter areas in cool forests. Tas, endemic. Spring, summer.

Stypandra glauca | Nodding Blue Lily

Erect perennial herb to 1m high. **Leaves** linear, 7–15cm long to 1cm wide, stem-clasping and arranged in 2 opposite rows along the stems. **Flowers** blue, about 2cm across, nodding, stamens 6 with yellow, woolly filaments, in loose branching clusters at the ends of the stems. Widespread and common from coast to ranges, in open forest, often in poor soils. Qld, NSW, Vic, SA, WA. Winter, spring.

Dianella caerulea

Dianella revoluta

Dianella tasmanica

Stypandra glauca

Thelionema grande

Tufted perennial herb to 1m high. **Leaves** linear, 20–60cm long and about 3mm wide, sheathing at the base and arranged in 2 opposite rows forming a fan-like arrangement at the base. **Flowers** deep blue or purple (rarely white), with 6 spreading segments and 6 stamens and yellow hairless filaments, in terminal cymes. Mainly at altitudes above 800m, usually in or near granite outcrops. NSW, Qld. Spring.

PITTOSPORACEAE | Pittosporum family

A family of 9 genera and about 250 species of shrubs, trees and twining plants occurring in tropical and warm temperate areas in Africa, Asia, Australia and the Pacific Islands. Most are endemic to Australia with 9 genera and about 42 species, the best-known genus being *Pittosporum* (about 11 species), which also extends beyond Australia. Leaves alternate or spirally arranged, simple and usually entire, stipules absent. Flowers bisexual, regular. Sepals 5. Petals 5, often cohering at the base, then spreading, forming a bell-shaped tube. Stamens 5. Ovary superior. Fruit a capsule or berry, sometimes brightly coloured. Many species have perfumed flowers and most are resinous in various parts.

Billardiera erubescens | Red Billardiera

Climber or scrambler with slender stems to 3m long. **Leaves** ovate–lanceolate, to 3.5cm long and 1.5cm wide, dark green and glossy, venation conspicuous, margins entire. **Flowers** tubular, deep red, about 2.5cm long, in loose clusters of up to 8 flowers. **Berry** flattish, about 1.5cm long. Wheatbelt region of southwest, usually in sandy heath. WA. Winter, spring.

Billardiera longiflora | Purple Appleberry

Climber or scrambler with stems to 4m long. **Leaves** variable, narrow–oblong, ovate to lanceolate, 2–7cm long and 5–10mm wide, dark green and glossy, margins flat or recurved. **Flowers** tubular, greenish-yellow, about 3cm long, usually solitary and pendulous on a long slender stalk. **Berry** oblong, to 2.5cm long, shiny purple when ripe. Widespread in woodland, open forest and margins of temperate rainforest. NSW, Vic, Tas. Spring, summer.

Billardiera scandens | Appleberry

Climber or scrambler with slender stems to 5m long. **Leaves** narrow–lanceolate to elliptic or ovate, 2–6cm long to 1.5cm wide, margins flat or recurved, sometimes wavy; young leaves hairy. **Flowers** bell-shaped, greenish-yellow, to 2.5cm long, solitary or 2–3 together, pendulous on long slender stalks. **Berry** cylindrical, to 4cm long, yellow to dark green and sometimes hairy. Widespread and common woodland and open forest, less common in coastal heath. NSW, Vic, Tas, SA. Spring, summer.

Thelionema grande

Billardiera erubescens

Billardiera longiflora

Billardiera scandens

Billardiera versicolor | Pale Appleberry

Climber or scrambler with slender stems to 2m long. **Leaves** lanceolate to narrow–lanceolate, 3–7cm long to 1cm wide, margins recurved, venation conspicuous. **Flowers** greenish-white sometimes tinged pink or purple, about 2cm across, in terminal umbel-like clusters of up to 12 flowers. **Berry** oblong, to 2.5cm long. Widespread in semi-arid districts, in mallee communities. NSW, Vic, SA. Spring, summer.

Hymenosporum flavum | Native Frangipani

Tall shrub to medium-size tree less than 20m high. **Leaves** obovate to oblanceolate, 8–16cm long to 4.5cm wide, dark green and glossy, margins entire, venation prominent, tip pointed. **Flowers** tubular with spreading lobes, pale cream aging to deep yellow, about 5cm across, highly fragrant, in loose terminal panicles about 20cm across. **Capsule** ovate to 3.5cm long, brown. Widespread in wet sclerophyll forest and in or near rainforest. Qld, NSW. Spring.

Pittosporum angustifolium | Weeping Pittosporum

Formerly *P. phylliraeoides*, which is now considered a coastal WA species. Large shrub or small tree to 10m high with pendulous branches. **Leaves** narrow–elliptic to oblong, 4–12cm long 4–12mm wide, margins flat, tip with small hooked point. **Flowers** tubular with spreading lobes, cream to yellow, about 1.2cm across, solitary or in small axillary or terminal clusters. **Capsule** ovoid to globular, to 1.8cm long, red or orange-red. Widespread in inland districts, mostly in woodland and mallee. All mainland States. Winter, spring.

Pittosporum revolutum | Yellow Pittosporum

Erect shrub to 3m high. **Leaves** elliptic to obovate, 5–15cm long and 1.5–6cm wide, young leaves and lower surface of mature leaves rusty hairy, venation prominent, margins slightly wavy, tip shortly pointed. **Flowers** tubular with spreading lobes, yellow, about 1.5cm across, in small terminal clusters, fragrant. **Capsule** ovoid, to 2cm long, rough, orange. Mainly coastal in wet and dry sclerophyll forest and rainforest. Qld, NSW, Vic. Spring, summer.

Pittosporum rhombifolium | Hollywood

Tall shrub or tree to 15m high. **Leaves** ovate to diamond-shaped, 6–11cm long and 3–5cm wide, alternate or clustered, dark green and glossy, margins irregularly toothed, tip shortly pointed. **Flowers** white with spreading petals, about 1cm across, in dense terminal clusters, fragrant. **Capsule** ovoid to globular, to 1cm long, yellow to orange, in dense clusters. Mainly coastal and slightly inland in woodland and rainforest. Qld, NSW. Spring, summer.

Pittosporum undulatum | Sweet Pittosporum

Tall shrub or tree to 15m high. **Leaves** elliptic to oblanceolate, 6–15cm long to 4cm wide, alternate or clustered, dark green and glossy, margins wavy, tip shortly pointed. **Flowers** creamy-white with spreading petals, about 1.5cm across, in terminal clusters. **Capsule** globular to obovate, to 1.5cm long, dark yellow to pale orange. Widespread on coast and ranges in wet and dry sclerophyll forest and rainforest. Qld, NSW, Vic, Tas. Spring.

Billardiera versicolor

Hymenosporum flavum

Pittosporum angustifolium

Pittosporum revolutum

Pittosporum rhombifolium

Pittosporum undulatum

Sollya heterophylla | Bluebell Creeper

Shrub or scrambler with twining stems to 2.5m long. **Leaves** linear–lanceolate to elliptic, 2–3cm long, tip pointed. **Flowers** blue, bell-shaped with 5 free petals, in pendulous terminal clusters of 4–12 flowers. **Capsule** blue, fleshy. Widespread in southwest in woodland and forest. WA. Spring, summer.

PROTEACEAE | Banksia family

A large family of about 80 genera and 1500 species with its main development in the Southern Hemisphere, with a few representatives in Asia, Africa, Central America and China. Australia has about 50 genera and 900 species occurring in all States. They are mostly woody shrubs and trees. Leaves alternate, scattered or sometimes opposite or whorled, simple or (rarely) compound, leathery, entire, toothed or lobed; stipules absent. Flowers bisexual, regular or strongly irregular, singly or in heads, spikes or racemes, sometimes surrounded by showy bracts. Sepals 4, petal-like, united into a cylindrical or swollen tube. Stamens 4, opposite and fused to the sepals, often with only the anthers free or with very short filaments. Style usually long, released as the flower splits open. Ovary superior. Fruit a nut, drupe or follicle.

Adenanthos detmoldii | Yellow Jugflower

Erect shrub to 4m high; branchlets and leaves hairy when young. **Leaves** linear–obovate, to 8cm long and 5mm wide, sessile, surface glandular. **Flowers** yellow and orange, tubular, about 4cm long, hairy, singly in leaf axils. **Fruit** an achene, to 7mm long. Southwest corner, in damp sandy places. Rare. WA. Winter, spring.

Adenanthos obovatus | Basket Flower

Erect multi-stemmed shrub to 1m high, stems smooth. **Leaves** obovate to elliptical, to 2cm long and 1cm wide, smooth, tip rounded with small point. **Flowers** orange to red, tubular, to 2.5cm long, slightly hairy, singly in leaf axils along stem; style hairy, to 4cm long. Southwest corner, in damp sandy places. WA. Winter, spring.

Adenanthos sericeus | Woollybush

Erect dense shrub 2–5m high. **Leaves** to 4.5cm long, divided into many soft grey-green terete segments, covered with closely appressed silky hairs. **Flowers** red, tubular, to 3cm long, singly and terminal, often partially concealed by foliage. Southwest coastal districts, often in deep sand. WA. Flowers most of year.

Sollya heterophylla

Adenanthos detmoldii

Adenanthos obovatus

Adenanthos sericeus

Adenanthos venosus

Multi-stemmed shrub 1–2m high; branchlets hairy when young. **Leaves** ovate to obovate, to 2cm long, sessile, leathery, longitudinal veins prominent. Young leaves reddish, especially near flowers. **Flowers** red, tubular, about 2.5cm long, terminal. Mainly Barren Ranges on south coast. WA. Spring.

Banksia aemula | Wallum Banksia

Tall shrub or small spreading tree to 8m high; bark rough and corky. **Leaves** narrow–obovate to oblong, 8–20cm long to 2cm wide, margins regularly toothed, hairy and rusty brown when young. **Flowers** pale yellow to greenish, in cylindrical heads 8–20cm long. **Cone** with persistent spent flowers; follicles large, up to 4.5cm long. Widespread in coastal areas, often on sand dunes. Qld, NSW. Autumn, winter.

Banksia baueri | Possum Banksia

Dense low shrub to 2m high. **Leaves** oblanceolate, to 15cm long and 2cm wide, stiff, margins serrated. **Flowers** pale yellow, grey-mauve or orange-brown, hairy, in dense cylindrical heads 12–30cm long and up to 20cm diameter, often partially concealed in foliage or close to the ground. **Cone** with persistent spent flowers; follicles small and furry. Widespread in southern districts, mostly in low shrubland and mallee. WA. Winter, spring.

Banksia baxteri | Bird's Nest Banksia

Spreading shrub to 4m high. **Leaves** 10–15cm long to 4cm wide, with deep triangular lobes to midrib, prickly, tip blunt and flat, tomentose below when young. **Flowers** yellow-green, in dense dome-shaped heads, about 12cm diameter, terminal, surrounded by leaves. **Cone** globular, spent flowers persistent; follicles few, but large and furry. Southern coastal areas, often in sandy, moist places. WA. Spring, summer, autumn.

Banksia coccinea | Scarlet Banksia

Erect shrub 2–4m high; branchlets with woolly white hairs. **Leaves** oblong, to 9cm long and 7cm wide, leathery, margins irregularly toothed, lower surface grey–tomentose. **Flowers** grey with bright red styles, arranged in vertical rows in squat spikes, to 12cm long and 15cm diameter, terminal. **Cone** ovoid, smooth; follicles small. South coast, from Albany to Hopetoun, often in deep sand. WA. Winter, spring, summer.

Adenanthos venosus

Banksia baueri

Banksia aemula

Banksia baxteri

Banksia coccinea

Banksia conferta var. *penicillata* |

Open shrub to 4m high; young growth rusty red and hairy. **Leaves** obovate, 4–12cm long to 4cm wide, in whorls, margins regularly toothed, smooth above, white–tomentose below, rusty hairs on lower midrib. **Flowers** grey-green in bud opening to yellow, in dense spikes to 19cm long. **Cone** with persistent spent flowers; small follicles numerous (often 100). Confined to upper Blue Mountains, in open forest. NSW. Autumn, winter.

Banksia ericifolia | Heath Banksia

Large bushy shrub or small tree to 6m high. **Leaves** linear, 1–2cm long and 1–2mm wide, margins revolute, tip notched with small point at each side, lower surface silvery. **Flowers** orange-red, in cylindrical spikes to 20cm long and 6cm diameter. **Cone** oblong, with some persistent flower parts; follicles oblong, to 2cm long. Common in sandy coastal areas, extending slightly inland to Blue Mountains. NSW. Autumn, winter.

Banksia hookerana | Hooker's Banksia

Dense shrub 2–3m high; branches hairy. **Leaves** narrow–linear, to 20cm long and 1cm wide, finely toothed halfway to midrib, lower surface tomentose on young leaves. **Flowers** pinkish-grey with bright orange styles, in oblong spikes 8–10cm long to 8cm diameter, terminal. **Cone** oblong, to 10cm long, spent flowers persistent; follicles small and hairy. Northern sandplains south of Geraldton. WA. Winter, spring, summer.

Banksia integrifolia | Coast Banksia

Tall shrub or tree 5–25m high; bark rough and light grey. **Leaves** narrow–obovate, 5–20cm long and 2–4cm wide, whorled, entire or occasionally with a few short teeth, lower surface white–tomentose. **Flowers** pale yellow, in cylindrical spikes 5–12cm long. **Cone** narrow, silvery-grey, smooth; prominent follicles open at maturity. Widespread along coast and nearby ranges. Qld, NSW, Vic, Tas. Summer, autumn, winter.

Banksia marginata | Silver Banksia

Shrub or small tree 2–10m high; branchlets hairy. **Leaves** linear to obovate, 2–6cm long to 1cm wide, margins entire or toothed when young, lower surface white–tomentose, tip flat. **Flowers** pale yellow, in oblong spikes 5–10cm long to 6cm diameter. **Cone** with persistent spent flowers; follicles small. Widespread from coast to mountains and farther inland. NSW, Vic, Tas, SA. Spring, summer, autumn.

Banksia media | Southern Plains Banksia

Bushy shrub 2–4m high; branchlets hairy. **Leaves** roughly wedge-shaped, 6–15cm long to 2cm wide, margins toothed, wavy, lower surface sometimes with brown hairs. **Flowers** yellow or golden brown, in dense cylindrical heads 12–20cm long to 10cm diameter. **Cone** same size as flowers, spent flowers persistent; follicles dark brown. Southern coastal districts in sandplain communities. WA. Autumn winter, spring.

Banksia conferta var. *penicillata*

Banksia ericifolia

Banksia hookerana

Banksia integrifolia

Banksia marginata

Banksia media

Banksia menziesii | Menzies' Banksia

Small gnarled tree to 15m high; bark rough and pebbled; branchlets woolly. **Leaves** oblong, 5–30cm long to 4cm wide, margins regularly toothed, wavy, lower surfaces rusty hairy. **Flowers** silvery-pink with golden styles, in acorn-shaped heads 10–15cm long to 12cm diameter. **Cone** broadest at base, smooth; follicles few but prominent. Common on sandplains north of Perth. WA. Autumn, winter, spring.

Banksia oblongifolia |

Multi-stemmed shrub 1–3m high; new growth with dense rusty hairs. **Leaves** obovate to oblong, 5–8cm long to 2cm wide, spreading, margins finely toothed (rarely entire), lower surface pale green or white. **Flowers** pale yellow, in spikes to 15cm long and 6cm diameter. **Cone** oblong, smooth; follicles velvety at first. Widespread and common in coastal areas, in open forest and heath. Qld, NSW. Autumn, winter.

Banksia occidentalis | Red Swamp Banksia

Erect bushy shrub or (rarely) small tree 3–7m high. **Leaves** linear, 5–15cm long to 3mm wide, in whorls, margins entire, except for a few teeth toward tip, lower surface white. **Flowers** yellow with bright red styles, in cylindrical spikes 10–14cm long to 9cm diameter. **Cone** oblong, spent flowers persistent; follicles numerous and crowded. Southern coastal areas, in swampy and wet places. WA. Summer, autumn.

Banksia ornata | Desert Banksia

Erect bushy shrub to 3m high. **Leaves** narrow–obovate, 3–11cm long to 2.5cm wide, margins toothed, lower surface hairy on midrib. **Flowers** vary from cream and yellow to rusty brown, in broad cylindrical spikes to 14cm long and 8cm diameter. **Cone** broad cylindrical, spent flowers persistent for a long time; follicles densely furry. Coastal and mostly inland districts in heath, woodland and mallee. Vic, SA. Winter, spring.

Banksia paludosa | Marsh Banksia

Small erect shrub to 1.5m high; branchlets rusty hairy. **Leaves** narrow–lanceolate to narrow–obovate, 4–13cm long to 3cm wide, alternate to whorled, toothed or entire, bright green and smooth above, white–tomentose and prominently veined below. **Flowers** golden-yellow, in narrow spikes to 13cm long and 4cm diameter. **Cone** narrow–oblong, spent flowers persistent; follicles smooth, widely spaced. Coast and nearby ranges, in heath or woodland in moist situations. NSW. Winter.

Banksia menziesii

Banksia oblongifolia

Banksia occidentalis

Banksia ornata

Banksia paludosa

Banksia petiolaris

Prostrate shrub with horizontal branches to 1m across. **Leaves** oblong, 10–30cm long to 2cm wide, held erect on long petiole, wavy, margins toothed, lower surface silvery-grey. **Flowers** yellow, in oblong spikes 10–20cm long, terminal on branches at ground level. **Cone** with spent flowers persistent; follicles prominent. Southern coastal areas, mainly in heath. WA. Spring, summer.

Banksia pilostylis

Dense shrub 2–4m high; branchlets densely hairy. **Leaves** narrow, wedge-shaped, 12–20cm long to 2cm wide, margins regularly toothed, lower surface silvery-grey. **Flowers** yellow or greenish-yellow, in oblong spikes 7–15cm long and 5–8cm diameter. **Cone** with spent flowers persistent; follicles prominent. Southern coastal areas between Ravensthorpe and Esperance. WA. Summer, autumn.

Banksia praemorsa | Cut-leaf Banksia

Large dense shrub to 4m high. **Leaves** oblong to wedge-shaped, 2–6cm long to 2cm wide, margins toothed, tip cut off, lower surface tomentose when young. **Flowers** deep red and greenish-yellow, in cylindrical spikes to 30cm long and 10cm diameter. **Cone** oblong, about same size as flower, spent flowers persistent, often concealing follicles. Confined to Albany district, often on coastal sand dunes and cliffs. WA. Winter, spring.

Banksia prionotes | Orange Banksia

Tall shrub or small tree 5–10m high; branches covered in dense white hairs. **Leaves** broad–linear, 10–30cm long to 2.5cm wide, margins with triangular teeth. **Flowers** woolly white with orange styles, in acorn-shaped heads 10–15cm long to 8cm diameter. **Cone** ovoid, spent flowers shed; follicles embedded. Widely distributed in southwest. WA. Autumn, winter.

Banksia petiolaris

Banksia pilostylis

Banksia praemorsa

Banksia prionotes

Banksia quercifolia | Oak-leaved Banksia

Erect shrub to 3m high; branchlets reddish-brown. **Leaves** narrowly wedge-shaped, 3–15cm long to 4cm wide, prominently toothed, tip blunt. **Flowers** grey maturing to orange-brown, in short oblong spikes, 5–10cm long to 6cm diameter. **Cone** oblong, to 6cm diameter, spent flowers persistent; follicles prominent, shortly pubescent, brown. Mainly coastal or near coastal in southwest corner, often in low-lying moist situations. WA. Autumn, winter.

Banksia repens | Creeping Banksia

Prostrate shrub with horizontal branches 2–3m across; young growth rusty brown. **Leaves** to 50cm long, erect on long petioles, deeply divided to rigid midrib, lobes sometimes toothed. **Flowers** pinkish-brown, on spikes to 15cm long to 7cm diameter, emerging at ground level. **Cone** with spent flowers persistent; follicles velvety, prominent. Widespread in southern coastal areas and slightly inland. WA. Spring, summer.

Banksia robur | Swamp Banksia

Open shrub to 2m high. **Leaves** obovate, to 30cm long and 10cm wide, thick and leathery, dark green above, strongly veined and rusty-hairy below, wavy, margins irregularly toothed. **Flowers** greenish-yellow, in spikes to 15cm long. **Cone** with spent flowers persistent; follicles prominent. Widespread in coastal areas, in heath and woodland in wet places. Qld, NSW. Summer, autumn, winter.

Banksia serrata | Saw Banksia

Large shrub or small gnarled tree 10–15m high; bark dark grey and rough. **Leaves** obovate, 5–20cm long to 4cm wide, stiff, bluntly toothed, lower surface velvety when young. **Flowers** creamy-grey, in spikes to 16cm long and 10cm diameter. **Cone** with spent flowers persistent; follicles prominent to 3.5cm long. Widespread and common in coastal regions in heath and open forest, on sandy soils. Qld, NSW, Vic, Tas. Summer, autumn, winter.

Banksia speciosa | Showy Banksia

Multi-branched spreading shrub 3–6m high; branchlets with woolly-white hairs. **Leaves** broad–linear, 20–40cm long, toothed to the midrib with prickly triangular lobes, lower surface white–tomentose. **Flowers** yellowish-grey, in cylindrical rounded heads to 15cm long and 12cm diameter. **Cone** with spent flowers persistent; follicles prominent, velvety brown. Locally common in coastal sandy heaths from Hopetoun to Israelite Bay. WA. Summer, autumn.

Banksia sphaerocarpa | Round-fruited Banksia

Spreading shrub to 2m high. **Leaves** narrow–linear, 2–10cm long to 1cm wide, margins entire and revolute, tip pointed. **Flowers** brownish-yellow, in rounded heads to 8cm diameter. **Cone** with spent flowers persistent; follicles hairy and prominent. Variable and widespread in southwest, in heath and open forest. WA. Spring, summer.

Banksia quercifolia

Banksia repens

Banksia robur

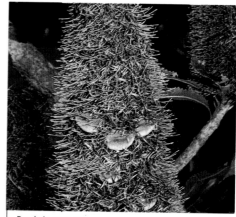

Banksia serrata

Banksia speciosa

Banksia sphaerocarpa

Banksia spinulosa | Hairpin Banksia

Multi-stemmed rounded shrub to 3m high. **Leaves** narrow–linear, 3–20cm long to 1cm wide, margins toothed in upper part, revolute. **Flowers** golden-yellow, in cylindrical spikes 6–15cm long; style yellow to black, distinctly hooked at the tip. **Cone** narrow–ovoid with spent flowers persistent; follicles crowded and somewhat flattened. Widely distributed in coastal heath, open forest and woodland. Qld, NSW, Vic. Autumn, winter.

Conospermum burgessiorum |

Spreading shrub 1–3m high; branchlets hairy when young. **Leaves** linear to narrow–oblanceolate, 10–20cm long to 1cm wide, slightly curved, veins prominent, tip pointed. **Flowers** cream to white, small and tubular, in dense terminal clusters. **Fruit** a small nut 2–3mm long, hairy. Gibraltar Range and Stanthorpe district, in woodland and open forest on granite soils. Qld, NSW. Spring.

Conospermum ericifolium |

Erect shrub to 1m high. **Leaves** linear to terete, to 2.5cm long, less than 1mm wide, crowded, tip pointed. **Flowers** cream to white, tubular, about 7mm long, hairy, in dense spikes, on stalks to 6cm long from upper leaf axils. Coastal, common in Sydney district, in woodland and heath. NSW. Spring.

Conospermum longifolium | Long-leaf Smokebush

Erect shrub 1–2m high; branchlets hairy. **Leaves** variable, linear to narrow–oblanceolate, 10–25cm long, 1–2cm wide, margins often wavy, tapering to base. **Flowers** white and bluish, tubular, about 1cm long, in dense terminal panicles on stalks to 30cm long held well above the leaves. Central and south coast and adjacent ranges, mainly in heath and open forest. NSW. Spring.

Conospermum mitchellii | Victorian Smokebush

Slender erect shrub to 2m high. **Leaves** linear, 5–15cm long to 3mm wide, stiff and curved upward from branchlets. **Flowers** creamy-white or tipped blue, tubular, about 5mm long, woolly, in dense, flat-topped clusters to 15cm wide. Endemic in southwestern Victoria, in heath and open forest. Vic. Spring, summer.

Conospermum patens | Slender Smokebush

Small erect shrub to 1m high. **Leaves** variable, linear, to 4cm long, initially hairy, crowded and spreading. **Flowers** blue to lilac, tubular, to 5mm long, hairy, in dense clusters about 7cm across, on slender branchlets above the foliage. Semi-arid regions, in heath. Vic, SA. Winter, spring.

Banksia spinulosa

Conospermum burgessiorum

Conospermum ericifolium

Conospermum longifolium

Conospermum mitchellii

Conospermum patens

Conospermum stoechadis | Common Smokebush

Erect dome-shaped shrub 1–2m high. **Leaves** terete, to 10cm long, rigid, tip pointed. **Flowers** whitish-grey, woolly, tubular, to 8mm long, in loose panicles on branchlets to 20cm long in upper leaf axils. Widely distributed throughout the southwest, in sand heath and woodland. WA. Spring.

Dryandra ashbyi |

Spreading shrub to 1.5m high. **Leaves** to 8cm long, curved back, with scattered, linear lobes, margins revolute, white–tomentose below, tips pungent-pointed. **Flowers** greenish-yellow, in dense heads to 4cm across toward branch ends; outer bracts dark brown and pointed. Geraldton District on gravelly hills. WA. Autumn, winter.

Dryandra carlinoides | Pink Dryandra

Dense spreading shrub to 1m high. **Leaves** linear or lanceolate, to 3cm long and 5mm wide, margins recurved with a few small prickly teeth toward tip. **Flowers** creamy-pink, in dense terminal heads about 3cm across; outer bracts grey-brown, hairy. Northern sandplains, among heath. WA. Spring.

Dryandra cuneata | Wedge-leaved Dryandra

Erect or spreading shrub to 2m high. **Leaves** wedge-shaped, 4–7cm long to 4cm wide, margins wavy, deeply toothed and prickly, green on both sides. **Flowers** yellow, in dense terminal heads to 4.5cm across, surrounded by short hairy bracts. Widespread in southern coastal heaths. WA. Autumn, winter, spring.

Dryandra formosa | Showy Dryandra

Erect open shrub 2–4m high. **Leaves** linear, to 20cm long and 1cm wide, deeply divided into triangular lobes to midrib, relatively soft, lower surface white–tomentose, white. **Flowers** golden orange, in dense terminal heads to 8cm across, surrounded by floral leaves. Stirling Ranges and stony hillsides around Albany. WA. Winter, spring.

Dryandra fraseri |

Semi-prostrate, spreading shrub to 1m high; branchlets hairy. **Leaves** to 10cm long with closely spaced prickly lobes, recurved margins, grey-green above, white–tomentose below. **Flowers** yellow to dull orange, silky-hairy, in heads about 5cm diameter; pinkish in bud. Widespread and common in southwest, in heath, open forest and woodland. WA. Winter, spring.

Conospermum stoechadis

Dryandra ashbyi

Dryandra carlinoides

Dryandra cuneata

Dryandra formosa

Dryandra fraseri

Dryandra nivea | Couch Honeypot

Prostrate or low spreading shrub to 1m high. **Leaves** linear, 10–30cm long to 1cm wide, margins with pointed triangular lobes divided to midrib, dark green above, lower surface whitish. **Flowers** yellow, orange or rusty brown, in terminal heads about 4cm diameter, surrounded by floral leaves; bracts numerous, brown and hairy. Widespread throughout the southwest. WA. Winter, spring.

Dryandra nobilis | Golden Dryandra

Multi-branched shrub to 5m high. **Leaves** linear, 10–30cm long to 1.5cm wide, margins with pointed triangular lobes divided to the midrib, dark green above, lower surface white–tomentose with prominent veins. **Flowers** orange-yellow, in heads about 7cm diameter, surrounded by floral leaves, on very short stalks in the leaf axils. Widespread throughout the southwest, usually in woodland on gravelly soils. WA. Winter, spring.

Dryandra polycephala | Many-headed Dryandra

Tall shrub to 4m high. **Leaves** narrow–linear, 5–20cm long to 6mm wide, margins recurved with well-spaced, narrow–triangular, prickly lobes. **Flowers** bright yellow, in heads about 4cm diameter, at ends of short branchlets along the branches; bracts brown. An understorey plant in wandoo woodland in the southwest. WA. Winter, spring.

Dryandra praemorsa | Urchin Dryandra

Large, bushy shrub 2–4m high; branches hairy. **Leaves** obovate, to 10cm long and 6cm wide, margins wavy and prickly toothed, lower surface white–tomentose, tip cut off. **Flowers** golden-yellow, in large terminal heads to 8cm diameter, surrounded by floral leaves; bracts small, about 1cm long. Jarrah forest in southwest. WA. Winter, spring.

Dryandra quercifolia | Oak-leaf Dryandra

Dense rounded shrub 2–4m high; branches hairy. **Leaves** obovate, to 10cm long and 4cm wide, margins wavy with deep, irregular prickly lobes, dark green and shiny above, green below, veins prominent. **Flowers** yellowish-green, in large terminal heads to 8cm diameter, surrounded by floral leaves; bracts conspicuous, reddish-brown. Southern coast, Fitzgerald River district. WA. Autumn, winter, spring.

Dryandra sessilis | Parrot Bush

Erect shrub 2–6m high. **Leaves** wedge-shaped, to 5cm long and 3cm wide, sessile, grey-green, margins wavy with deep, prickly teeth toward the tip. **Flowers** pale yellow, in terminal heads to 3cm long, surrounded by floral leaves; bracts short, pale brown. Widespread in southwest, common in jarrah forest and coastal limestone. WA. Winter, spring.

Dryandra nivea

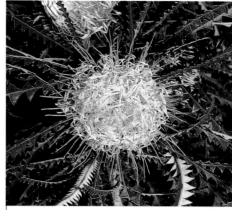

Dryandra nobilis

Dryandra polycephala

Dryandra praemorsa

Dryandra quercifolia

Dryandra sessilis

Dryandra speciosa | Shaggy Dryandra

Open spreading shrub to 1.5cm high. **Leaves** narrow–linear, to 10cm long and 2mm wide, dark green above, paler below, margins entire and recurved, tip pointed. **Flowers** silvery-pink to yellow, in pendent heads to 7cm diameter, surrounded by shaggy grey-brown bracts to 5cm long. Northern wheatbelt district, mainly in gravelly heath. WA. Winter, spring.

Grevillea alpina | Mountain Grevillea

(Grampians form pictured.) Very variable shrub from prostrate to 2m high. **Leaves** oblong to elliptic, to 3cm long and 1cm wide, sessile, margins entire, recurved, upper surface sometimes hairy, lower surface paler and hairy, tip rounded with small point. **Flowers** cream, green, yellow, orange, pink or red (or combination of these), about 1.2cm long, in pairs or short terminal racemes; style hairy, to 1.6cm long. Widespread in southeast, in woodland, heath and open forest. NSW, Vic. Winter, spring.

Grevillea anethifolia | Spiny Cream Spider Flower

Multi-stemmed shrub to 2m high; branchlets velvety. **Leaves** 2–5cm long, divided into 3–5 linear prickly lobes, which are again divided, margins strongly recurved. **Flowers** creamy-white, in short cylindrical terminal or axillary racemes to 2cm long; style white, straight, with cylindrical pollen presenter. Widespread in southern mallee communities. NSW, SA, WA. Winter, spring.

Grevillea aquifolium | Holly Grevillea

Variable shrub from prostrate and spreading or erect up to 4m high. **Leaves** ovate to oblong, 2–10cm long, 1–4cm wide, glabrous or hairy above with conspicuous veins, lower surface hairy, margins wavy with prickly teeth or lobes. **Flowers** green, yellow to red, in toothbrush-like racemes to 5cm long; style red, hairless, to 2cm long. Heath and woodland. Vic, SA. Winter, spring.

Grevillea argyrophylla | Silvery-leaved Grevillea

Spreading shrub 2–6m high; branchlets silky-hairy. **Leaves** linear to obovate, 2–6cm long to 1.5cm wide, dark green above, lower surface with white silky hairs, margins recurved, tip rounded or notched. **Flowers** creamy-white, in rounded racemes about 2cm across, in upper leaf axils; style cream, hooked at tip. Northern Irwin district, mainly in coastal heath on sandy soil. WA. Winter, spring.

Grevillea aspera | Rough-leaf Grevillea

Small dense shrub to 1m high; branchlets and new growth hairy. **Leaves** oblong to obovate, 3–8cm long to 1cm wide, dark green and rough above, lower surface silky-hairy, margins recurved, tip rounded with small point. **Flowers** red and cream, hairy, in pendent, axillary or terminal racemes about 4cm long; style green then red, stout and slightly curved. Widespread in Flinders Ranges and Eyre Peninsula in heath and woodland. SA. Winter, spring.

Dryandra speciosa

Grevillea alpina

Grevillea anethifolia

Grevillea aquifolium

Grevillea argyrophylla

Grevillea aspera

Grevillea aspleniifolia | Fern Leaf Grevillea

Large spreading shrub 3–5m high; branchlets and new growth hairy. **Leaves** linear–lanceolate, 15–30cm long, toothed or lobed, often entire, dark green above, lower surface with dense hairs, margins recurved. **Flowers** purplish-pink and silky, in toothbrush-like racemes to 5cm long; style red to 2cm long with green tip. Mainly central and southern tablelands in rocky open places in woodland. NSW. Winter, spring.

Grevillea banksii | Red Silky Oak

Spreading shrub or small slender tree 3–10m high; sometimes prostrate. **Leaves** pinnately lobed, to 30cm long with 4–12 linear, pointed lobes to 15cm long, dark green above, lower surface silky, margins recurved. **Flowers** creamy-white or red (sometimes pinkish), in cylindrical spike to 12cm long and 10cm wide; style red or cream, curved to about 4cm long, with yellow tip. Widely distributed in coastal areas. Qld. Winter, spring.

Grevillea baueri | Bauer's Grevillea

Small spreading shrub to 1m high and 2m across. **Leaves** oblong–elliptic, to 3cm long and 1cm wide, sessile, smooth above, paler below, margins slightly recurved, tip rounded with small point. **Flowers** red and cream, in terminal or axillary clusters to 4cm long; style red and hairy, about 2.5cm long. Central and southern coast and tablelands, in woodland or heath. NSW. Winter, spring.

Grevillea buxifolia | Grey Spider Flower

Erect open shrub 1–2m high; branchlets hairy. **Leaves** ovate to elliptic, to 3.5cm long and 1cm wide, sessile, margins entire and slightly recurved, lower surface hairy, tip softly pointed. **Flowers** woolly, grey and brown, in terminal racemes 3–4cm across; style densely hairy with reflexed tip. Central coast and tablelands, in open forest and heath. NSW. Winter, spring.

Grevillea chrysophaea | Golden Grevillea

Erect open shrub to 1.5m high; branchlets and young growth hairy. **Leaves** oblong to elliptic, 1–6cm long to 1.5cm wide, sessile, slightly glandular and minutely hairy above, lower surface hairy, margins recurved, tip rounded with small point. **Flowers** golden-yellow, 2–8 per raceme, usually pendent, to 3cm across; style yellowish-brown and hairy, to 2cm long. Widespread, mainly in the south, in open forest and heath. Vic. Winter, spring, summer.

Grevillea crithmifolia |

A spreading shrub to 2.5m high; branchlets hairy. **Leaves** pinnate, to 3cm long with 3–5 linear lobes, grey-green and smooth above, lower surface hairy, margins recurved, tip pointed. **Flowers** white to soft pink, in terminal globular racemes about 3cm diameter; style white, very fine, to 3mm long. Around Perth, in woodland and coastal heath, usually on limestone. WA. Winter, spring.

Grevillea aspleniifolia

Grevillea banksii

Grevillea baueri

Grevillea buxifolia

Grevillea chrysophaea

Grevillea crithmifolia

Grevillea dryophylla | Goldfields Grevillea

Erect spreading shrub 1–2m high; branchlets and young growth silky-hairy. **Leaves** to 6.5cm long and 5cm wide, divided into segments, each segment with up to 3 triangular pointed lobes, sparsely hairy both sides, margins slightly recurved. **Flowers** greenish-brown, silky, in terminal 1-sided racemes to 3.5cm long, usually pendent; style yellow, pink or red, smooth, to 1cm long, strongly curved. Central and western goldfield districts in box–ironbark forest. Vic. Winter, spring.

Grevillea floribunda | Rusty Spider Flower

Erect open shrub to 2m high; branchlets hairy. **Leaves** oblong to ovate, 2–7cm long to 2cm wide, lower surface silky-hairy, margins entire and slightly recurved, tip rounded with short point. **Flowers** greenish-orange, densely hairy, in terminal pendent racemes to 5cm long; style brown with rusty hair. Widespread in inland areas in open forest and woodland, often in stony soils. Qld, NSW. Winter, spring.

Grevillea hilliana | White Silky Oak

Tree 8–25m high. **Leaves** variable; juvenile leaves to 40cm long are deeply divided with 3–10 lobes; adult leaves oblong to obovate, 10–20cm long to 6cm wide, wavy, entire or sometimes 4–6 lobed, glossy dark green above, lower surface silky, veins conspicuous. **Flowers** creamy-white, in dense cylindrical racemes to 22cm long, usually pendent; style white, curved. Rainforest, mainly in coastal districts. NSW, Qld. Spring, summer.

Grevillea juncifolia | Honeysuckle Grevillea

Erect shrub 2–6m high; branchlets whitish-grey, hairy. **Leaves** linear, 10–30cm long, sometimes divided into linear lobes to 2mm wide, grey-green and hairy, margins revolute, tip sharply pointed. **Flowers** bright yellow to orange, in loose terminal racemes 7–20cm long; style yellow to orange, to 2.5cm long. Widespread in inland regions, on sand dunes and sandy plains. Qld, NSW, SA, WA, NT. Winter, spring.

Grevillea dryophylla

Grevillea floribunda

Grevillea hilliana

Grevillea juncifolia

Grevillea juniperina

Low prostrate to erect shrub to 2.5m high; branchlets hairy. **Leaves** lanceolate or linear, to 3.5cm long and 6mm wide, sessile, margins entire and recurved, tip sharply pointed. **Flowers** red, pink, orange, yellow or cream, in terminal pendent clusters to 6cm across; style smooth, to 2.5cm long. Widespread on coast and tablelands, in moist places. NSW. Winter, spring.

Grevillea lanigera | Woolly Grevillea

Spreading shrub from prostrate to 1.5m high; branchlets hairy. **Leaves** linear to narrow–oblanceolate, 1–3cm long, to 5mm wide, sessile, grey-green, margins entire, revolute, lower surface hairy. **Flowers** deep pink and cream, sometimes greenish-yellow and cream, in spidery clusters to 6cm across; style red, sometimes green, hairy, to 2cm long. Widespread in coastal heath and subalpine woodland. NSW, Vic. Winter, spring.

Grevillea lavendulacea | Lavender Grevillea

Variable low spreading or upright shrub to 1m high; branchlets hairy. **Leaves** variable, narrow–linear to narrow–obovate, to 4cm long and 1cm wide, sessile, margins entire, recurved, lower surface hairy, tip usually pointed. **Flowers** pink, red or (rarely) white, often with cream or paler tips; style pink, red or white, usually smooth, to 2.5cm long. Widespread in drier areas in open woodland and mallee country. Vic, SA. Winter, spring.

Grevillea longifolia | Long-leaf Grevillea

Spreading shrub 2–5m high; branchlets reddish, silky. **Leaves** linear to narrow–lanceolate, 7–20cm long to 2.5cm wide, margins serrated (rarely entire), lower surface with silky hairs. **Flowers** pink to red, in toothbrush-like racemes to 8cm long; style red to deep pink, smooth, to 2cm long with green tip. Restricted to near Sydney and Blue Mountains, often near creeks in open forest. NSW. Winter, spring.

Grevillea longistyla | Long-style Grevillea

Erect open shrub 2–5m high; branchlets silky. **Leaves** linear, 15–25cm long, either simple or pinnately divided into linear lobes to 17cm long and 4mm wide, margins recurved, lower surface white with silky hairs. **Flowers** red, in loose cylindrical racemes to 10cm long; style red, smooth, to 4cm long. Open forest and woodland, often on sandstone ridges and plains. Qld. Spring, summer.

Grevillea juniperina

Grevillea lanigera

Grevillea lavendulacea

Grevillea longifolia

Grevillea longistyla

Grevillea macrostylis | Mount Barren Grevillea

Erect shrub to 2m high; branchlets glandular with felted hairs. **Leaves** to about 5cm long, usually divided into 3 lobes (rarely entire), sparsely silky above, lower surface silky, midvein prominent. **Flowers** orange-red and yellow, slightly hairy, 2–6 per raceme, terminal and in leaf axils; style orange-red, smooth, to 4cm long. Confined to southern coastal areas, often in heath and open woodland. WA. Winter, spring.

Grevillea mucronulata | Green Spider Flower

Spreading shrub to 2.5m high; branchlets reddish, hairy. **Leaves** elliptic to ovate to almost circular, 1–4cm long to 2cm wide, rough above, hairy below, margins recurved, tip with short point. **Flowers** green, in spider-like racemes about 5cm across, terminal or axillary; style dark purplish-red, hairy, to 2cm long, with green tip. Widespread from coast to mountains, in open forest and woodland. NSW. Winter, spring.

Grevillea paniculata | Kerosene Bush

Erect or spreading prickly shrub 1–3m high; branchlets sometimes reddish. **Leaves** to 6cm long, light green, usually divided into 3 linear–terete segments to 4cm long (occasionally twice divided), tip sharply pointed. **Flowers** white, loosely clustered in axillary racemes; style white, short. Widespread in inland areas of the southwest. WA. Winter, spring.

Grevillea petrophiloides | Pink Pokers

Erect or spreading open shrub 1–3m high. **Leaves** to 25cm long, deeply divided several times into linear–terete lobes to about 2cm long, tip pointed. **Flowers** pink, in dense cylindrical racemes about 10cm long and 3cm wide, open first from the top, usually terminal on leafless stems; style pink, smooth, about 1.5cm long. Widespread in inland areas of the southwest. WA. Winter, spring.

Grevillea prasina |

Small multi-stemmed shrub 1–2m high. **Leaves** ovate, 3–9cm long to 4cm wide, pale green, margins wavy with well-spaced prickly teeth, veins conspicuous. **Flowers** creamy-green, slightly hairy, in pendulous racemes to 5cm long, in upper leaf axils; style light green, curved, about 1.5cm long. Tropical north, from eastern Kimberley region to Victoria River district on sandstone ridges and open woodland. WA, NT. Winter, spring.

Grevillea pteridifolia | Golden Grevillea

Extremely variable, from prostrate shrub to small open tree to 10m high. **Leaves** to 40cm long, pinnately divided into numerous narrow–linear segments 15–25cm long, midvein prominent, margins recurved, lower surface silky. **Flowers** orange, in toothbrush-like racemes to 20cm long, terminal or in upper axils; style bright yellow or orange, curved, 2–3cm long. Widespread across northern Australia, in open forest and woodland, in seasonally wet places. Qld, WA, NT. Winter, spring.

Grevillea macrostylis

Grevillea mucronulata

Grevillea paniculata

Grevillea petrophiloides

Grevillea prasina

Grevillea pteridifolia

Grevillea quercifolia | Oak-leaf Grevillea

Low spreading shrub to 80cm high; branchlets reddish and silky when young. **Leaves** ovate to oblong, 4–20cm long to 6cm wide, with well-spaced prickly lobes, lateral veins and midvein prominent. **Flowers** deep pink to purple, in erect cylindrical racemes 2–6cm long; style pink, short and twisted. Widespread in southwest, in forest, often in damp places. WA. Spring.

Grevillea robusta | Silky Oak

Erect tree 10–35m high. **Leaves** 10–30cm long, 2 or 3 times divided into oblong–linear lobes, dark green above, lower surface paler and silky-hairy, veins prominent. **Flowers** bright orange, in toothbrush-like racemes 10–15cm long with flowers facing upward, often several together; style orange-yellow, erect, to 2cm long. Coast and inland ranges in subtropical rainforest and dry rainforest. Qld, NSW. Spring, summer.

Grevillea rosmarinifolia | Rosemary Grevillea

Variable shrub from 30cm to 2m high; branchlets reddish, silky-hairy. **Leaves** linear to narrow–oblong, 1–4cm long to 3mm wide, margins recurved, rough above, lower surface silky grey, tip sharply pointed. **Flowers** pink, red, cream or green, sometimes pink and cream, in terminal pendent racemes to 4cm across; style red, pink, cream or green, about 2cm long. Inland regions in woodland and mallee country. NSW, Vic. Winter, spring.

Grevillea sericea | Silky Grevillea

Erect shrub to 2.5cm high; branchlets angular, silky. **Leaves** linear to narrow–obovate, 2–7cm long to 1cm wide, margins entire and recurved, lower surface silky, tip pointed. **Flowers** pale to deep pink (rarely white), in terminal, spider-like racemes to 5cm across; style pink, curved at end, about 2cm long. Widespread and common from the central coast to nearby mountains, in heath and open forest. NSW. Winter, spring.

Grevillea speciosa | Red Spider Flower

Erect shrub 1–3m high; branchlets reddish, silky-hairy. **Leaves** narrow–elliptic or obovate, 1–4cm long up to about 1.5cm wide, lower surface silky-hairy, margins recurved, tip rounded with small point. **Flowers** red or deep pink, in spider-like pendent racemes to 4cm long; style red or deep pink, to 3cm long. Common and endemic to Sydney district, in open forest and heath usually in sand. NSW. Winter, spring.

Grevillea stenobotrya | Sandhill Spider Flower

Open shrub to small tree 3–6m high. **Leaves** narrow–linear, 5–25cm long to 2mm wide, leathery, margins strongly revolute, tip pointed. **Flowers** cream to pale yellow, in cylindrical racemes 8–25cm long, with 5–20 together in branched panicles at the ends of branches; style cream to pale yellow, curved, to 1.5cm long. Widespread throughout the inland, usually on red sand dunes. Qld, NSW, WA, NT. Winter, spring.

Grevillea quercifolia

Grevillea robusta

Grevillea rosmarinifolia

Grevillea sericea

Grevillea speciosa

Grevillea stenobotrya

Grevillea tetragonoloba

Spreading shrub 1–2.5m high; branchlets silky-hairy. **Leaves** 6–12cm long, divided into 3–5 narrow–linear pointed segments, upper surface ribbed, margins recurved. **Flowers** pale brown and hairy, in terminal toothbrush-like racemes to 12cm long; style bright red, curved, to 2.5cm long. Southern coastal districts in mallee heath and open woodland, mostly on granite soils. WA. Winter, spring.

Grevillea trifida

Erect or spreading shrub to 1.5m high; branchlets silky-hairy. **Leaves** 2–10cm long, extremely variable, entire or divided into 3 spreading lobes, they may be again divided; segments linear to triangular, margins recurved, tip pointed. **Flowers** creamy-white, in axillary or terminal clusters about 2cm across; style white, often S-shaped. Widespread in southwestern corner, in a variety of habitats. WA. Winter, spring.

Grevillea triloba

Spreading shrub to 2m high and across; branchlets with dense woolly white hairs. **Leaves** to 7cm long, divided into 3 spreading lobes, upper surface slightly hairy and prominently veined, lower surface densely hairy, margins recurved, tip pointed. **Flowers** white, in terminal or axillary racemes about 3cm long, perfumed; style white, constricted near tip and base. Irwin district in coastal and near-coastal sand heath. WA. Autumn, winter.

Grevillea uncinulata

Small branched shrub to about 50cm high; branchlets terete, hairy. **Leaves** narrow–lanceolate to linear–terete, to 3cm long and 3mm wide, sessile, upper surface rough, lower surface hairy, margins revolute, tip hooked. **Flowers** cream, densely hairy, in terminal or axillary umbel-like racemes, to 1.5cm long, profuse; style cream, hairy about 1cm long; tip yellow aging to red. Widespread in southwest, in heath and low shrubland. WA. Winter, spring.

Grevillea vestita

Spreading shrub 1–4m high; branchlets densely hairy. **Leaves** wedge-shaped, 1–5cm long, with 3–6 lobes or teeth near tip, grey-green and slightly hairy above, lower surface densely hairy, tips pointed. **Flowers** white, in open clusters about 2cm across, on short axillary branchlets; style white, constricted near tip and base. Widespread in southwest in coastal heath, woodland and limestone hills. WA. Winter, spring.

Grevillea victoriae | Royal Grevillea

Spreading shrub to 2m high and 3m across; branchlets silky-hairy. **Leaves** lanceolate to obovate, 2–14cm long to 5cm wide, grey-green and usually smooth above, lower surface silky, margins flat, wavy or slightly recurved, veins prominent. **Flowers** orange-red or deep pink, rusty-hairy, in terminal pendent racemes to 5cm across; style red, smooth, to 2.5cm long. Subalpine regions, mainly at high altitudes in wet forest and woodland. NSW, Vic. Spring, summer.

Grevillea tetragonoloba

Grevillea trifida

Grevillea triloba

Grevillea uncinulata

Grevillea vestita

Grevillea victoriae

Grevillea wilsonii | Wilson's Grevillea

Dense spreading shrub to 1.5m high; branchlets angular, mostly smooth. **Leaves** bipinnately lobed, to 6cm long and wide, somewhat entangled, segments narrow–linear, margins revolute, tip sharply pointed. **Flowers** bright red, in terminal umbel-like racemes to 7cm across; style red, hairy, to 3.5cm long. Confined to the Darling Range, in jarrah forest and woodland. WA. Winter, spring.

Hakea amplexicaulis |

Straggly shrub to 3m high. **Leaves** ovate–oblong, to 20cm long and 7cm wide, sessile and stem-clasping, heart-shaped at base, grey-green, margins wavy with prickly spines, midvein pale and conspicuous. **Flowers** white to deep pink, in axillary clusters about 6cm across; style creamy-white, curved, about 6mm long. **Fruit** ovoid, to 3cm long, beak pointed. Confined to southwest corner, in jarrah forests. WA. Winter, spring.

Hakea baxteri | Fan-leaf Hakea

Straggly to erect shrub 1.5–5m high. **Leaves** fan-shaped, 4–8cm long to 6cm across, light green, thick and rigid, margins wavy and prickly toothed. **Flowers** pinkish-brown, silky, in small axillary clusters on the old wood, scented; style green, smooth, about 8mm long. **Fruit** globular, to 4cm long, beak short. Widespread in southwest, mostly in sand heath. WA. Winter, spring.

Hakea bucculenta | Red Pokers

Erect open shrub 2–5m high. **Leaves** narrow–linear, 12–18cm long to 2mm wide, flat, leathery, 1 distinct central vein, tip pointed. **Flowers** red, in axillary spike-like racemes to 15cm long; style red, slightly curved, to 2cm long. **Fruit** ovoid, grey, to 2cm long, beak blunt. Irwin district between Mingenew and Shark Bay, in tall shrublands in sandy soil. WA. Winter, spring.

Hakea chordophylla | Bootlace Tree

Small open tree 5–8m high; bark corky. **Leaves** terete, 15–40cm long, dark green, drooping, tip sharply pointed. **Flowers** greenish-yellow, in pendulous cylindrical racemes to 16cm long, on old wood; style greenish-yellow, smooth, to 3cm long. **Fruit** narrow–ovoid, to 3.5cm long, beak slightly curved. Widespread in northern arid regions, in open woodland. Qld, WA, NT. Winter, spring.

Hakea cinerea | Ashy Hakea

Erect stiff shrub 2–3m high; branchlets covered in grey hairs. **Leaves** oblanceolate, 10–15cm long to 2cm wide, grey-green and yellow at base, 3 longitudinal veins prominent, tip sharply pointed. **Flowers** greenish-yellow, in rounded axillary clusters about 5cm across; style yellow, smooth, to 3cm long. **Fruit** narrow, about 2cm long, beak pointed. Common on sand heath, between Esperance and Hopetoun. WA. Winter, spring.

Grevillea wilsonii

Hakea amplexicaulis

Hakea baxteri

Hakea bucculenta

Hakea chordophylla

Hakea cinerea

Hakea clavata | Coastal Hakea

Spreading shrub 1–2m high; branchlets short and reddish-brown. **Leaves** succulent, terete, 3–7cm long to about 6mm wide, dark green, tip sharply pointed. **Flowers** pale pink, in rounded axillary and terminal clusters, about 3cm across; style white, smooth, to 1cm long. **Fruit** ovoid, to 2cm long, tip with 2 small horns. Southern coasts between Esperance and Israelite Bay, on granite hills. WA. Winter, spring.

Hakea coriacea | Pink Spike Hakea

Erect shrub or small tree 4–7m high. **Leaves** linear, 10–20cm long to 1.5cm wide, flat, 8–13 longitudinal veins, tip pointed. **Flowers** pale to deep pink, in spike-like axillary racemes 8–12cm long; style cream or pale pink, smooth, about 2cm long. **Fruit** ovoid, about 2cm long, beak rounded. Wheatbelt, mostly in gravelly soils. WA. Winter, spring.

Hakea corymbosa | Cauliflower Hakea

Rounded dense shrub to 2m high; branchlets short and hairy. **Leaves** narrow–oblanceolate, 3–8cm long to 8mm wide, thick, central vein prominent, margins thickened, tip sharply pointed. **Flowers** greenish-cream, in dense clusters about 2.5cm across, in upper leaf axils, prolific; style cream, smooth, to 1cm long. **Fruit** ovoid, about 2cm long, beak tapering to small point. Widespread in southern coastal regions, in sandy heath often with mallee. WA. Winter, spring.

Hakea dactyloides | Finger Hakea

Shrub 1–3m high. **Leaves** linear–lanceolate to oblanceolate, 5–12cm long to 2cm wide, stiff, flat, 3 or more longitudinal veins prominent, tip rounded with small hard point. **Flowers** creamy-white, in small axillary clusters; style white, smooth, to 5mm long. **Fruit** ovoid, to 3cm long, warty, beak short. Widespread from coast to mountains, in open forest, heath and woodland. Qld, NSW, Vic. Spring, summer.

Hakea drupacea | Sweet-scented Hakea

Formerly *H. suaveolens*. Erect shrub 2–5m high. **Leaves** terete, to 12cm long, divided into numerous segments to 3mm wide, tip sharply pointed. **Flowers** white, in rounded axillary racemes about 2.5cm long, some forms pink in bud, scented; style white, smooth, about 3mm long. **Fruit** ovoid, shiny, to 2.5cm long, beak with 2 small curved horns. Southern coastal areas, on granite hills. WA. Winter, spring.

Hakea florulenta |

Shrub 1–3m high. **Leaves** narrow–elliptic to lanceolate, 5–15cm long to 3.5cm wide, pale green, leathery, tips rounded with small point. **Flowers** white, in axillary clusters of about 20 flowers; style white, smooth, about 7mm long. **Fruit** ovoid, to 2.5cm long, spotted and warty, beak upturned. Coast and nearby ranges in wet forest, open forest and heath. Qld, NSW. Spring.

Hakea clavata

Hakea coriacea

Hakea corymbosa

Hakea dactyloides

Hakea drupacea

Hakea florulenta

Hakea francisiana | Grass-Leaf Hakea

Erect shrub or small tree 3–6m high. **Leaves** linear, 8–25cm long to 6mm wide, flat, silvery-green, with 5–7 longitudinal veins, tip rounded with small point. **Flowers** deep pink or red, in erect, spike-like racemes to 10cm long; style pink, straight, to 2cm long. **Fruit** ovoid, to 2.5cm long, beak blunt. Widespread in semi-arid and arid regions of southern Australia, in a wide range of habitats. SA, WA. Winter, spring.

Hakea gibbosa | Rock Hakea

Erect bushy shrub 1–3m high; branchlets hairy. **Leaves** terete, 2–9cm long to 1mm wide, dull green, hairy (especially when young), stiff, tip sharply pointed. **Flowers** creamy-white, in small axillary clusters about 1cm long; style creamy-white, about 1cm long, curved. **Fruit** rounded, to 3cm long, wrinkled or warty, beak distinct. Central coastal districts, mainly on sandstone in heath. NSW. Spring.

Hakea laurina | Pincushion Hakea

Tall shrub or small tree 3–8m high; branchlets spreading or sometimes pendulous. **Leaves** oblanceolate, 8–15cm long to 2.5cm wide, leathery, longitudinal veins prominent, tip pointed. **Flowers** cream at first turning bright red, in dense rounded racemes about 6cm across, in upper leaf axils; style creamy-white, smooth and straight, to 2cm long. **Fruit** almost rounded, about 2.5cm long, sparsely spotted, beak short. Widespread in southwest, mostly on sandplains. WA. Autumn, winter.

Hakea lissocarpha | Honeybush

Spreading open shrub to 1.5m high and across. **Leaves** linear–terete, to 3.5cm long, divided into 3–7 stiff segments, tips sharply pointed. **Flowers** white to pale pink, in axillary clusters to 2cm long, scented; style white, straight, to 4mm long. **Fruit** narrow–ovoid, about 1.5cm long, beak with 2 small horns. Widespread in southwest in a range of habitats. WA. Winter, spring.

Hakea multilineata | Grass-leaf Hakea

Tall erect shrub or small tree to 5m high. **Leaves** broad–linear, 10–20cm long to 1.5cm wide, mid-green, flat, up to 15 longitudinal veins visible, tip rounded. **Flowers** deep pink to red, in spike-like racemes to 4cm long; style pale pink, straight, about 1.5cm long. **Fruit** almost rounded, to 2cm long, beak curved upward. Southern wheatbelt district, in gravelly heath. WA. Winter, spring.

Hakea nitida | Frog Hakea

Spreading shrub 1–3m high. **Leaves** obovate to narrow–obovate, 3–10cm long to 2cm wide, grey-green, thick, margins entire or with irregular prickly teeth, tip sharply pointed. **Flowers** white, in almost globular, axillary clusters to 3cm across; style white, about 4mm long. **Fruit** ovoid, about 3cm long, roughly spotted, beak with 2 prominent horns. Widespread in southern sand heaths, among mallees or on granite hills. WA. Winter, spring.

Hakea francisiana

Hakea gibbosa

Hakea laurina

Hakea lissocarpha

Hakea multilineata

Hakea nitida

Hakea petiolaris | Sea Urchin Hakea

Erect shrub or small tree 2–6m high. **Leaves** broadly ovate, 6–12cm long to 6cm wide, grey-green, veins prominent, tip finely pointed. **Flowers** cream at first then pink or purple, in rounded axillary racemes about 6cm across, often on older wood; style cream, straight, to 2cm long. **Fruit** narrow ovoid, to 3cm long, beak curved and pointed; often in clusters. Widespread in southwest, always on granite hills. WA. Autumn, winter.

Hakea plurinervia |

Erect open shrub 1–3m high. **Leaves** narrow–obovate, 8–18cm long to 3cm wide, often sickle-shaped, leathery, 5–9 longitudinal veins conspicuous, tip with small point. **Flowers** white, in globular, axillary racemes along the stems; scented; style white, smooth, about 4mm long. **Fruit** ovoid, about 3.5cm long, distinctly curved toward beak. Widespread in coastal districts and nearby ranges, mostly in sandy soils in open forest. Qld. Spring.

Hakea prostrata | Harsh Hakea

Low spreading or erect shrub 1–5m high; branchlets reddish-brown. **Leaves** obovate, 3–7cm long to 4cm wide, stem-clasping, margins wavy with scattered prickly teeth, tip sharply pointed. **Flowers** creamy-white, in axillary clusters about 2.5cm across, scented; style greenish-white, smooth, about 8mm long, curved. **Fruit** ovoid, about 3.5cm long, dotted with projections, beak elongated, upturned. Widespread in southwest, on sandy soils. WA. Spring.

Hakea purpurea |

Erect shrub 2–3m high. **Leaves** terete, 3–10cm long, entire or divided into 2–4 segments, each with a sharp pointed tip. **Flowers** reddish-purple, in axillary clusters to 3cm long, profuse; style reddish, smooth, to 3cm long. **Fruit** ovoid, to 4cm long, slightly wrinkled, beak short. Western side of Dividing Range in open forest. Qld. Winter, spring.

Hakea rostrata | Beaked Hakea

Dome-shaped shrub to 2m high; branchlets hairy. **Leaves** terete or linear, 2–15cm long to 1.5mm wide, sharply pointed. **Flowers** white, in small axillary clusters of 1–10 flowers; style white, smooth, about 1cm long, slightly curved. **Fruit** ovoid, to 4.5cm long and 3cm wide, beak strongly curved back into the fruit. Southern Australia in heath, open forest and mallee country. Vic, Tas, SA. Winter, spring.

Hakea scoparia |

Erect shrub 2–3m high. **Leaves** linear to terete, to 20cm long and 2mm wide, grey-green, stiff, with 5 longitudinal ridges, tip sharply pointed. **Flowers** cream, pink or purplish, in rounded axillary racemes to 4cm across; style cream, straight, to 1.5cm long. **Fruit** ovoid, to 2.5cm long, warty, beak long and tapered. Widespread in drier inland districts of southwest, mostly in heath or open woodland. WA. Winter, spring.

Hakea petiolaris

Hakea plurinervia

Hakea prostrata

Hakea purpurea

Hakea rostrata

Hakea scoparia

Hakea sericea | Silky Hakea

Spreading shrub 1–3m high; branchlets with silky white hairs. **Leaves** terete, 2–7cm long to 1mm wide, stiff, dark green, tip with sharp black point. **Flowers** white (rarely pink), in axillary clusters about 2cm long; style white, to 1cm long. **Fruit** slightly rounded, to 3cm long, wrinkled, beak with 2 upturned points. Widespread in the east, from coast to nearby ranges, mostly in heath and dry forest. NSW, Vic, Tas, SA. Winter, spring.

Hakea suberea | Long-leaf Corkwood

Tall shrub or small tree 3–8m high; bark dark brown, corky. **Leaves** terete, 12–40cm long to 3mm wide, mostly entire, rarely divided with 2–5 segments, grey-green, hairy, usually pointing upward, tip with short point. **Flowers** creamy-green, in pendulous axillary racemes 4–12cm long, scented; style cream, straight, to 3cm long. **Fruit** rounded, to 3.5cm long, beak curved. Widespread on inland plains, ridges or escarpments. SA, WA, NT. Winter, spring.

Hakea teretifolia | Dagger Hakea

Dense or spreading prickly shrub 1–3m high. **Leaves** terete, 2–7cm long to 2mm wide, stiff and spreading, tip sharply pointed. **Flowers** white, in axillary racemes to 1.5cm long; style white, to 1cm long, curved. **Fruit** narrow, about 3cm long, beak elongated and pointed. Widespread from coast to ranges, often in damp places in heath or dry forest. NSW, Vic, Tas. Spring, summer.

Hakea trifurcata | Two-leaf Hakea

Open erect shrub 2–3m high. **Leaves** variable, terete or flat, to 7cm long, dark green, entire or divided into 2–3 pointed segments, some leaves may be oblong or obovate on the same plant. **Flowers** creamy-white, silky, in axillary racemes to 2.5cm across; style red, smooth, to 8mm long. **Fruit** flattish, to 1.5cm long, beak pointed. Widespread in southwest, in heath and open woodland. WA. Winter, spring.

Hakea ulicina | Gorse Hakea

Prostrate or erect shrub to 3m high; branchlets hairy. **Leaves** variable, linear, 2–10cm long to 5mm wide, flat and stiff, twisted near base, 1–3 veins prominent, tip sharply pointed. **Flowers** creamy-white, in axillary racemes clustered along the stems; style white, to 5mm long. **Fruit** oblong, to 2.5cm long, beak short. Coastal heath and dry forests farther inland. NSW, Vic, Tas. Winter, spring.

Hakea varia | Variable-leaved Hakea

Erect or spreading shrub 1–3m high. **Leaves** variable, flat or terete, 2–5cm long, simple with tip toothed, or divided into prickly lobes. **Flowers** creamy-white, in axillary clusters about 3cm across, strongly scented; style white, to 4mm long. **Fruit** ovoid, about 2cm long, beak with 2 distinct horns. Widespread in southwest. WA. Winter, spring.

Hakea sericea

Hakea suberea

Hakea teretifolia

Hakea trifurcata

Hakea ulicina

Hakea varia

Hakea victoria | Royal Hakea

Erect shrub to 3m high; branchlets short and hairy. Leaves rounded, to about 15cm across, leathery, margins wavy and prickly, veins conspicuous; variegated from cream, yellow and green, upper leaves aging to orange and bright red. **Flowers** creamy-white, in axillary clusters about 5cm across; style cream, about 2.5cm long. **Fruit** almost rounded, rough, about 2.5cm long. Confined to Fitzgerald River National Park and Stirling Range. WA. Winter, spring.

Isopogon anemonifolius | Broad-leaf Drumsticks

Erect shrub to 2m high. **Leaves** flat, 5–10cm long, usually divided into 3 segments, again divided and lobed near tip, pointed but not prickly. **Flowers** yellow, in terminal sessile rounded heads about 4cm across. **Cone** rounded, to 2cm across. Widespread and common from coast to ranges, in heath and dry forest. NSW. Spring, summer.

Isopogon anethifolius | Narrow-leaf Drumsticks

Erect bushy shrub to 3m high. **Leaves** terete, 4–15cm long, divided into slender segments with point upward, tip pointed. **Flowers** yellow, in terminal sessile rounded heads about 4cm across. **Cone** rounded, to 2.5cm across. Common on central and southern coast and tablelands, in heath or open forest, often on sandstone. NSW. Winter, spring.

Isopogon buxifolius |

Erect shrub 1–2m high. **Leaves** variable, linear, obovate or spoon-shaped, to 3.5cm long and 3–15mm wide, leathery, tip rounded with sharp point. **Flowers** pink, mauve or creamy-white, silky-hairy, in clusters to 3cm across, either terminal or in upper leaf axils. **Cone** about 1cm diameter. Widespread in southwest, in heath and shrubland, often in moist places. WA. Autumn, spring.

Isopogon ceratophyllus | Horny Cone Bush

Spreading prickly shrub to 1.2m high. **Leaves** flat, to 4–8cm long, divided 3 times into linear to triangular sharply pointed segments. **Flowers** yellow, sessile, in terminal or axillary heads, about 3cm across, surrounded and partially hidden by leaves. **Cone** about 2cm diameter. Confined to southeast, mostly in heath or woodland. Vic, Tas, SA. Winter, spring, summer.

Isopogon cuneatus |

Erect bushy shrub to 2.5m high. **Leaves** obovate, to 10cm long and 2.5cm wide, thick, tip rounded ending in short hard point. **Flowers** pale pink to purplish-pink, in terminal heads to 5.5cm across. **Cone** about 3.5cm across. South coast around Albany and the Stirling Range, common in heath. WA. Winter, spring.

Hakea victoria

Isopogon anemonifolius

Isopogon anethifolius

Isopogon buxifolius

Isopogon ceratophyllus

Isopogon cuneatus

Isopogon dawsonii | Nepean Cone Bush

Erect shrub or small tree 1–4m high. **Leaves** 8–12cm long, usually divided into flattened linear segments about 3mm wide. **Flowers** creamy-yellow, silky-hairy, in terminal sessile heads about 4.5cm across. **Cone** rounded, to 2cm diameter. Central coast and nearby tablelands, also central western slopes, in dry forest and heath on sandstone. NSW. Winter, spring.

Isopogon divergens | Spreading Cone Bush

Erect or spreading shrub to 1.5m high. **Leaves** terete, to 10cm long, deeply lobed into needle-like segments. **Flowers** pale pink to mauve, silky, in terminal sessile heads to 5cm across. **Cone** barrel-shaped, to 2cm diameter. Northern part of southwest, usually in heath and open woodland. WA. Winter, spring.

Isopogon dubius | Pincushion Cone Flower

Small erect shrub to 1.5m high. **Leaves** to 7cm long, divided into 3 segments, may again be divided into 3 lobes, tips prickly pointed. **Flowers** pink to deep pink, silky, in terminal or axillary heads to 5cm across. **Cone** rounded, about 3cm diameter. Darling Ranges, in heath, open woodland and jarrah forest. WA. Winter, spring.

Isopogon formosus | Rose Cone Flower

Erect shrub to 2m high. **Leaves** to 6cm long, much divided into narrow, terete segments, tips prickly pointed. **Flowers** mauve, pink or red, in terminal or axillary heads about 6cm across. **Cone** rounded, about 2cm diameter. Widespread in southwest, most common in woodland. WA. Winter, spring.

Isopogon petiolaris |

Spreading shrub to 1m high. **Leaves** to 15cm long, divided in upper half into many flat, linear segments, longitudinal veins prominent, tips sharply pointed. **Flowers** yellow, in rounded terminal heads about 2cm across. **Cone** rounded, to 2cm diameter. Widespread in northwestern slopes and plains, tablelands and coast, in heath and dry forest. NSW. Spring, summer.

Isopogon prostratus |

Prostrate shrub to 30cm high; branchlets pubescent. **Leaves** to 10cm long, divided in upper half into flat, linear segments, usually upright, tips softly pointed. **Flowers** yellow, in rounded terminal heads about 3.5cm across. **Cone** rounded, to 2cm diameter. Coast and nearby ranges near Sydney, south to Gippsland, in heath and dry forest. NSW, Vic. Spring, summer.

Isopogon dawsonii

Isopogon divergens

Isopogon dubius

Isopogon formosus

Isopogon petiolaris

Isopogon prostratus

Isopogon teretifolius | Nodding Cone Flower

Erect shrub to 2m high. **Leaves** terete, 4–8cm long, simple or much divided in upper half into widely spreading, needle-like segments. **Flowers** yellow or various shades of pink, hairy, in rounded terminal heads to 4cm across, becoming pendent. **Cone** rounded, about 2.5cm diameter. Widespread throughout the southwest, often in sandplains. WA. Spring.

Lambertia formosa | Mountain Devil

Erect shrub to 2m high; branchlets hairy. **Leaves** linear to narrow–oblanceolate, 3–7cm long to 5mm wide, usually in whorls of 3, dark green and shiny above, lower surface paler and hairy, margins entire, tip sharply pointed. **Flowers** tubular, red, in terminal clusters of 7, surrounded by reddish-green bracts about 5cm long. **Fruit** to 2.5cm long, shortly beaked with 2 prominent horns. Widespread on the coast and nearby ranges, in heath and open forest. NSW. Spring, summer.

Lambertia inermis | Chittick

Tall shrub or small tree 3–7m high. **Leaves** obovate to spoon-shaped, to 2.5cm long and 7mm wide, dark green above, paler and hairy below. **Flowers** orange or yellow, in terminal clusters of 5–7, surrounded by thin creamy-orange bracts to 2cm long. **Fruit** smooth, about 1cm long. Common in southern coastal districts, often on deep sands in heath. WA. Winter, spring.

Lambertia multiflora | Many-flowered Honeysuckle

Erect bushy shrub to 2m high. **Leaves** linear, oblong to narrow–obovate, to 4cm long and 5mm wide, dark green, network of veins visible, tip sharply pointed. **Flowers** yellow or reddish-orange, usually 7 per terminal cluster, surrounded by short brownish bracts. **Fruit** smooth, to 2cm long, beaked. Widespread in Irwin and Darling districts, in heath and woodland. WA. Winter, spring.

Lomatia myricoides | River Lomatia

Bushy shrub or small tree to 5m high. **Leaves** linear to lanceolate, 5–20cm long to 2cm wide, dark green and smooth above, paler below, margins entire or irregularly toothed, tip pointed. **Flowers** greenish-yellow, in axillary or terminal clusters to 10cm long, usually shorter than the leaves. **Fruit** a cylindrical follicle to 3cm long. Widespread on coast and nearby ranges, often along watercourses and in gullies. NSW, Vic. Summer.

Lomatia tinctoria | Guitar Plant

Sparsely branched erect shrub to 1.5m high. **Leaves** to 8cm long, pinnately divided into 3–7 pairs, which may be entire or again divided. **Flowers** white or cream, in terminal racemes to 20cm long; style green, curved. **Fruit** dark brown, about 2cm long, opens into a guitar shape. Endemic and widespread in Tasmania, on hillsides and open forest. Tas. Summer.

Isopogon teretifolius

Lambertia formosa

Lambertia inermis

Lambertia multiflora

Lomatia myricoides

Lomatia tinctoria

Persoonia falcata | Wild Pear

Slender shrub or small tree 3–5m high. **Leaves** linear to oblanceolate, 10–20cm long to 3cm wide, sickle-shaped, leathery, mid-vein prominent, tip with small point. **Flowers** yellow, tubular, to 1.5cm long, singly in upper leaf axils or in dense terminal racemes to 10cm long. **Fruit** a yellowish-green ovoid drupe, to 2cm long. Widespread in tropical regions, in savanna woodland and open forest. Qld, WA, NT. Winter, spring.

Persoonia levis | Broad-leaved Geebung

Erect or spreading shrub or small tree to 5m high; bark flaky revealing a deep red beneath. **Leaves** oblanceolate to obovate, 6–18cm long to 8cm wide, often sickle-shaped, thick, smooth, tip rounded with small point. **Flowers** yellow, singly on short stalks to 8mm long. **Fruit** a green, rounded drupe, to 1cm long. Widespread from coast to nearby ranges, in heath and dry open forest. NSW, Vic. Spring.

Persoonia linearis | Narrow-leaved Geebung

Erect open shrub 2–5m high; branchlets downy-hairy. **Leaves** linear, 2–9cm long to 6mm wide, flat, becoming smooth, tip softly pointed. **Flowers** yellow, singly on short stalks to 8mm long, near the ends of branchlets. **Fruit** a green rounded drupe about 1.5cm diameter. Widely distributed and common from coast to nearby ranges, in woodland and dry open forest. NSW, Vic. Spring, summer.

Persoonia media |

Tall shrub or small tree 3–8m high. **Leaves** linear to obovate, 3–14cm long to 3.5cm wide, flat, becoming smooth, tip softly pointed. **Flowers** yellow, singly on short stalks to 6mm long, in leaf axils. **Fruit** a green and purple drupe, to 1.5cm long. Mainly on the ranges, in rainforest or dry open forest. Qld, NSW. Spring, summer.

Persoonia oxycoccoides |

Prostrate to low spreading shrub to 1m high. **Leaves** broadly elliptical to ovate, to 1.2cm long and 6mm wide, margins recurved, tip softly pointed. **Flowers** yellow, singly on short stalks to 1.2cm long, sometimes nodding. **Fruit** a green drupe, about 1cm long. Central tablelands, mainly in dry open forest and heath. NSW. Summer.

Persoonia pinifolia | Pine-leaved Geebung

Tall erect shrub 3–5m high; branchlets often drooping. **Leaves** terete, 3–7cm long, less than 1mm wide, deep green, becoming smooth, tip softly pointed. **Flowers** golden-yellow, in leaf axils toward ends of branches. **Fruit** a drupe, initially green, aging to red, about 1.5cm long. Confined to Sydney district, in heath and dry open forest. NSW. Summer, autumn, winter.

Persoonia falcata

Persoonia levis

Persoonia linearis

Persoonia media

Persoonia oxycoccoides

Persoonia pinifolia

Petrophile diversifolia

Spreading open shrub to 3m high. **Leaves** to 11cm long, pinnate often again divided into flat prickly lobes; juvenile leaves fern-like and often reddish. **Flowers** creamy-white (rarely pink), hairy, in axillary heads to 2.5cm long, on whitish, hairy stalks to 2cm long. **Cone** ovoid, to 3cm long. Southwest corner, in dry open forest and shrubland, often in poorly drained places. WA. Spring.

Petrophile linearis | Pixie Mops

Small erect shrub to 80cm high. **Leaves** narrow–obovate to 12cm long and 1cm wide, thick, curved, tip rounded with short recurved point. **Flowers** greyish-pink to mauve, hairy, in terminal or axillary heads about 5cm across, sessile. **Cone** ovoid, to 2.5cm long. Common on the coastal plain and Darling Range, in heath and open woodland. WA. Winter, spring.

Petrophile media

Low spreading shrub to 80cm high. **Leaves** terete, 7–30cm long to 2mm wide, smooth, often curved upward, tip sharply pointed. **Flowers** cream or yellow, hairy, in terminal heads to 2.5cm across, sessile, profuse. **Cone** ovoid, to 2.5cm long, sessile. Southwest corner, in heath, shrubland and open woodland. WA. Winter, spring, summer.

Petrophile pulchella

Erect shrub to 3m high. **Leaves** terete, 4–10cm long, smooth, highly divided into erect segments in upper half, tips softly pointed. **Flowers** cream, silky, in spike-like heads to 5cm long, terminal or axillary, solitary or in small clusters. **Cone** cylindrical, about 5cm long and 2cm wide. Widespread in coastal areas, in heath and dry open forest. NSW. Winter, spring, summer.

Petrophile serruriae

Erect or spreading shrub to 1.5m high. **Leaves** terete, to 3.5cm long, highly divided into short segments, tips sharply pointed. **Flowers** yellow or greyish-pink, silky, terminally in clusters, about 1cm across, and in upper leaf axils. **Cone** globular to 1.2cm across. Widespread along southwest coast and slightly inland, in heath, shrubland and open woodland. WA. Winter, spring.

Petrophile sessilis | Prickly Conesticks

Erect shrub to 3m high. **Leaves** terete, spreading at right angles to the stem, 3–10cm long, highly divided into stiff, widely spaced segments, tips prickly. **Flowers** yellow, hairy, in ovoid heads to 4cm across, terminal or axillary, sessile. **Cone** oblong–ovoid, about 5cm long, sessile. Coast and tablelands south of Sydney, in heath, open woodland and dry open forest on sandstone. NSW. Spring, summer.

Petrophile diversifolia

Petrophile linearis

Petrophile media

Petrophile pulchella

Petrophile serruriae

Petrophile sessilis

Petrophile squamata

Erect shrub to 1.5m high. **Leaves** to 7cm long, deeply divided in the upper half into broadly linear lobes, tips prickly pointed. **Flowers** cream or yellow, silky-hairy, in small clusters to 2cm long, sessile, in the upper leaf axils. **Cone** globular, about 1cm diameter. Widespread in southwest, in heath and woodland, sometimes in damp places. WA. Winter, spring.

Stenocarpus sinuatus | Firewheel Tree

Tree to 30m high; bark slightly rough, greyish-brown. **Leaves** dark green and glossy and very variable, either entire and oblong–lanceolate to 20cm long, or deeply lobed to 45cm long. **Flowers** orange to bright red, tubular, arranged into a wheel-like umbel to 10cm across, terminally on stalks to 10cm long. **Fruit** a cylindrical follicle, 5–10cm long. Scattered, in a variety of coastal rainforests. Qld, NSW. Spring, summer.

Telopea mongaensis | Monga Waratah

Branched shrub to 5m high. **Leaves** linear to oblanceolate, 5–15cm long to 2cm wide, margins entire or slightly lobed, tip rounded. **Flowers** red, up to 65 per flattened head, about 10cm across, surrounded by a ring of pink and/or green bracts. **Fruit** an oblong follicle to 6.5cm long. Confined to the Braidwood district, in sheltered forests and rainforest margins. NSW. Spring.

Telopea speciosissima | Waratah

Erect slender shrub to 3m high. **Leaves** obovate to spoon-shaped, 8–25cm long to 6cm wide, leathery, strongly veined, margins toothed. **Flowers** red, up to 250 per dome-shaped head, to 15cm diameter, surrounded by a conspicuous ring of bright red bracts to 9cm long. **Fruit** a boat-shaped follicle to 15cm long. Common in Sydney district and Blue Mountains, also south coast, mostly in dry open forest. NSW. Spring.

Petrophile squamata

Stenocarpus sinuatus

Telopea mongaensis

Telopea speciosissima

RANUNCULACEAE | Buttercup family

Large family of about 70 genera and 3000 species with a world-wide distribution. Australia has about 5 genera and 50 species, the best known being species of *Ranunculus* and *Clematis*. They are mostly herbs or woody climbers. Leaves alternate or opposite, often lobed or dissected in a basal rosette, or compound with bases forming a sheath; stipules usually absent. Flowers regular, with the parts typically arranged in spirals along a rather elongated or globular receptacle. Sepals 4 or 5, often petal-like (petals then absent). Petals (if present) 5 (sometimes more), free, usually with a nectary-bearing stalk. Stamens numerous, free. Ovary comprising mostly numerous free carpels, superior. Fruit a cluster of achenes, sometimes with plumed styles.

Clematis aristata | Austral Clematis

Woody climber to 10m high. **Leaves** mostly trifoliate with glossy, dark green, ovate leaflets, 2–10cm long and 1–4cm wide, margins entire or irregularly toothed. **Flowers** white with 4 petal-like sepals, to 4cm across, on long slender stalks forming short, axillary panicles; anther appendages long. **Fruit** a rounded head of achenes, each with a silky tail to 4cm long. Widespread from the coast to the mountains, in sheltered situations in forests. Qld, NSW, Vic, Tas, SA. Spring.

Clematis gentianoides | Bushy Clematis

Small branching shrub to 40cm high. **Leaves** simple, lanceolate, to 8cm long, leathery, margins entire or toothed. **Flowers** white with 4–8 petal-like sepals, to 5cm across, terminal on slender stalks. **Fruit** a rounded head of achenes each with a plumed tail to 2.5cm long. Endemic in Tasmania, widespread on rocky hillsides in open forest. Tas. Spring.

Clematis glycinoides | Forest Clematis

Woody climber to 3m high. **Leaves** trifoliate with glossy dark green ovate leaflets, to 12cm long and 8cm wide, thin-textured, margins mostly entire, occasionally with a few teeth. **Flowers** white with 4 petal-like sepals, to 3cm across, forming short axillary panicles; anther appendages absent or short. **Fruit** a rounded head of achenes, each with a plumed tail to 6cm long. Widespread from coast to mountains, common in moist forests. Qld, NSW, Vic. Spring.

Clematis microphylla | Small-leaved Clematis

Woody climber to 4m high. **Leaves** divided into narrow–oblong leaflets to 5cm long and 1.5cm wide, margins mostly entire. **Flowers** creamy-white with 4 petal-like sepals, 2–4cm across, in short axillary panicles. **Fruit** a rounded head of achenes, each with a plumed tail to 6cm long. Widespread, mostly on ranges and farther inland. Qld, NSW, Vic, Tas, SA, WA. Spring.

Clematis aristata

Clematis gentianoides

Clematis glycinoides

Clematis microphylla

Clematis pubescens | Western Clematis

Woody climber to 6m high; stems hairy. **Leaves** trifoliate with dull green ovate leaflets 3–6cm long to 1.5cm wide, hairy, margins toothed. **Flowers** white with 4 petal-like sepals, to 4cm across, forming short but showy axillary panicles. **Fruit** a rounded head of achenes, each with a plumed tail to 4cm long. Widespread and common in jarrah and karri forests in the southwest. WA. Winter, spring.

Ranunculus anemoneus | Anemone Buttercup

Perennial herb to 30cm high. Basal **leaves** palmately divided into overlapping, coarsely toothed lobes, 4–8cm across on stems 5–15cm long; stem-clasping upper leaves becoming smaller with narrower segments. **Flowers** white, to 6cm diameter, with 15–30 overlapping petals, solitary on stout stems. **Fruit** an ovoid head of numerous achenes. Confined to alpine herbfields and subalpine woodland, often near snow patches. NSW. Summer.

Ranunculus graniticola | Granite Buttercup

Perennial tufted herb to 30cm high. **Leaves** mostly basal, ovate to elliptic, 1–4cm long, simple and toothed, or deeply dissected into 2 or 3 spreading lobes, on hairy stems to 20cm long. **Flowers** golden-yellow, 1–3.5cm across, petals 5–8, on hairy stems. **Fruit** a globular cluster of numerous achenes. Alpine and subalpine areas and adjacent ranges, in grassland and woodland. NSW, Vic. Summer.

Ranunculus gunnianus | Gunn's Alpine Buttercup

Perennial herb to 25cm high. **Leaves** mostly basal, bright green, divided 2 or 3 times into numerous linear, semi-terete segments, on grooved stems to 15cm long. **Flowers** shiny golden-yellow, about 4.5cm across, on stems to 10cm long. **Fruit** in dense clusters of up to 80 achenes. Common in subalpine and alpine herbfield and grassland, usually in damp situations. NSW, Vic, Tas. Summer.

Ranunculus inundatus | River Buttercup

Perennial clumping herb 7–30cm high. **Leaves** to 3.5cm across, divided into numerous narrow segments less than 2mm wide, on stems to 20cm long. **Flowers** golden-yellow, to 1.5cm across, petals 5–9, on smooth stems to 30cm long. **Fruit** a globular cluster of 11–40 achenes. Widespread from coast to mountains, in swampy soils often with roots submerged in water. Qld, NSW, Vic, SA. Spring, summer.

Ranunculus lappaceus | Common Buttercup

Perennial herb to 50cm high. **Leaves** ovate, to 8cm across, divided into numerous lobes with toothed segments, on stems to 30cm long. **Flowers** golden-yellow, to 3cm across, petals 5, on branched stems to 50cm high. **Fruit** a globular cluster of 20–50 achenes, each with a recoiled beak. Widespread from coast to ranges, in grassland and forest. Qld, NSW, Vic, Tas, SA. Spring, summer.

Clematis pubescens

Ranunculus anemoneus

Ranunculus graniticola

Ranunculus gunnianus

Ranunculus inundatus

Ranunculus lappaceus

RHAMNACEAE | Buckthorn family

Cosmopolitan family of 58 genera and 900 species, mainly in tropical and subtropical regions. About 18 genera and 150 species are widely distributed throughout Australia, the largest and best known being *Pomaderris* (53 species). They are mainly shrubs and trees. Leaves simple, usually alternate, with stipules. Flowers small, regular, bisexual. Sepals 5. Petals 5, free, often small and reduced or absent. Stamens 5, opposite the petals. Ovary superior, sometimes sunken into the disc. Fruit a drupe.

Pomaderris elliptica

Spreading shrub 1–4m high; stems with short, whitish hairs. **Leaves** elliptic to ovate, 3–12cm long to 4.5cm wide, glabrous above, lower surface with fine whitish hairs, margins entire or with shallow rounded teeth, veins prominent, tip rounded to pointed. **Flowers** pale yellow, in conspicuous terminal panicles about 12cm across; petals present. Widespread from coast to tablelands, often in open forest. NSW, Vic, Tas. Spring.

Pomaderris eriocephala

Spreading shrub to 3m high; stems with brownish long and short hairs. **Leaves** ovate to almost round, about 3cm long and 2cm across, dark green with depressed veins, lower surface with white and brownish hairs, margins usually entire or faintly toothed. **Flowers** pale yellow, hairy, in compact globular clusters about 1.5cm across; petals absent. Mainly on the ranges, in open forest and woodland. NSW, Vic. Spring.

Pomaderris intermedia

Shrub to 3m high; stems with close white, woolly hairs. **Leaves** elliptic to ovate, 4–12cm long, 1–5cm wide, dark green and glabrous above, lower surface with close whitish hairs and some long simple hairs, especially along veins, margins flat, veins distinct. **Flowers** bright yellow, in terminal panicles, about 15cm across; petals present. Widespread on coast and ranges, in heath, woodland and open forest. NSW, Vic, Tas. Spring.

Pomaderris lanigera

Shrub or small open tree 1–5m high; stems with rusty hairs. **Leaves** ovate to elliptic, 3–10cm long, to 3cm wide, dull green with sparse hairs, lower surface with velvety rusty hairs, margins flat, veins prominent. **Flowers** golden-yellow, in showy, terminal panicles to 12cm across; petals present. Widespread on coast and ranges, in heath, woodland and open forest. Qld, NSW, Vic. Winter, spring.

Pomaderris elliptica

Pomaderris eriocephala

Pomaderris intermedia

Pomaderris lanigera

Pomaderris phylicifolia | Narrow-leaved Pomaderris

Erect shrub to 2m high; stems densely hairy. **Leaves** linear to narrow–oblanceolate, to 2cm long and 3mm wide, dark green and bristly above, lower surface with velvety grey hairs, margins recurved, tip rounded. **Flowers** pale yellow, hairy, in small axillary clusters; petals absent. Coast and tablelands, in open forest and woodland. NSW, Vic, Tas. Spring.

Pomaderris velutina | Velvety Pomaderris

Shrub to 2m high; stems densely hairy with long rusty hairs. **Leaves** elliptic, 1–3cm long to 1.5cm wide, faintly hairy above, lower surface with longer grey hairs, tip rounded or notched. **Flowers** pale yellow, in loose terminal panicles to 8cm long; sepals persistent, petals absent. Mainly at higher altitudes on the ranges, in woodland and open forest. NSW, Vic. Spring.

Spyridium parvifolium | Dusty Miller

Shrub to 3m high. **Leaves** elliptic to circular, to about 1cm long and across, dull green and hairy above, whitish below, strongly veined, margins recurved, tip rounded or notched. **Flowers** whitish, woolly, in small heads forming terminal leafy clusters about 3cm across, surrounded by creamy-white floral leaves. Widespread in eastern Australia, in open forest. NSW, Vic, Tas, SA. Spring.

Spyridium vexilliferum | Winged Spyridium

Slender shrub to 1m high. **Leaves** narrow–linear, to 1.5cm long and 1–2mm wide, scattered, dark green, midrib deeply depressed, margins recurved, tip pointed. **Flowers** whitish, in small heads to 6mm wide, with 1 to 3 white-velvety floral leaves. Widespread in southeastern Australia, in sandy heath, mallee, woodland and open forest. Vic, Tas, SA. Spring, summer.

Pomaderris phylicifolia

Pomaderris velutina

Spyridium parvifolium

Spyridium vexilliferum

RUTACEAE | Citrus family

Large family of woody plants of about 150 genera and 1800 species, widespread in tropical and temperate regions, especially in the Southern Hemisphere. This family includes the important *Citrus* genus and a large number of ornamental plants. About 40 genera and 320 species occur in Australia, the largest and best known being *Boronia* (about 100 species). They are mostly shrubs and trees. Leaves opposite or alternate, simple or compound, usually gland-dotted and aromatic when crushed; without stipules. Flowers regular, bisexual; disc present between stamens and ovary. Sepals 4 or 5, free or united at the base forming a cup. Petals 4 or 5 usually free, but united into a tube in most species of *Correa*. Stamens 4 or 5, or up to 10. Ovary superior with 4 or 5 lobes. Fruit a berry, drupe or capsule.

Asterolasia asteriscophora | Lemon Starbush

Erect slender shrub 1–2m high; branches covered in brown stellate hairs. **Leaves** obovate, to 3cm long and 1cm wide, both surfaces with stellate hairs, dull green above, paler below, tip rounded or notched. **Flowers** yellow, star-shaped, with 5 petals, about 2cm across, hairy on outside; stamens 10. Mainly tablelands, in rocky areas in open forest. NSW, Vic. Spring.

Asterolasia hexapetala

Erect spreading shrub 1–2m high; branches covered in brown stellate hairs. **Leaves** oblong to obovate, 2–6cm long to 1.5cm wide, both surfaces with stellate hairs, dark green above, paler below, tip rounded. **Flowers** cream or pale yellow, star-shaped, with 5 petals, to 2cm across, hairy on outside, mostly terminal; stamens 10. Confined to northwestern slopes and plains, in woodland and open forest. NSW. Spring.

Boronia algida

Small shrub to 1.5m high; branchlets pubescent, often warty. **Leaves** pinnate, usually with 5 spoon-shaped leaflets to 7mm long and 4mm wide, dark green, margins entire and recurved, tip rounded. **Flowers** white, pale pink to bright pink, with 4 spreading petals, singly or a few together, terminal. Mainly at higher altitudes in heath and dry open forest, often in rocky situations. NSW, Vic. Spring, summer.

Boronia amabilis

Small spreading shrub to 1m high; branchlets with mixture of simple and stellate brownish hairs. **Leaves** pinnate, with about 7 narrow–oblong leaflets, each about 1cm long, both surfaces with stellate hairs, margins recurved, tip rounded. **Flowers** bright pink, with 4 spreading petals, in pairs. Confined to the Darling Downs district, among granite outcrops. Qld. Spring.

Asterolasia asteriscophora

Asterolasia hexapetala

Boronia algida

Boronia amabilis

Boronia anemonifolia | Sticky Boronia

Erect strong-smelling shrub to 2m high; branchlets hairy, warty. **Leaves** usually with 3 linear to wedge-shaped leaflets, each about 1cm long with 3 teeth at tip, margins incurved, resinous and aromatic. **Flowers** white to pale pink, with 4 spreading petals, about 1.5cm across, often in pairs in upper leaf axils. Widespread in southeastern Australia, in heath, woodland and dry forest. NSW, Vic, Tas. Spring, summer.

Boronia barkeriana | Barker's Boronia

Small shrub to 1m high. **Leaves** narrow–elliptic to obovate, 1–3cm long to 1cm wide, glabrous, margins minutely toothed, tip pointed. **Flowers** bright pink, with 4 spreading petals, about 2cm across, often in clusters, terminal or in upper leaf axils, on stalks to 2cm long. Scattered along coast and tablelands, in wet sandy places. Qld, NSW. Winter, spring.

Boronia crenulata |

Small erect shrub to 1m high. **Leaves** obovate or wedge-shaped, to 1.5cm long and 7mm wide, margins entire or shallowly toothed, aromatic. **Flowers** bright pink, with 4 spreading petals, to 1.5cm across, terminal or axillary, on very short stalks. Lower slopes of the Stirling Range, in mallee heath. WA. Winter, spring.

Boronia cymosa | Granite Boronia

Small twiggy shrub to 1m high. **Leaves** linear–terete, to 2.5cm long, sessile, entire, usually crowded in clusters. **Flowers** pale pink to dark pink, with 4 spreading petals, to 1cm across, in cymes on long slender stalks. Widespread in southwest corner. WA. Winter, spring.

Boronia denticulata |

Erect shrub to 2.5m high. **Leaves** linear or narrow–lanceolate, to 4cm long and 2mm wide, flat, finely toothed, tip pointed, strongly aromatic. **Flowers** mauve to deep pink, with 4 spreading petals, to 1cm across, terminal, on short stalks. Widespread in southwest corner. WA. Winter, spring.

Boronia floribunda | Pale-pink Boronia

Many-stemmed shrub to 1m high. **Leaves** pinnate, to 5cm long, 5–9 narrow–oblong leaflets to 1.5cm long, dark green, tip pointed, glandular–warty and aromatic. **Flowers** pale pink (sometimes white or deep pink), with 4 spreading petals, to 2cm across, 2–3 together in axillary clusters. Confined to Sydney district and Blue Mountains, in heath and open forest. NSW. Spring.

Boronia anemonifolia

Boronia barkeriana

Boronia crenulata

Boronia cymosa

Boronia denticulata

Boronia floribunda

Boronia glabra

Erect twiggy shrub to 1.5m high; branchlets with stellate hairs. **Leaves** narrow–oblong, to 3cm long and 6mm wide, sessile, margins recurved, tip blunt. **Flowers** pink, with 4 spreading petals, to 2cm across, singly in upper leaf axils, profuse. Widespread from northwestern slopes and plains to central Qld, in open woodland and dry forest. Qld, NSW. Winter, spring.

Boronia heterophylla | Red Boronia

Erect shrub to 2m high. **Leaves** simple or pinnate, to 5cm long, often with 3 narrow leaflets. **Flowers** deep pink to reddish, bell-like with overlapping petals, to 1cm long, singly on pendent axillary stalks, slightly fragrant. Confined to Kalgan and King River districts near Albany. WA. Winter, spring.

Boronia keysii | Key's Boronia

Erect open shrub to 2m high; branchlets with stellate hairs. **Leaves** to 4cm long, very variable from simple or pinnate, with 3–9 lanceolate leaflets on winged stalks. **Flowers** deep pink, with 4 spreading petals, to 2cm across, on short axillary stalks. Confined to Wide Bay district, in dry open forest. Qld. Winter, spring.

Boronia ledifolia | Sydney Boronia

Erect shrub to 1.5m high; branchlets with stellate hairs. **Leaves** simple or pinnate, with 3–11 linear–elliptic leaflets, dark green above, lower surface hairy, margins recurved, strongly aromatic. **Flowers** bright pink, with 4 spreading petals, to 2cm across, usually singly on felted stalks to 6–12mm long. Widespread from coast to mountains, in heath and open forest; most often on coastal sandstone. NSW, Vic. Winter, spring.

Boronia megastigma | Brown Boronia

Erect or spreading shrub to 2m high. **Leaves** pinnate, with 3–5 soft, narrow leaflets to 1.5cm long. **Flowers** deep brown to yellow-green outside, golden-green inside, bell-like with overlapping petals, to 1cm across, singly on short axillary, pendent stalks, highly fragrant. Chiefly around Albany district, in sandy swampy places. WA. Winter, spring.

Boronia microphylla | Small-leaved Boronia

Spreading shrub to 1m high; branchlets glandular. **Leaves** pinnate, with 5–15 oblong to spoon-shaped leaflets, dark green, tip rounded with short point. **Flowers** bright pink, with 4 spreading petals, to 1cm across, in clusters of up to 5 in upper leaf axils. Widespread from coast to tablelands, in heath and dry open forest. Qld, NSW. Spring, summer.

Boronia glabra

Boronia heterophylla

Boronia keysii

Boronia ledifolia

Boronia megastigma

Boronia microphylla

Rutaceae/Citrus family 377

Boronia mollis | Soft Boronia

Erect shrub to 2m high; branchlets with brown stellate hairs. **Leaves** pinnate, to 4cm long, with 3–9 broad–oblong leaflets, terminal leaflet longest and broadest, hairy, margins recurved, tip rounded. **Flowers** bright pink, with 4 spreading petals, to 2cm across, in clusters of 2–6 in leaf axils. Coastal districts in dry open forest, often in gullies. NSW. Winter, spring.

Boronia molloyae | Tall Boronia

Erect or spreading shrub to 4m high; branchlets hairy. **Leaves** pinnate, to 5cm long, with 5–15 narrow, hairy leaflets to 1cm long, strongly aromatic. **Flowers** deep pink, bell-like with overlapping petals, singly on pendent stalks to 5mm long in leaf axils. Widespread in southwest, along stream banks and wet places. WA. Spring, summer.

Boronia muelleri | Forest Boronia

Shrub to 3m high; branchlets often glandular. **Leaves** pinnate, to 5cm long, with 7–17 narrow-elliptic leaflets to 2.5cm long, warty, margins finely toothed and recurved, tips point-ed. **Flowers** pale pink, with 4 spreading petals, to 2cm across, in clusters of up to 7 in leaf axils, profuse. Chiefly coastal, in dry open forest on moist sandy soils. NSW. Vic. Winter, spring.

Boronia pinnata | Pinnate Boronia

Erect shrub to 1.5m high; branchlets glabrous. **Leaves** pinnate, to 5cm long, with 5–11 oblong–linear leaflets to 2.5cm long, tips pointed, strongly aromatic; leaf stalk flattened. **Flowers** bright pink, with 4 spreading petals, to 2cm across, 3–8 per cluster in upper leaf axils. Chiefly coastal, in heath and dry open forest on sandstone. NSW. Winter, spring, summer.

Boronia pulchella | Smooth Boronia

Spreading shrub to 1.5m high; branchlets reddish. **Leaves** pinnate, to 2cm long, with 5–9 linear leaflets to 8mm long, glandular, tips pointed. **Flowers** bright pink, with 4 spreading petals, to 1.5cm across, singly on axillary stalks shorter than leaves. Stirling Range. WA. Spring.

Boronia rosmarinifolia |

Open twiggy shrub to 1.5m high; branchlets with stellate hairs. **Leaves** linear–oblong, to 4cm long and 3mm wide, dark green above, paler and hairy below, margins recurved, tip rounded. **Flowers** bright pink, with 4 spreading petals, to 1cm across, singly on axillary stalk to 7mm long. Chiefly coastal, in dry open forest on sandy soils. Qld, NSW. Winter, spring.

Boronia mollis

Boronia molloyae

Boronia muelleri

Boronia pinnata

Boronia pulchella

Boronia rosmarinifolia

Boronia serrulata | Native Rose

Small shrub to 1.5m high; branchlets glabrous. **Leaves** broad–ovate, to 2cm long and 1cm wide, sessile, thick, often reddish, margins finely toothed, tip pointed. **Flowers** bright pink, bell-like, with overlapping petals, about 12mm long, in terminal clusters, perfumed. Confined to Sydney district, mainly coastal in moist heath. NSW. Winter, spring.

Boronia thujona |

Tall shrub to 4m high; branchlets glabrous. **Leaves** pinnate, with 3–15 narrow–elliptic leaflets to 3cm long, margins entire or minutely toothed, recurved, tip pointed, strongly aromatic. **Flowers** bright pink, with 4 cupped petals, to 2cm across, in axillary clusters of 2–6 flowers. From Sydney district to south coast, in dry open forest, often in damp shady places. NSW. Winter, spring.

Chorilaena quercifolia | Chorilaena

Shrub 1–3m high; branchlets with brown stellate hairs. **Leaves** oak-like, 2–4cm long to 3cm wide, lobed, slightly hairy above, lower surface densely hairy. **Flowers** yellowish-green or red, in heads to 1.5cm long, surrounded by narrow, hairy bracts, on pendulous, hairy stalks. Between Augusta and Albany, common in karri forest and coastal heaths. WA. Spring.

Correa alba | White Correa

Erect or spreading shrub to 1.5m high; branchlets rusty hairy. **Leaves** obovate to round, to 3.5cm long and 3cm across, glabrous or sparsely hairy above, rusty–tomentose below, tip rounded. **Flowers** white, with 4 spreading petals, to 1.5cm across; calyx cup-shaped, 4-lobed. Widespread in southeastern Australia, coastal headlands and sandy situations near the coast. NSW, Vic, Tas. Winter, spring.

Correa baeuerlenii | Chef's Cap Correa

Shrub to 2.5m high; branchlets covered in short brown hairs. **Leaves** ovate, 2–6cm long to 2cm wide, glandular, dark green and glossy above, sparsely hairy below, tip rounded or pointed. **Flowers** greenish-yellow, tubular, to 3cm long, singly, on short pendulous stalks; calyx cylindrical, 4-lobed, with flattened rim at the base. Restricted to southern coastal districts, in dry open forest, often in damp places. NSW. Autumn, winter, spring.

Correa glabra | Rock Correa

Erect shrub to 3m high. **Leaves** oblong to obovate, 1–4cm long to 1.5cm wide, dark green and usually glabrous above, densely hairy below, tip rounded. **Flowers** pale green or yellowish, tubular, to 3cm long, singly on short pendulous stalks; calyx cup-shaped, unlobed. Chiefly on inland ranges, often in woodland on rocky sites. Qld, NSW, Vic, SA. Autumn, winter.

Boronia serrulata

Boronia thujona

Chorilaena quercifolia

Correa alba

Correa baeuerlenii

Correa glabra

Correa lawrenciana var. *lawrenciana* | Mountain Correa

Shrub to 3m high; branchlets densely hairy. **Leaves** elliptic, 2–7cm long 1–3cm wide, leathery, glabrous, tip rounded. **Flowers** yellowish-green, tubular, to 2.5cm long, velvety; calyx cup-shaped, lobed, rusty hairy. Chiefly on ranges, in dry open forest. NSW, Vic, Tas. Autumn, winter.

Correa lawrenciana var. *glandulifera* |

Shrub or small tree to 3–6m high. **Leaves** ovate, 4–8cm long to 3.5cm wide, tip pointed. **Flowers** greenish-yellow, tubular, to 3cm long, velvety; calyx small with prominent glandular dots. Chiefly on ranges, in dry open forest. Qld, NSW. Winter, spring.

Correa pulchella |

Prostrate to upright shrub to 1m high. Leaves ovate, 1–2cm long, shiny. Flowers orange to deep pink (rarely white), tubular to 2.5cm long, usually pendulous, petal tips curled back; calyx cup-shaped, green; stamens short. Kangaroo Island; Yorke Peninsula; Mount Lofty Range. SA. Autumn, winter.

Correa reflexa | Common Correa

Spreading or erect shrub to 1.5m high; branchlets rusty hairy. **Leaves** ovate, 1–5cm long to 3cm wide, heart-shaped at base, dark green and rough above, stellate hairs below. **Flowers** deep red with green tips or green, tubular, to 4cm long, velvety, usually pendulous, petal tips curled back; calyx cup-shaped. Widespread in southeastern Australia, in heath and dry open forest. Qld, NSW, Vic, Tas, SA. Autumn, winter, spring.

Crowea angustifolia var. *dentata* |

Shrub to 3m high; branchlets glabrous. **Leaves** elliptic to obovate, 2–4cm long to 1cm wide, dark green, margins toothed. **Flowers** white, with 5 spreading petals, to 1.5cm across, singly on short axillary stalks, profuse. Between Pemberton and Albany, common in karri forest in moist places. WA. Winter, spring.

Crowea exalata | Small Crowea

Small shrub to 1m high; branchlets slightly angular. **Leaves** narrow–obovate to linear, 1.5–5cm long to 5mm wide, glabrous, tip rounded. **Flowers** pink, with 5 spreading, waxy petals, to 3cm across, singly, axillary or terminal on short stalks. Widespread along coast and farther inland, in dry open forest. NSW, Vic. Summer, autumn, winter.

Correa lawrenciana var. *lawrenciana*

Correa lawrenciana var. *glandulifera*

Correa pulchella

Correa reflexa

Crowea angustifolia var. *dentata*

Crowea exalata

Crowea saligna

Slender small shrub to 1.5m high; branchlets conspicuously angular. **Leaves** narrow–elliptic, about 5cm long and 1.5cm wide, sessile, midvein prominent, tip rounded with small point. **Flowers** pink (rarely white), with 5 spreading waxy petals, to 3.5cm across, singly in leaf axils. Confined to coastal regions around Sydney, in open forest on sandstone. NSW. Autumn, winter.

Diplolaena angustifolia | Yanchep Rose

Erect shrub to 1m high; branchlets densely hairy. **Leaves** linear, 2–5cm long, margins recurved, lower surface with white felty hairs, tip rounded. **Flowers** in dense pendent heads, to 3.5cm across, surrounded by 3 or 4 rows of bracts; stamens red to pale orange, to 3cm long. From Dongara to Perth on sand and limestone. WA. Winter, spring.

Diplolaena grandiflora

Spreading shrub to 3m high; branchlets densely hairy. **Leaves** oblong to obovate, to 5cm long, dark green and hairy above, densely hairy below, tip rounded. **Flowers** in dense pendent heads, about 4cm across, surrounded by rows of hairy bracts, often reddish; stamens pink to red. Irwin district. WA. Winter, spring.

Diplolaena microcephala | Lesser Diplolaena

Shrub to 1.5m high; branchlets densely hairy. **Leaves** elliptic or obovate, 1–4cm long to 1.5cm wide, hairy above, densely hairy below, tip rounded. **Flowers** in dense pendent heads, about 2.5cm across, surrounded by rows of green bracts; stamens pink, orange or green. Widespread in southwest, in various habitats. WA. Winter, spring.

Eriostemon australasius | Pink Wax Flower

Erect shrub 1–2m high; branchlets angular. **Leaves** narrow–oblong to elliptic, 2–8cm long to 1.5cm wide, glandular, tip pointed. **Flowers** pale pink, waxy, with 5 spreading veined petals, to 4cm across, singly in upper leaf axils, profuse. Widespread, mostly along coast in heath and dry open forest. Qld, NSW. Winter, spring.

Eriostemon buxifolius

Small shrub to 1.5m high; branchlets terete with bristly hairs. **Leaves** obovate to rounded, to 1.5cm long and 1.2cm wide, sessile, thick, lower surface glandular, tip rounded with short point. **Flowers** white to pale pink, waxy, with 5 spreading petals, to 3cm across, singly in leaf axils on short stout stalks. From Gosford to near Jervis Bay, mainly in coastal heath on sandstone. NSW. Winter, spring.

Crowea saligna

Diplolaena angustifolia

Diplolaena grandiflora

Diplolaena microcephala

Eriostemon australasius

Eriostemon buxifolius

Eriostemon difformis

Shrub to 2m high; branchlets glandular and finely hairy. **Leaves** variable, linear–oblong, ovate or subterete, to 1cm long and 2mm wide, warty, tip rounded. **Flowers** white, with 5 spreading petals, to 1cm across, 1–4 per sessile cluster. Widespread, mainly in inland districts. Qld, NSW, Vic. Autumn, winter.

Eriostemon myoporoides | Long-leaf Wax Flower

Bushy shrub to 2m high; branchlets terete, glandular. **Leaves** narrow–elliptic to oblong, 2–12cm long to 2cm wide, sessile, dark green, glandular, midvein prominent, tip pointed. **Flowers** white, waxy, with 5 spreading petals, to 2.5cm across, in clusters of 2–8, on common stalk to 2cm long, from leaf axils, profuse; buds deep pink. Widespread from coast, ranges to farther inland, chiefly in mountainous regions. Qld, NSW, Vic. Autumn, winter, spring.

Eriostemon obovalis

Small shrub to 1m high; branchlets terete, slightly hairy. **Leaves** obovate, to 1cm long and 6mm wide, thick, smooth above, slightly warty below, tip notched. **Flowers** white tinged with pink, with 5 spreading petals, to 1.2cm across, singly in leaf axils. Confined to Blue Mountains, in heath and dry open forest on sandstone. NSW. Spring.

Eriostemon scaber

Small shrub to 60cm high; branchlets terete, softly hairy. **Leaves** narrow, almost terete, to 2.5cm long and 1–5mm wide, sessile, concave, lower surface very warty, tip pointed. **Flowers** white to pink, with 5 spreading petals, to 1.5cm across, singly in leaf axils. Chiefly coastal, from Sydney to Nowra, in dry open forest and heath on sandy soils. NSW. Winter, spring.

Eriostemon spicatus | Spiked Eriostemon

Open shrub to 1.5m high; branchlets slender. **Leaves** linear, to 2cm long, sessile, concave, glandular, tip pointed. **Flowers** deep pink, mauve or white, with 5 spreading petals, to 1cm across, in a loose terminal spike to 20cm long. Widespread in southwest, often near the coast. WA. Winter, spring.

Eriostemon trachyphyllus

Shrub to small tree 2–7m high; branchlets terete, warty. **Leaves** oblong, elliptic or obovate, 3–6cm long to 1cm wide, sessile, warty, glabrous, tip rounded with short point. **Flowers** white, with 5 spreading petals, to 1.5cm across, singly or in clusters of 3, on stalks to 1.2cm long, in leaf axils. Scattered and uncommon, mainly in coastal ranges, on rocky hillsides. NSW, Vic. Spring.

Eriostemon difformis

Eriostemon myoporoides

Eriostemon obovalis

Eriostemon scaber

Eriostemon spicatus

Eriostemon trachyphyllus

Eriostemon verrucosus | Fairy Wax Flower

Shrub 1–2m high; branchlets terete, very glandular. **Leaves** obovate, to 2cm long and 1cm wide, sessile, thick, concave, lower surface extremely warty, tip notched. **Flowers** white or pale pink, with 5 spreading petals, to 2cm across, singly in leaf axils; buds rose-pink. Scattered, mostly in inland districts. Vic, Tas, SA. Winter, spring.

Phebalium coxii

Dense shrub 1–3m high; branchlets slender, angular. **Leaves** narrow–elliptic to oblanceolate, 3–7cm long to 1.5cm wide, glossy green above, midrib depressed, margins finely toothed, tip pointed. **Flowers** creamy-white, in terminal heads of 10–30. Southern tablelands, in open forest along creek banks. NSW. Spring, summer.

Phebalium elatius | Tall Phebalium

Shrub 2–5m high. **Leaves** narrow–obovate or oblong, 1–3.5cm long to 5mm wide, smooth and glossy above, midrib prominent below, tip rounded or rarely notched, sometimes aromatic. **Flowers** white, in terminal heads to 2cm across. Mainly on the ranges. Qld, NSW. Spring.

Phebalium nottii | Pink Phebalium

Dense shrub 1–3m high; branchlets with silvery-brown scales. **Leaves** oblong–elliptic, 2–5cm long to 1.5cm wide, midrib depressed above, lower surface with silvery scales, tip rounded, aromatic. **Flowers** pale pink or dark pink, in sessile clusters of 1–6 flowers; buds and outside of petals rusty-scaly. Widespread in dry open forest, often on sandstone. Qld, NSW. Spring.

Phebalium obcordatum | Club-leaved Phebalium

Shrub to 1.5m high; branchlets with rusty scales. **Leaves** obovate to obcordate, small to 4mm long and 2mm wide, warty above, scaly below, tip rounded or notched. **Flowers** white to pale yellow, in small sessile clusters; petals with silvery scales outside. Rare plant in central inland areas, usually in woodland. NSW, Vic. Spring.

Phebalium rotundifolium | Round-leaved Phebalium

Erect bushy shrub to 2m high; branchlets slightly hairy. **Leaves** broadly obovate to rounded, to 1cm long and 6mm wide, deep green and glabrous, tip rounded. **Flowers** white to pale yellow, in terminal rounded clusters to 1.5cm across; petals glandular. Northern Tablelands and Darling Downs district, usually associated with granite outcrops. Qld, NSW. Spring.

Eriostemon verrucosus

Phebalium coxii

Phebalium elatius

Phebalium nottii

Phebalium obcordatum

Phebalium rotundifolium

Phebalium squamulosum | Scaly Phebalium

(*Phebalium squamulosum* subsp. *parvifolium* pictured.) Shrub to small tree 1–7m high; branchlets with rusty scales, becoming smooth. **Leaves** extremely variable, from narrow–oblong, elliptic to obovate, 1.5–5cm long and 2–10mm wide, upper surface mainly smooth, (glandular–warty in subsp. *verrucosum*), lower surface usually with rusty or silvery scales, tip pointed, rounded or notched. **Flowers** pale to bright yellow, in terminal clusters. Widespread, mainly in heath and dry open forest. Qld, NSW, Vic. Spring.

Phebalium stenophyllum | Narrow-leaved Phebalium

Erect or spreading shrub to 1.5m high; branchlets with brownish scales. **Leaves** narrow–oblong, somewhat terete, to 2cm long and 2mm wide, glabrous above, scaly below, margins recurved to revolute, tip rounded. **Flowers** yellow, in sessile terminal heads of 3–10 flowers; petals with rusty scales on outside. Widespread in semi-arid regions, in heath and open woodland. NSW, Vic, SA. Spring.

Phebalium whitei |

Spreading open shrub to 1m high; branchlets with brownish scales. **Leaves** narrow–oblong, 1–6cm long to about 1cm wide, glabrous and midrib depressed above, scaly below, tip rounded. **Flowers** bright yellow, conspicuous, in sessile terminal clusters of 1–6; buds rusty-scaly. Restricted to border ranges, in association with granite outcrops. Qld. Spring.

Zieria arborescens | Stinkwood

Tall shrub or small tree to 10m high; branches with short dense hairs. **Leaves** trifoliate, narrow–elliptic, to 10cm long and 1.5cm wide, dark green and glabrous above, hairy below, margins recurved, tip pointed. **Flowers** white, with 4 spreading, pubescent petals to 6mm long, in branched clusters. Widespread from coast to ranges, in wet open forest and near rainforest. Qld, NSW, Vic, Tas. Spring, summer.

Zieria cytisoides | Downy Zieria

Erect bushy shrub 1–2m high; branchlets covered in soft greyish hairs. **Leaves** trifoliate, each leaflet ovate to broad–elliptic, about 4cm long and 1.5cm wide, grey-green and velvety hairy on both surfaces, tip rounded or slightly pointed. **Flowers** pale pink (rarely white), in dense clusters of 3–30 flowers, on common axillary stalk to 2cm long. Widespread, in heath, woodland and dry open forest, often in rocky places. Qld, NSW, Vic. Winter, spring.

Zieria laevigata |

Erect shrub to 1.5m high; branchlets slightly angular, hairless. **Leaves** trifoliate, each leaflet linear–elliptic to 4cm long and 3mm wide, dark green and glabrous above, paler and velvety below, margins revolute, tip pointed. **Flowers** white or pale pink, with 4 spreading petals to 5mm long, usually 3 per cluster. Widespread, often coastal in heath or dry open forest on sandstone or granite outcrops. Qld, NSW. Winter, spring.

Phebalium squamulosum subsp. *parvifolium*

Phebalium stenophyllum

Phebalium whitei

Zieria arborescens

Zieria cytisoides

Zieria laevigata

Zieria smithii | Sandfly Zieria

Erect shrub to 2m high; branchlets glandular, hairless. **Leaves** trifoliate, each leaflet narrow–elliptic or lanceolate, 2–5cm long and 4–10mm wide, dark green, glabrous and dotted with oil glands on both surfaces, margins recurved, tip pointed; strongly aromatic. **Flowers** white, with 4 spreading pubescent petals to 4mm long, 7–60 per axillary cluster. Widespread from coast to ranges, in wet open forest and rainforest margins. Qld, NSW, Vic. Winter, spring.

Zieria southwellii |

Tall shrub or small tree to 5m high; branchlets becoming smooth. **Leaves** trifoliate, each leaflet elliptic, 4–9cm long to 2.5cm wide, dark green and mostly glabrous on both surfaces, dotted with oil glands below, tip rounded. **Flowers** white, with 4 spreading pubescent petals to 6mm long, in dense axillary clusters. Mainly coastal, in sheltered wet forest and rainforest margins. Qld, NSW. Winter, spring.

SAPINDACEAE | Hop Bush family

Large family of about 150 genera and 2000 species with a world-wide distribution, mainly in tropical and subtropical regions. It includes important edible fruits, such as the lychee and rambutan; some species yield valuable timbers and several contain saponin, used as a foaming agent and as a fish poison. Australia has 30 genera and about 190 species, the largest and best known being *Dodonaea* (about 60 species) found in all States, often in arid and semi-arid regions. They are mostly trees, shrubs and climbers. Leaves alternate, simple or more often compound, without stipules. Flowers regular, small, unisexual or bisexual, usually with a disc outside the stamens. Stamens usually 8, but there may be 5 to many, arising from the disc. Ovary superior. Fruit a drupe or dry capsule, sometimes with wing-like outgrowths. Seeds often with arils.

Atalaya hemiglauca | Whitewood

Small tree 5–10m high; bark pale grey, rough and fissured. **Leaves** pinnate, grey-green, divided into 2–6 narrow–elliptic leaflets, to 15cm long and 1.5cm wide; sometimes simple on juveniles. **Flowers** white, about 1cm across, numerous on large, dense panicles to 20cm long. **Fruit** a 2-lobed, yellowish-green capsule, with distinct wings to 4cm long. Widespread in dry inland and semi-arid regions, in a wide range of habitats. Qld, NSW, SA, WA, NT. Winter, spring.

Dodonaea baueri |

Small rigid shrub to 1m high. **Leaves** obovate, 6–18mm long to 1cm wide, dark green above, paler below, margins wavy and irregularly toothed. **Flowers** small, solitary, drooping on short stalks. **Capsule** globular, 3–5 angled, without distinct wings, dark red to brown when mature. Endemic to Flinders Ranges, southern districts and Kangaroo Island, on rocky hillsides. SA. Summer, autumn.

Zieria smithii

Zieria southwellii

Atalaya hemiglauca

Dodonaea baueri

Dodonaea boroniifolia | Fern Leaf Hop Bush

Erect or spreading shrub to 2m high. **Leaves** pinnate, to 3.5cm long, divided into 8–12 obovate leaflets, each leaflet to 7mm long, dark green and resinous, with 3–6 teeth at tip. **Flowers** small, 2–3 per axillary cluster. **Capsule** to 2cm across with 4 rounded wings, red to purplish-red when mature. Widespread in eastern States in heath, woodland or dry open forest in sandy soils or on sandstone. Qld, NSW, Vic. Winter, spring.

Dodonaea coriacea |

Small spreading shrub to 2m high; branchlets angular, light brown, sticky. **Leaves** wedge-shaped, to 3cm long and 1cm wide, sessile, glandular, toothed toward tip. **Flowers** small, in clusters at branch ends. **Capsule** flattened, to 2cm across, with 3 prominent rounded wings, creamy-yellow when mature. Widespread in northern arid regions. Qld, WA, NT. Autumn, winter.

Dodonaea falcata |

Erect shrub to 2m high. **Leaves** linear, 4–9cm long to 1cm wide, sessile, curved, concave above, tip rounded and often recurved. **Flowers** small, 3–4 per terminal cluster. **Capsule** to 1.5cm across, with 4 rounded wings, reddish-brown when mature. Scattered from coast near Sydney, northwestern slopes to Darling Downs. Qld, NSW. Spring, summer.

Dodonaea lobulata |

Erect shrub 1–3m high. **Leaves** linear–oblanceolate, 2–5cm long to 2.5mm wide, sessile, often sticky, margins with numerous small, rounded lobes, tip rounded. **Flowers** small, 2–3 per axillary cluster. **Capsule** to 2cm across, with 3 (rarely 4) rounded wings, deep pink or reddish-brown when mature. Widespread in semi-arid regions, in open woodland usually in rocky places. NSW, SA, WA. Autumn, winter.

Dodonaea pinnata | Pinnate Hop Bush

Spreading shrub to 1.5m high; branchlets hairy. **Leaves** pinnate, 2–4cm long, 10–16 leaflets, each leaflet narrow–obovate to 1cm long, densely hairy, margins recurved. **Flowers** small, solitary, on hairy stalks to 7mm long. **Capsule** to 2cm across, with 4 rounded wings, reddish-brown when mature. Confined to central coast, usually in dry open forest on sandstone-derived soils. NSW. Spring.

Dodonaea sinuolata |

Spreading shrub to 3m high; branchlets glandular and sticky. **Leaves** pinnate, 2–4cm long, 6–14 leaflets, each leaflet linear, to 1.5cm long, margins irregular and wavy, tip rounded. **Flowers** small, 3–6 per axillary cluster. **Capsule** to 1.5cm across, with 3 (rarely 4) rounded wings, reddish-brown when mature. Slightly inland on northwestern slopes and plains, in dry open forest and woodland, usually in rocky situations. Qld, NSW. Summer, autumn.

Dodonaea boroniifolia

Dodonaea coriacea

Dodonaea falcata

Dodonaea lobulata

Dodonaea pinnata

Dodonaea sinuolata

Dodonaea tenuifolia | Feathery Hop Bush

Spreading shrub 1–3m high. **Leaves** pinnate, to 10cm long, with 9–25 linear leaflets, sticky, each leaflet linear, 1–3cm long and less than 2mm wide, margins entire. **Flowers** small, in dense axillary clusters. **Capsule** to 2cm across, with 4 rounded wings, reddish-purple when mature. Confined to the southeast, on rocky hillsides and ranges. Qld. Autumn.

Dodonaea triquetra | Large-leaf Hop Bush

Erect shrub 1–3m high. **Leaves** elliptic, lanceolate or ovate, 5–12cm long and 1–5cm wide, midrib prominent, margins entire or wavy, tip pointed. **Flowers** small, in axillary clusters. **Capsule** to 1.5cm across, with 3 rounded wings, yellowish-green at first, purplish-brown when mature. Mainly in coastal areas, in open forest on sandy soils. Qld, NSW, Vic. Summer, autumn.

Dodonaea viscosa |

Erect or spreading shrub or small tree 1–6m high. **Leaves** extremely variable, linear, elliptic to obovate, 1–15cm long and 1–4cm wide, shiny, margins entire or toothed or irregularly wavy, tip rounded or pointed. Subsp. *cuneata* (pictured) has wedge-shaped leaves. **Flowers** small, in terminal clusters. **Capsule** to 3cm across, with 3 or 4 rounded wings, dark pink, red or purplish-red when mature. Widespread from the coast to the dry inland, extremely variable in the field and a number of subspecies exist. All States. Winter, spring.

Dodonaea viscosa subsp. *angustissima* |

Erect bushy shrub to 2–4m high. **Leaves** linear to narrow–oblong, 3–10cm long to 6mm wide, sessile, margin slightly toothed or wavy. **Capsule** to 1.5cm across, with 3 (rarely 4) rounded wings, green turning red to purplish when mature. Widespread in arid and semi-arid areas, in open woodland, sandplains and rocky situations. Qld, NSW, Vic, SA, WA, NT. Spring.

Dodonaea tenuifolia

Dodonaea triquetra

Dodonaea viscosa

Dodonaea viscosa subsp. *angustissima*

SCROPHULARIACEAE | Speedwell family

Large cosmopolitan herbaceous family of about 250 genera and up to 5000 species found mainly in temperate regions. Australia has 49 genera and about 200 species. They are mostly herbs or rarely shrubs, sometimes semi-parasitic. Leaves alternate, opposite or whorled, without stipules. Flowers irregular, bisexual. Calyx 3-lobed to 5-lobed, or sepals 4 or 5 and free. Corolla tubular, often 2-lipped or 3-lobed to 5-lobed. Stamens 4, usually with 2 longer than the others. Ovary superior. Fruit a many-seeded capsule.

Derwentia derwentiana | Derwent Speedwell

Formerly *Parahebe derwentiana*. Erect woody perennial to 1.5m high. **Leaves** lanceolate to ovate, to 5–20cm long to 4.5cm wide, opposite, sessile, base sometimes heart-shaped, margins toothed, tip pointed. **Flowers** white or with a purple tinge, with 4 spreading lobes, in dense terminal racemes to 25cm long. Widespread from coast to ranges, in open forest to alpine herbfields. Qld, NSW, Vic, Tas, SA. Summer.

Derwentia perfoliata | Digger's Speedwell

Formerly *Parahebe perfoliata*. Erect woody perennial to 1.2m high. **Leaves** ovate, 3–5cm long to 4cm wide, opposite, sessile and often heart-shaped at the base, margins entire or finely toothed, tip pointed. **Flowers** deep blue, with 4 spreading lobes, in loose racemes to 45cm long from the upper leaf axils. Widespread on slopes and tablelands, in open forest, woodland, heath and alpine grassland. NSW, Vic. Spring, summer.

Euphrasia collina subsp. *diversicolor* |

Semi-parasitic perennial herb to 40cm high; branches glandular or hairy. **Leaves** ovate to broad–oblong, to 1.2cm long and 1cm wide, opposite, margins with 4–8 teeth, tip pointed. **Flowers** white or purple to pink with a white tube, often with a yellow blotch on lower lip, about 2cm long, in densely arranged terminal racemes. Alpine and subalpine areas in heath, grassland and herbfields. NSW. Summer.

Euphrasia collina subsp. *glacialis* |

Semi-parasitic perennial herb to 20cm high; stems hairy. **Leaves** wedge-shaped to obovate, about 1cm long and 6mm wide, margins with 3–5 teeth, tip pointed. **Flowers** usually white, sometimes lilac in bud, with yellow blotch on lower lip, about 1.2cm long, in racemes of up to 12 flowers. Confined to alpine herbfields in the Kosciusko area. NSW. Summer.

Derwentia derwentiana

Derwentia perfoliata

Euphrasia collina subsp. *diversicolor*

Euphrasia collina subsp. *glacialis*

Mimulus prostratus | Small Monkey-flower

Prostrate annual or perennial herb with stems rooting at the nodes and forming dense mats to 2m across. **Leaves** obovate to elliptic, 2–6mm long to 3mm wide, opposite, sessile, margins entire, tip pointed. **Flowers** blue, pink or purple, with 5 spreading lobes, to 1.5cm across, solitary in leaf axils. Widespread in inland districts, usually in moist depressions and margins of swamps. Qld, NSW, Vic, SA. Winter, spring.

Stemodia florulenta | Bluerod

Formerly *Morgania floribunda*. Erect perennial herb to 80cm high. **Leaves** narrow–oblanceolate to narrow–elliptic, 1–5cm long to 5mm wide, sessile, opposite or in whorls, margins entire or slightly toothed. **Flowers** bright blue or purple with darker streaks, the lower lip spreading, with 3 recurved lobes, singly or in small axillary clusters. Widespread in inland regions, often in seasonally flooded situations. All mainland States. Spring, summer.

SOLANACEAE | Potato family

Large cosmopolitan family of about 90 genera and more than 2600 species, widespread in tropical and temperate regions, especially in Central and South America. The family is noted for important food plants, such as potato, tomato, eggplant, chilli and capsicum. Some species have a high alkaloid content and have medicinal or narcotic properties, such as *Duboisia* spp. and tobacco (*Nicotiana* spp.). Australia has 23 genera and about 200 species, the largest and best-known genus being *Solanum* (about 100 species). They are mostly herbs, shrubs or small trees, with or without prickles. Leaves alternate, simple to pinnate, often strongly scented when crushed. Flowers regular or irregular, usually bell-shaped, tubular or funnel-shaped. Petals usually 5 (3–9), united. Stamens usually 5, arising from the corolla tube and alternate with lobes. Ovary superior. Fruit a many-seeded berry or spiny capsule.

Anthocercis viscosa | Sticky Tail Flower

Erect or spreading sticky shrub to 3m high; branchlets glandular hairy. **Leaves** obovate to ovate, 2–6cm long and 1–3cm wide, thick, sometimes shallowly toothed. **Flowers** white to creamy–white, bell-shaped to 5cm long, with 5 spreading lobes and green striations at throat, fragrant. **Capsule** ovoid, to 2cm long, opening in 2 valves. Southern coastline between Albany and Cape Arid, associated with granite outcrops. WA. All year round.

Anthotroche pannosa |

Erect or spreading shrub to 2m high; branchlets densely covered with woolly white hairs. **Leaves** ovate to almost rounded, 1–3cm long to 1.5cm wide, hairy on both sides. **Flowers** deep purple to black, with 5 spreading lobes to 1.5cm across, hairy, 1–3 per axillary cluster. **Capsule** ovoid, to 7mm long, smooth, opening in 4 valves. Widespread in arid and semi–arid regions, in heath, shrubland and woodland, on sandy soils. WA. Winter, spring.

Mimulus prostratus

Stemodia florulenta

Anthocercis viscosa

Anthotroche pannosa

Anthotroche walcottii

Erect or spreading shrub to 2m high; branchlets densely covered in grey or rusty hairs. **Leaves** ovate to almost rounded, to 2cm long and 1.5cm wide, densely hairy on both sides. **Flowers** deep violet and white, with 5 spreading lobes, to 1.5cm across, hairy, 1–3 per axillary cluster. **Capsule** broadly ovoid, to 8mm long, opening in 4 valves. Coastal sandplains between Geraldton and Shark Bay. WA. Winter, spring.

Cyphanthera anthocercidea | Large-leaf Ray Flower

Erect shrub to 2m high; branchlets minutely hairy. **Leaves** lanceolate to narrow–ovate, 1–3.5cm long to 1cm wide, midvein prominent, sparsely hairy. **Flowers** white with purple striations at throat, bell-shaped with 5 spreading lobes, to 1.5cm across, perfumed. **Capsule** globular, to 5mm across. Mainly western districts, in dry open forest and rocky places. Vic. Winter, spring.

Duboisia myoporoides | Corkwood

Tall shrub or small tree to 12m high; bark corky. **Leaves** obovate to elliptic, 4–15cm long, 1–4cm wide, dark green and glabrous, tip rounded. **Flowers** white with purple striations at throat, bell-shaped with 5 spreading petals, about 6mm across, in branched panicles. **Berry** globular, to 6cm long, purple-black. Widespread from coast to ranges, on rainforest margins and wet open forest. Qld, NSW. Winter, spring.

Solanum aviculare | Kangaroo Apple

Erect shrub 2–4m high; prickles absent. **Leaves** to 30cm long, variable from deeply lobed with pointed segments to entire and narrow–lanceolate; entire leaves usually on upper parts. **Flowers** blue-violet, with spreading pointed lobes, to 4cm across. **Berry** ovoid, to 1.5cm across, bright orange to red. Widespread in eastern Australia, in coastal rainforest and farther inland. Qld, NSW, Vic, SA, WA. Spring.

Solanum brownii | Violet Nightshade

Erect shrub to 2m high; stems densely pubescent; prickles present but sparse on stems. **Leaves** lanceolate, 8–12cm long, 1–3cm wide, dark green and sparsely hairy above, dense and woolly below. **Flowers** pale blue or purple, with 5 spreading pointed petals to 4cm across, in clusters of up to 10 flowers. **Berry** globular, to 2cm across, greenish-white. Along the Great Dividing Range, in woodland, dry open forest and disturbed rainforest. Qld, NSW, Vic. Winter, spring.

Solanum cleistogamum

Annual or perennial herb to 60cm high; prickles mostly present on stems, petioles and calyx tube. **Leaves** ovate to lanceolate, 3–10cm long, 1–4cm wide, grey-green and densely hairy. **Flowers** pale lavender with rounded petals, to 1.5cm across, often remaining closed. **Berry** globular, to 1.5cm across, green or purplish. Widespread in arid regions, often in rocky or gravelly areas. Qld, NSW, SA, WA, NT. Summer, autumn.

Anthotroche walcottii

Cyphanthera anthocercidea

Duboisia myoporoides

Solanum aviculare

Solanum brownii

Solanum cleistogamum

Solanum elegans | Spiny Kangaroo Apple

Erect shrub to 1m high; prickles scattered on stems, leaves and flowering stalks. **Leaves** linear to lanceolate, 4–6cm long to 1.5cm wide, entire or weakly lobed, sparsely hairy above, dense greyish hairs below. **Flowers** purple, with 5 shallowly pointed lobes, to 3cm across. **Berry** globular, to 1.5cm across, red. Widespread from coast to ranges, in dry open forest on rocky soil. Qld, NSW, Vic. Spring, summer.

Solanum ferocissimum |

Erect open shrub to 1m high; prickles on stems, leaves and flowering stalks. **Leaves** linear, 3–6cm long, 2–7mm wide, entire or with 1 or 2 lobes at base, lower surface hairy. **Flowers** white, pale blue or pale mauve, with 5 spreading pointed lobes, to 2cm across. **Berry** globular, to 8mm across, red to black. Scattered throughout arid and semi-arid regions. Qld, NSW, SA, NT. All year round.

Solanum laciniatum | Large-flowered Kangaroo Apple

Shrub to 3m high; branches often purplish; prickles absent. **Leaves** variable in shape from deeply lobed to 38cm long, or entire and lanceolate, 5–20cm long, 1–4cm wide. **Flowers** purplish-blue, with rounded notched lobes, to 5cm across, in clusters of up to 11 flowers. **Berry** ovoid, to 2cm across, yellow to orange. Widespread in southeastern Australia. NSW, Vic, Tas, SA, WA. Spring, summer.

Solanum linearifolium | Mountain Kangaroo Apple

Erect shrub to 4m high; sparsely hairy; prickles absent. **Leaves** variable in shape from deeply lobed to 40cm long, or entire and narrow–elliptic to linear, 5–10cm long to 1cm wide, decurrent along stem. **Flowers** purple-violet, with broad rounded lobes, to 4.5cm across, in clusters of up to 11 flowers. **Berry** globular, to 2cm across, yellow and deep red in upper half. Coastal ranges and tablelands. NSW, Vic. Spring, summer.

Solanum quadriloculatum |

Erect or sprawling shrub to 50cm high; stems with dense covering of stellate hairs; prickles present on stems, leaves, flowering stalks and calyx. **Leaves** ovate, 5–9cm long to 4cm wide, grey-green, entire and slightly wavy, densely hairy. **Flowers** purple, with spreading pointed lobes, to 2.5cm across, in clusters of up to 20. **Berry** globular, to 1.5cm across, brownish-yellow. Widespread in arid regions, often near seasonally flooded watercourses. Qld, NSW, SA, WA, NT. Winter, spring.

Solanum sturtianum | Thargomindah Nightshade

Erect shrub to 3m high; stems densely hairy; prickles present on stems. **Leaves** lanceolate, 3–6cm long to 1.5cm wide, grey-green, slightly wavy. **Flowers** purple with shallowly pointed lobes, to 4cm across, in clusters of up to 12. **Berry** globular, to 1.5cm across, yellow to dark brown. Widespread in arid areas. Qld, NSW, SA, WA, NT. All year round.

Solanum elegans

Solanum ferocissimum

Solanum laciniatum

Solanum linearifolium

Solanum quadriloculatum

Solanum sturtianum

STACKHOUSIACEAE

Small family of 3 genera and about 25 species in Indonesia, the Philippines, New Guinea, New Zealand, Australia and Micronesia; 24 occur in Australia. Annual or perennial herbs, with slender ribbed stems. Leaves alternate, simple, margins entire, sometimes succulent. Flowers bisexual, usually regular. Sepals 5, free. Petals 5, usually united into a tube with spreading lobes. Stamens 5, free, alternate with petals. Ovary superior. Fruit a schizocarp, separating into up to 5 nutlets.

Stackhousia monogyna | Creamy Candles

Erect perennial herb to 70cm high. **Leaves** linear to lanceolate, to 3cm long and 2–4mm wide, usually scattered along stems. **Flowers** white to yellow, tubular, with 5 spreading lobes, in terminal cylindrical spikes on hairless stems 3–10cm long, perfumed. **Fruit** separates into 3 nutlets. Widespread in varied habitats. Qld, NSW, Vic, Tas, SA, WA. Winter, spring, summer.

Stackhousia pulvinaris | Alpine Stackhousia

Prostrate perennial herb forming dense mats to 5cm high; stems rooting at nodes. **Leaves** narrow–oblong or narrow–obovate, 5–10mm long, 1–2mm wide, bright green and fleshy. **Flowers** creamy-yellow, with 5 spreading lobes, to 1cm across, sessile, singly in upper axils, sweetly scented. **Fruit** separates into 3 nutlets. Alpine herbfields and subalpine grasslands, often in wet places. NSW, Vic, Tas. Summer.

STERCULIACEAE | Kurrajong family

A family of 65 genera and about 1100 species found mainly in tropical and subtropical regions. Cocoa and chocolate are extracted from the roasted seeds of the cocoa-tree *Theobroma cacao*, native to tropical America. Australia has 21 genera and about 160 species. Trees or shrubs, mostly with star-shaped hairs. Leaves alternate, simple or palmately lobed. Flowers regular, bisexual or unisexual. Sepals usually 5. Petals 5, often twisted in bud, often minute or absent. Stamens 5–30, either free or united into a short tube; when 5 they are opposite the petals and sometimes alternate with 5 staminoides. Ovary superior. Fruit a capsule.

Keraudrenia hermanniifolia | Crinkled-leaved Firebush

Shrub to 1m high; branchlets with dense rusty hairs. **Leaves** oblong to ovate, 5–15mm long to 7mm wide, with deep wavy margins, undersurface densely hairy, tip rounded. **Flowers** have conspicuous mauve to purplish-blue sepals, to 1.5cm across, in loose clusters. **Capsule** globular, to 1.5cm across, densely hairy. Northern wheatbelt region, often in heath. WA. Winter, spring.

Keraudrenia integrifolia | Common Firebush

Shrub 1m high; branchlets with dense rusty hairs. **Leaves** oblong or oblong–elliptic to 5cm long, to 1.2cm wide, finely hairy above, densely hairy below, concave, tip rounded or notched. **Flowers** have conspicuous bluish to purplish sepals, to 2.5cm across, in loose terminal or axillary clusters. **Capsule** globular, to 1.2cm across, densely hairy. Widespread in inland regions. Common in disturbed areas and after fire. Qld, NSW, SA, WA, NT. Winter, spring, summer.

Stackhousia monogyna

Stackhousia pulvinaris

Keraudrenia hermanniifolia

Keraudrenia integrifolia

Keraudrenia nephrosperma

Shrub to 1m high; branchlets densely hairy. **Leaves** oblong or ovate, 2–4cm long to 2.5cm wide, slightly hairy above, densely hairy below, margins wavy to lobed, sometimes heart-shaped at base, tip rounded. **Flowers** lacking petals, have conspicuous rose-pink to purple sepals, to 1.5cm across, in many-flowered clusters. **Capsule** globular, readily separates into nutlets. Widespread in arid and semi-arid regions, in sandy soils or rocky places. WA, NT. Winter, spring.

Lasiopetalum drummondii

Small shrub to 60cm high; branchlets rusty–hairy. **Leaves** oblong–lanceolate, 2–5cm long to 1.5cm wide, sometimes heart-shaped at base, dark green and glabrous above, rusty to grey hairs below, margins recurved, tip rounded or pointed. **Flowers** with enlarged white to pinkish sepals, to 1.2cm across, in short drooping clusters. Wheatbelt region, often in sandy heaths. WA. Winter, spring.

Lasiopetalum macrophyllum

Erect shrub 1–2m high; branchlets densely hairy. **Leaves** oblong–lanceolate, 5–12cm long, 1–4cm wide, often heart-shaped at base, slightly scaly or becoming glabrous above, densely hairy below, veins prominent, tip pointed. **Flowers** with enlarged cream sepals, to 1.2cm across, with dense, rusty hairs on outer surface, in short compact clusters. Widespread in eastern Australia, in heath, woodland and open forest. NSW, Vic, Tas. Spring.

Rulingia dasyphylla | Kerrawang

Erect shrub 1–2m high; stems with soft hairs. **Leaves** ovate to lanceolate, 3–7cm long to 3cm wide, rough above, hairy below, margins coarsely toothed, veins prominent. **Flowers** pinkish, with 5 spreading petals, to 8mm across, in loose, axillary clusters. **Capsule** to 7mm across, with rigid bristles. Widespread from coast to ranges, often in rocky places in gullies. Qld, NSW, Vic. Winter, spring.

Rulingia hermanniifolia

Prostrate shrub with trailing hairy stems to 1m long. **Leaves** oblong to lanceolate, to 2cm long and 1.5cm wide, strongly wrinkled above, hairy below, margins shallowly toothed, recurved, tip rounded. **Flowers** pinkish-white, with 5 small spreading petals, to 8mm across, in compact, axillary clusters. **Capsule** to 4mm across, with bristles. Coastal areas, mainly on cliffs or in heath on sandy soils. NSW. Winter, spring.

Thomasia grandiflora | Large-flowered Thomasia

Spreading shrub to 1m high; young growth stellate–hairy. **Leaves** oblong to ovate, 2–5cm long to 1.5cm wide, often heart-shaped at base, smooth above, hairy below. **Flowers** lacking petals have conspicuous, pinkish-mauve broad calyx lobes with stellate hairs, to 2cm across, in small nodding clusters in leaf axils. Widespread in near-coastal areas in south-west, in open forest. WA. Winter, spring.

Keraudrenia nephrosperma

Lasiopetalum drummondii

Lasiopetalum macrophyllum

Rulingia dasyphylla

Rulingia hermanniifolia

Thomasia grandiflora

Thomasia macrocarpa | Large-fruited Thomasia

Erect shrub to 2m high, young growth stellate–hairy. **Leaves** ovate, 4–8cm long to 5.5cm wide, heart-shaped at base, upper surface with white hairs when young, densely stellate–hairy below, margins irregularly toothed or lobed. **Flowers** lacking petals have conspicuous mauve calyx lobes with stellate hairs, to 2cm across, 2–6 per drooping raceme. Jarrah forest, particularly Darling Scarp near Perth. WA. Winter, spring.

Thomasia pauciflora | Few-flowered Thomasia

Erect shrub to 1.5m high, stems densely hairy when young. **Leaves** lanceolate to narrow–lanceolate, to 6cm long and 2.5cm wide, heart-shaped at base, rough above, with rusty stellate hairs along the veins of both surfaces. **Flowers** lacking petals have conspicuous deep pink to purple calyx lobes, to 1.5cm across, stellate–hairy on both surfaces, 1–3 per drooping raceme. Widespread along the coast from Perth to Albany in damp situations. WA. Winter, spring.

Thomasia petalocalyx | Paper Flower

Spreading shrub to 80cm high; stems densely hairy. **Leaves** oblong, 2–4cm long to 1cm wide, veins prominent, margins wavy and recurved, tip rounded. **Flowers** with minute petals have conspicuous pinkish-mauve, strongly veined calyx lobes, to 1.5cm across, a few together in drooping racemes. Widespread in semi-arid regions. Vic, SA, WA. Spring, summer.

Thomasia purpurea |

Rounded shrub to 50cm high; stems stellate–hairy. **Leaves** oblong, 1–3cm long to 7mm wide, with stellate hairs along the veins on both surfaces, margins wavy. **Flowers** small, lacking petals, calyx lobes pinky-mauve, to 1cm across, in drooping racemes of 3–8 flowers. Widespread in coastal regions in southwest. WA. Winter, spring.

Thomasia pygmaea | Tiny Thomasia

Small shrub to 60cm high; stems wiry with scaly hairs. **Leaves** rounded, to 1cm across, often heart-shaped at base, glabrous above. **Flowers** small, lacking petals, calyx lobes pinky-mauve with tiny red dots, 1–3 per drooping cluster. Southern areas in sandy shrubland. WA. Winter, spring.

Thomasia stelligera |

Shrub to 1m high; stems with scaly hairs. **Leaves** linear or oblong–lanceolate, to 2cm long, glabrous above, star-shaped hairs and blackish scales below. **Flowers** small, lacking petals, calyx lobes pink and rough on outside, 1–3 per drooping cluster. Coolgardie district. WA. Spring.

Thomasia macrocarpa

Thomasia pauciflora

Thomasia petalocalyx

Thomasia purpurea

Thomasia pygmaea

Thomasia stelligera

THYMELAEACEAE | Rice Flower family

A cosmopolitan family of 50 genera and 500 species, mainly centred in tropical and subtropical regions of the world. About 9 or 10 genera and 95 species occur in Australia; *Pimelea*, with about 90 species, accounts for the great majority of species. Herbs, shrubs or small trees, often with a tough fibrous bark. Leaves simple, entire, alternate or opposite, without stipules. Flowers regular, mostly bisexual, tubular, often in dense heads. Sepals 4 or 5, petal-like and usually with spreading lobes. Petals small and scale-like, arising from the mouth between the calyx lobes; often absent. Stamens 8–10 inserted in the tube, or 2 in *Pimelea*. Ovary superior. Fruit 1-seeded, dry or fleshy, remains closed.

Pimelea alpina | Alpine Rice Flower

Prostrate to erect shrub to 30cm high; stems smooth and often tangled. **Leaves** narrow–elliptic, to 1cm long, 2–4mm wide, opposite, concave, tip pointed. **Flowers** pink (rarely white), in terminal heads to 1.5cm across, perfumed; floral bracts ovate to elliptic, green and smooth, to 7mm long. Alpine and sub-alpine regions, in herbfields, grassland, or heath. NSW, Vic. Summer.

Pimelea ferruginea

Erect compact shrub to 1.5m high. **Leaves** narrow–elliptic to elliptic, to 2cm long and 8mm wide, opposite, glossy green above, paler below, margins recurved, tip pointed. **Flowers** deep pink, in terminal heads to 3cm across; floral bracts ovate, green and reddish, to 2cm long. Widespread in coastal and near-coastal areas in southwest, often on sand dunes or rocky soils. WA. Winter, spring.

Pimelea flava | Yellow Rice Flower

Slender erect shrub to 2.5m high. **Leaves** narrow–elliptic to almost rounded, to 2cm long to 1cm across, opposite, light green and glossy, tip rounded or pointed. **Flowers** yellow, in small terminal heads to 1.5cm across; floral bracts elliptic, greenish-yellow to 1.2cm long. Widespread in southern coastal and near-coastal areas, often in moist forests. Vic, Tas, SA. Winter, spring.

Pimelea floribunda

Erect shrub to 1m high. **Leaves** ovate to narrow–elliptic, to 4cm long and 1.5cm wide, opposite, blue-green, tip tapering to soft point. **Flowers** white or cream in dense terminal nodding heads to 6cm across, lightly scented; floral bracts ovate, reddish-green, to 2cm long. Between Geraldton and Perth, in coastal and near-coastal areas, often in woodland on sand. WA. Winter, spring.

Pimelea humilis | Common Rice Flower

Spreading low shrub to 50cm high; stems hairy. **Leaves** elliptic to lanceolate, 5–15mm long to 8mm wide, opposite, glabrous, tip rounded with small point. **Flowers** creamy-white, hairy on outside, in small or dense terminal heads to 2.5cm across; floral bracts ovate, green, to 2cm long, tip hairy. Widespread in heath and woodland. NSW, Vic, Tas, SA. Spring, summer.

Pimelea alpina

Pimelea ferruginea

Pimelea flava

Pimelea floribunda

Pimelea humilis

Pimelea ligustrina | Tall Rice Flower

Shrub 1–2.5m high; stems glabrous. **Leaves** oblanceolate or narrow–elliptic, 1–9cm long to 2cm wide, opposite, glabrous, tip pointed. **Flowers** white, hairy on outside, in rounded terminal heads, to 4cm across, on nodding stalks to 6cm long; floral bracts ovate, green to reddish-brown, to 2cm long. Widespread and common on coast and ranges, mainly in forested areas. Qld, NSW, Vic, Tas, SA. Spring, summer.

Pimelea linifolia | Slender Rice Flower

Prostrate to small shrub to 1.5m high; stems glabrous. **Leaves** narrow–elliptic to oblanceolate, to 3cm long and 2–8mm wide, opposite, glabrous, midrib prominent, tip pointed. **Flowers** white or occasionally pink, in terminal heads to 4cm across, on stems to 4cm long; floral bracts ovate, green sometimes with reddish tinge, to 2cm long. Widespread and common from coast to mountains, in various habitats. Qld, NSW, Vic, Tas, SA. Winter, spring, summer.

Pimelea nivea | Round-leaf Rice Flower

Erect or spreading shrub to 2m high; branchlets covered with dense white hairs. **Leaves** elliptic to rounded, to 1.5cm long and 1.2cm wide, dark green and glossy above, woolly-white hairy below. **Flowers** white or pale pink, in dense terminal heads to 3cm across, perfumed; floral bracts leaf-like. Widespread and common on hillsides, often in rocky soils. Tas. Spring, summer.

Pimelea physodes | Qualup Bell

Erect slender shrub to 1.5m high, but usually less. **Leaves** narrow–elliptic to ovate, 1–3cm long and 5–15mm wide, opposite, blue-green, glabrous, midrib prominent, tip blunt or pointed. **Flowers** greenish-yellow, wholly enclosed in bracts forming a bell-like pendent head to 6cm long; floral bracts elliptic, pale green or yellow with reddish tinge of varying degrees. Confined to Ravensthorpe district, on sandheath or rocky hills. WA. Winter, spring.

Pimelea rosea | Rose Banjine

Erect slender shrub to 1m high. **Leaves** narrow–elliptic, 1–2cm long to 6mm wide, opposite, scattered, blue-green, glabrous, tip pointed. **Flowers** white, pale to deep pink, in terminal heads to 4cm across; floral bracts ovate, green with reddish base, margins hairy. Widespread from near Perth to Albany district, mainly on coastal plain. WA. Winter, spring, summer.

Pimelea sericea | Silky Pimelea

Erect shrub to 80cm high; branches many, often with silky hairs. **Leaves** broad–elliptic to 1.2cm long and 6mm wide, dark green and glabrous above, white silky hairs below, tip pointed. **Flowers** white to pink, silky, in terminal heads to 2cm across; floral bracts green and similar to leaves. Common in mountainous areas. Tas. Spring, summer.

Pimelea ligustrina

Pimelea linifolia

Pimelea nivea

Pimelea physodes

Pimelea rosea

Pimelea sericea

Pimelea spectabilis

Erect open shrub to 1.5m high. **Leaves** narrow–elliptic, 1–4cm long to 6mm wide, light green and glabrous above, paler below, tip pointed. **Flowers** creamy-white to pink, minutely hairy, in dense terminal heads, to 7cm across, sometimes nodding, profuse; floral bracts ovate, green to bronzy-pink. Southwest, mostly in the Darling Ranges. WA. Winter, spring.

TREMANDRACEAE

Small endemic Australian family of 3 genera and 25 species, the largest being *Tetratheca* (20 species). They are small heath-like undershrubs. Leaves alternate, opposite or in whorls, simple, sometimes reduced to scales; stipules absent. Flowers regular, axillary, solitary, 3–5 or numerous. Stamens twice as many as the petals. Ovary superior. Fruit a flattened capsule.

Tetratheca ciliata

Small clump-forming, erect shrub to 80cm high; stems ridged, hairy. **Leaves** ovate to rounded, to 2cm long and 1.5cm wide, arranged in 3s or 5s around the stems. **Flowers** deep pink, bell-like, singly or 2 or 3 together, pendent on hairy stalks in leaf-axils. Mostly in southern Australia, in heath and dry open forest. NSW, Vic, Tas, SA, WA. Spring, summer.

Tetratheca glandulosa

Small shrub 20–50cm high; stems ridged, hairy. **Leaves** mostly opposite or alternate, to 2cm long and 2mm wide, margins revolute with stiff glandular hairs giving a finely toothed appearance. **Flowers** deep pink, bell-like, singly, on stalks with dark red, glandular hairs, in upper leaf axils; sepals also with glandular hairs. Confined to central coast, mostly in heath. NSW. Winter, spring.

Tetratheca neglecta

Small shrub to 50cm high; stems 4-angled, hairy. **Leaves** linear, to 1.5cm long and less than 1mm wide, arranged in 4s or 6s around the stems, sessile, margins revolute. **Flowers** deep pink, bell-like, singly, on hairless stalks to 1.5cm long, in upper leaf axils. Common in Sydney district, in heath and dry open forest. NSW. Winter, spring.

Pimelea spectabilis

Tetratheca ciliata

Tetratheca glandulosa

Tetratheca neglecta

Tetratheca thymifolia | Black-eyed Susan

Erect shrub to 1m high; stems with dense spreading hairs. **Leaves** elliptic, to 2cm long and 8mm wide, arranged in 3s or 5s around the stem, glabrous to densely hairy, margins recurved. **Flowers** deep pink (occasionally white), bell-like, usually singly (rarely paired) in upper leaf axils. Widespread in eastern Australia, in sandy heath and dry open forest. Qld, NSW, Vic. Winter, spring.

VIOLACEAE | Violet family

Family of herbs and shrubs of about 22 genera and 900 species with a worldwide distribution and including the well-known cultivated exotic violets and pansies (*Viola* spp.). There are 3 Australian genera and about 26 species. Leaves alternate; stipules present. Flowers irregular, mostly bisexual. Sepals 5. Petals 5, free, the lowest often the largest. Stamens 5, partly fused and alternating with the petals. Ovary superior. Fruit a capsule or berry containing many fine seeds.

Hybanthus aurantiacus | Orange Spade Flower

Small erect shrub to 40cm high; stems rough and hairy when young. **Leaves** linear to lanceolate, to 7mm long and 5mm wide, glabrous to hairy, margins toothed or entire. **Flowers** golden-orange, with lower petal largest and spade-shaped, to 1.5cm long, singly in upper leaf axils. Widespread in northern tropical and central arid regions. Qld, SA, WA, NT. Winter, spring.

Hybanthus floribundus | Shrub Violet

Small shrub to 1.5m high, usually less. **Leaves** linear, oblong or lanceolate, to 3.5cm long and 7mm wide, margins slightly recurved, tip pointed and recurved. **Flowers** pale blue or mauve, with spoon-shaped lower petals to 1cm long, in clusters (sometimes singly) in upper leaf axils. Widespread in semi-arid regions, in sandy soils often in mallee communities. NSW, Vic, SA, WA. Winter, spring, summer.

Viola betonicifolia |

Erect perennial herb to 10cm high. **Leaves** broad–lanceolate, to 6cm long and 2.5cm wide, arising from the base of the plant on narrow stalks, margins shallowly toothed. **Flowers** violet or purple (occasionally white), to 1.5cm across on erect slender stalks; lateral petals bearded inside. Widespread in eastern Australia, from coast to ranges, in woodland and forest. Qld, NSW, Vic, Tas, SA. Winter, spring.

Tetratheca thymifolia

Hybanthus aurantiacus

Hybanthus floribundus

Viola betonicifolia

Viola hederacea | Ivy-leaved Violet

Erect perennial herb; stems spread by runners. **Leaves** kidney-shaped to almost rounded, to 2cm long and 3cm across, heart-shaped at base, on stalks 2–6cm long. **Flowers** purple and white, to 2cm across, on erect slender stalks to 10cm long; lateral petals bearded inside. Widespread and common from coast to ranges, often in sheltered moist situations. Qld, NSW, Vic, Tas, SA. Spring, summer.

XANTHORRHOEACEAE | Grasstree family

Small endemic Australian family of a single genus *Xanthorrhoea*, the distinctive and well-known grasstrees or blackboys. They are stout perennials with either woody underground or above-ground trunks, often impregnated with resin. Leaves linear, grass-like, often angular in cross-section, arising from the tip of the trunk. Flowers 6 to numerous, creamy-white, surrounded by floral bracts and embedded in a tall spike-like inflorescence. Stamens free. Ovary superior. Fruit a woody capsule with 1–2 black seeds. Leaves are not illustrated in this family as they are too similar for identification purposes.

Xanthorrhoea australis | Austral Grass Tree

Perennial with stout trunk usually 1–3m high, sometimes to 7m; sometimes branched. **Leaves** narrow, grass-like, up to 1m long and 1–2mm wide, quadrangular in cross-section. **Flowers** small, white, surrounded by brown floral bracts, in dense spike to 1.5m long on a stout stalk shorter than the spike. **Capsule** shiny brown, pointed. Widespread in eastern Australia. NSW, Vic, Tas, SA. Spring, summer, or after fire.

Xanthorrhoea glauca |

Perennial with branched or single trunk 1–5m high. **Leaves** grass-like, to 5mm wide, diamond-shaped in cross-section, blue-green and glaucous. **Flowers** creamy-white, surrounded by triangular bracts, in spike 1–2m long, on a stout stalk shorter than the flowering spike. Widespread from the coast, tablelands to slopes and plains. NSW. Spring, summer, or after fire.

Xanthorrhoea resinosa |

Perennial herb with underground trunk. **Leaves** grass-like, to 4mm wide, quadrangular or convex–triangular in cross-section. **Flowers** creamy-white, surrounded by velvety brown floral bracts, in a dense spike up to 1.8m long on a stout stalk longer than the flowering spike, to 2m long. Widespread from coast to ranges, usually in swamps and wet places on sandy soils. NSW, Vic. Spring, summer, or after fire.

Xanthorrhoea preisii | Common Blackboy

Erect perennial to 5.5m high; sometimes branched. **Leaves** grass-like, angular in cross-section, to 1m long. **Flowers** creamy-white, surrounded by brown bracts, in dense spike to 2m long, on stout stalk shorter than flower spike. Widespread in southwest in many habitats. WA. Spring, or after fire.

Viola hederacea

Xanthorrhoea australis

Xanthorrhoea glauca

Xanthorrhoea resinosa

Xanthorrhoea preisii

FURTHER READING

Aboriginal Communities of the Northern Territory (1993) *Traditional Aboriginal Medicines in the Northern Territory of Australia*, Conservation Commission of the Northern Territory of Australia, Darwin.

Althofer, G.W. (1978) *Cradle of Incense, The Story of Australian Prostanthera*, The Society for Growing Australian Plants, Sydney.

Armitage, I. (1978) *Acacias of New South Wales*, New South Wales Region, Society for Growing Australian Plants, Sydney.

Australian Daisy Study Group (1987) *Australian Daisies for Gardens and Floral Art*, Lothian Publishing Co., Melbourne.

Australian Systemic Botany Society (1981) *Flora of Central Australia*, (ed. J. Jessop) A.H. & A.W. Reed, Sydney.

Beadle, N.C.W., Evans, O.D. and Carolin, R.C. (1972) *Flora of the Sydney Region*, A.H. & A.W. Reed, Sydney.

Beard, J.S. (1990) *Plant Life of Western Australia*, Kangaroo Press, Kenthurst.

Bishop, A. (1996) *Field Guide to the Orchids of New South Wales and Victoria*, University of New South Wales Press, Sydney.

Black, J.M. (1943-57) *Flora of South Australia*, Parts 1-4, Government Printer, Adelaide.

Black, J.M. (1978) *Flora of South Australia*, Part 1 (3rd edition), Government Printer, Adelaide.

Blackall, W.E. (1954) *How to Know Western Australian Wildflowers*, Part 1, University of Western Australia Press, Perth.

Blackall, W.E. and Grieve, B.J. (1956-80) *How to Know Western Australian Wildflowers*, Parts 2-4, University of Western Australia Press, Perth.

Blombery, A.M. (1967) *A Guide to Native Australian Plants*, Angus & Robertson, Sydney.

Boland, D.J. et al. (1984) *Forest Trees of Australia*, 4th edition, Thomas Nelson (Australia) Ltd., Melbourne, and CSIRO Melbourne.

Brooker, M.I.H. & Kleinig, D.A., *Field Guide to Eucalypts: Vol. 1. Southeastern Australia*, Inkata Press, Melbourne, 1983.

Burbidge, N.T. and Gray, M. (1970) *Flora of the Australian Capital Territory*, Australian National University Press, Canberra.

Chippendale, G.M. (1973) *Eucalypts of the Western Australian Goldfields*, Australian Government Publishing Service, Canberra.

Cochrane, R.G., Fuhrer, B.A., Rotherham, E.R., Simmons, J. & M., and Willis, J.H. (1980) *Flowers and Plants of Victoria and Tasmania*, A.H. & A.W. Reed, Sydney.

Costermans, L.F., (1981) *Native Trees and Shrubs of South Eastern Australia*, Rigby, Adelaide.

Costin, A.B., Gray, M., Totterdell, C.J., and Wimbush, D.J. (1979) *Kosciusko Alpine Flora*, CSIRO, Melbourne, and William Collins, Sydney.

Cunningham, G.M., Mulham, W.E., Milthorpe, P.L. and Leigh, J.H. (1981) *Plants of Western*

New South Wales, Soil Conservation Service of New South Wales.

Elliot, W.R. and Jones, D.L. (1980-97) *Encyclopaedia of Australian Plants Suitable for Cultivation* Vol. 1-7. Lothian Publishing Co., Melbourne.

Erickson, R. (1968) *Plants of Prey in Australia*, Lamb Publications, Osborne Park, WA.

Erickson, R., George, A.S., Marchant, N.G. and Morcombe, M.K. (1973) *Flowers and Plants of Western Australia*, A.H. & A.W. Reed, Sydney.

Fairley, A. and Moore, P. (1989) *Native Plants of the Sydney District, An Identification Guide*, Kangaroo Press, Kenthurst in association with The Society for Growing Plants – NSW Ltd.

Flora of Australia Series (1981-) Australian Government Publishing Service (1981-94), Australian Biological Resources Study with CSIRO (1995-), Melbourne.

Galbraith, J. (1977) *Collins Field Guide to the Wild Flowers of South-East Australia*, William Collins, Sydney.

Gardner, C.A. (1975) *Wildflowers of Western Australia*, Western Australian Newspapers Ltd., Perth.

George, A.S. (1984) *The Banksia Book*, Kangaroo Press, Kenthurst, NSW.

Harden, G.J. (ed.) (1990-93) *Flora of New South Wales, Vol. 1-4. New South Wales* University Press, Sydney.

Harmer, J. (1975) *North Australian Plants* Part 1, The Society for Growing Australian Plants, Sydney.

Hill, K.D., and Johnson, L.A.S. 'Systemic studies in the eucalypts: A revision of the bloodwoods, genus *Corymbia* (*Myrtaceae*)' in *Telopea* 6 (2-3), 185-469.

Holliday, I. (1989) *A Field Guide to Melaleucas*, Hamlyn Australia, Melbourne.

Holliday, I. and Watton, G. (1975) *A Field Guide to Banksias*, Ribgy, Adelaide.

Isaacs, J. (1987) *Bush Food, Aboriginal Food and Herbal Medicine*, Weldons, Sydney.

Jones, D.L. (1986) *Ornamental Rainforest Plants in Australia*, Reed Books, Sydney.

Jones, D.L. and Gray, B. (1988) *Climbing Plants in Australia*, Reed Books, Sydney.

Jones, D.L. (1988) *Native Orchids of Australia, Reed Books, Sydney.*

Launceston Field Naturalists Club (1981) *Guide to Flowers and Plants of Tasmania*, M. Cameron (ed.) A.H. & A.W. Reed, Sydney.

Marchant, N.G. et al. (1987) *Flora of the Perth Region*, 2 Vols, Western Australian Herbarium, Department of Agriculture, Perth.

Nuytsia (1970-) Bulletin of the Western Australian Herbarium, Department of Conservation & Land Management, Western Australia, Government Printer, WA.

Olde, O. & Marriott, N. (1994-95) *The Grevillea Book*, Volumes 1-3, Kangaroo Press, Kenthurst, NSW.

Rotherham, E.R., Briggs, B.C., Blaxell, D.F. and Carolin, R.C. (1975) *Flowers & Plants of New South Wales and Southern Queensland*, A.H. & A.W. Reed, Sydney.

Sainsbury, R.M. (1987) *A Field Guide to Isopogons and Petrophiles*, University of Western Australia Press, Perth.

Simmons, M.H. (1981) *Acacias of Australia*, Thomas Nelson Australia, Vic.

Society for Growing Australian Plants, *Australian Plants, Quarterly*, The Society for Growing Australian Plants, Sydney.

Specht, R.L. (1972) *Vegetation of South Australia*, 2nd edition, Government Printer, Adelaide.

Telopea (1975-) Contributions from the National Herbarium of New South Wales, Government Printer, NSW.

Walsh, N.G. & Entwisle, T.J. (eds) (1994-96) *Flora of Victoria*, Volumes 2 & 3, Inkata Press, Melbourne.

Webb, L.J. (1968) 'Environmental Relationships of the Structural Types of Australian Rain Forest Vegetation' *Ecology* 49, 296-311.

Webb, L.J. (1978) 'A General Classification of Australian Rainforests' *Australian Plants* 9, 349-63.

Wheeler, J.R. (ed.) (1992) *Flora of the Kimberley Region*, Department of Conservation and Land Management, Perth.

Whibley, D.J.E. (1980) *Acacias of South Australia*, Government Printer, Adelaide.

Williams, K.A.W. (1979-87) *Native Plants of Queensland*, Volumes 1-3, K.A.W. Williams, North Ipswich, Qld.

Willis, J.H. (1972) *A Handbook to Plants in Victoria*, Vol. 2, Melbourne University Press, Melbourne.

Woolcock, D. *A Fieldguide to Native Peaflowers of Victoria and Southeastern Australia*, Kangaroo Press, Kenthurst in association with The Society for Growing Australian Plants – NSW Ltd.

Wrigley, J.W. & Fagg, M. (1993) *Bottlebrushes, Paperbarks & Tea Trees*, Angus & Robertson, Sydney.

Wrigley, J.W. & Fagg, M. (1989) *Banksias, Waratahs and Grevilleas*, William Collins, Sydney.

GLOSSARY

achene a small, dry, one-seeded fruit that does not split open, as in Asteraceae and Ranunculaceae.

acute sharp, having a short sharp point.

alternate (of leaves) arranged at different levels along a stem; not opposite.

alternate leaves

annual a plant that completes its life cycle from germination to fruiting and then dying within a single year.

anther the top part of the stamen where pollen is produced.

apex the tip of an organ.

appressed lying close to or pressed flat against another organ.

arboreal living or situated among trees.

aril the fleshy outer covering of some seeds, often brightly coloured.

ascending growing at an angle at first, then upwards.

awn a slender bristle-like projection.

axil the upper angle between a stem and leaf.

axillary in, or arising from, an axil.

barbed bearing sharp, spine-like hooks that are bent backwards.

beak a long, pointed projection, often applied to the extension of a fruit.

bearded with tufts of stiff hairs.

berry a fleshy, many-seeded fruit with a soft outer portion.

bipinnate (of leaves) when the first divisions of a leaf are further divided.

bipinnate leaves

bisexual having both sexes, as in a flower bearing both male (stamens) and female (pistil) reproductive organs.

bloom a thin layer of white waxy powder on some stems, leaves and fruit.

bract a small leaf-like structure that surrounds or encloses a flower or group of small individual flowers.

bracteole small bract-like structure on the stalk or calyx of a flower.

bristle a short stiff hair.

bulb a swollen underground organ comprising a short stem surrounded by tightly overlapping leaf bases.

burr a prickly fruit.

buttress (of roots) a flattened expansion of the lower part of the trunk and root in rainforest trees.

callus (plural calli) in orchids, a thickening in the labellum, in the form of a ridge, bump or club.

calyculus a whorl or ring of tissue just below the perianth of the flower of Loranthaceae.

calyx the outer series of floral leaves, each one a sepal.

campanulate bell-shaped.

canopy the topmost layer of branches and foliage of a community of trees.

capsule a dry fruit that, when mature, dries and splits open to release seeds.

carpel female reproductive organ, comprising the stigma, style and ovary.

drupe

caudex a thick, erect trunk.

ciliate fringed with hairs.

compound leaf a leaf divided into two or more separate leaflets.

cone a woody fruit of a conifer, made up of overlapping scales. Also applied to other woody fruits such as those of banksias and casuarinas.

cordate heart-shaped.

corolla all the petals of a flower.

corymb a type of inflorescence where the flower stalks arise at different points, but flowers are at the same final level, giving a flat-top arrangement.

crenate the margins scalloped into shallow rounded teeth or lobes.

crown all the branches of a tree.

cyme a type of inflorescence in which each flower terminates a branch and further growth is from one or two lateral buds which themselves end in a flower.

deciduous shedding seasonally, e.g. leaves and bark of some trees, parts of the flower.

decumbent spreading horizontally, but with the tips growing upward.

decurrent extending down along a stem after joining with it, as of leaf bases.

decussate in pairs alternately at right angles.

dehiscent opening at maturity to release the contents.

dentate having coarse, sharp teeth.

dicotyledon one of the two major subdivisions of flowering plants; dicotyledons are those plants bearing two seed leaves at the seedling stage. Called dicot, for short.

diffuse open and loosely spreading in habit.

disc floret one of the inner tubular flowers of the flower heads of some Asteraceae, as distinct from the outer ray florets.

drupe a succulent fruit with a stone enclosing one or more seeds.

elliptic (of leaves) oval and flat, broadest across the middle and tapered equally at both ends.

endemic confined to a specific country, region or location.

entire (of leaves) having smooth margins without teeth or division.

epiphyte a plant that grows on another plants but is not parasitic.

exotic introduced from a foreign country.

exserted protruding from surrounding parts, e.g. when the valves project above the rim of a eucalypt capsule.

falcate (of leaves) curved and tapered to a point like a sickle, e.g many eucalypt leaves.

filament the thread-like stalk of a stamen bearing the anther.

filiform thread-like.

flower the part of the plant that contains the reproductive organs; some flowers are single-sexed (unisexual) but most contain organs of both sexes (bisexual).

follicle a dry fruit that splits open along one side only and contains more than one seed.

free not united with any other part.

fruit the seed-containing structure formed from the ovary after the flower is pollinated.

fused joined and growing together.

genus (plural genera) a subdivision of a family; a group of species that are closely related to each other because they share a number of similarities.

glabrous smooth and hairless.

gland a liquid-secreting organ, usually on leaves, stems and flowers.

gland-dotted having translucent or coloured dots when viewed against the light.

glaucous covered with bloom, often giving a greyish or powdery appearance.

habitat the place or environment in which particular plants and animals normally live.

heath a plant community dominated by small shrubs.

herb a plant that does not produce a woody stem.

hirsute covered with long, coarse, spreading hairs.

hoary covered with short hairs giving the surface a greyish appearance.

incurved (of leaves) curved or bent inwards or upwards.

indehiscent not opening at maturity.

inferior ovary one that lies below the point of attachment of the calyx.

inflorescence the structure that carries the flowers, which may be arranged in a number of ways, e.g. a spike or umbel.

inrolled (of leaves) curved inward or upward.

involucre leaf-like structure enclosing a flower.

irregular (of flowers) asymmetrical; where one or more of its segments differs in shape from the others.

keel 1. a boat-like structure, with a prominent longitudinal ridge. 2. the two loosely united lower petals of the flowers of the Fabaceae.

kino a dark, reddish resin-like substance developed in the veins of bark or wood, especially common in eucalypts.

labellum the lip or lower petal of an orchid flower, which is usually modified and distinctively different.

lanceolate (of leaves) shaped like the blade of a lance, usually broadest in the lowest half.

leaf a lateral organ borne on a stem, numbers of which make up the foliage of a plant.

leaflet one of the several segments into which a compound leaf is divided. A leaf has a bud in its axil; a leaflet does not.

legume having a dry fruit that splits open along two sides to form two halves, sometimes called a pod.

pod of legume

linear (of leaves) long and narrow with more or less parallel sides.

lithophyte a plant growing on rocks.

littoral growing on or near the shoreline.

lobe (of leaves) having curved or rounded edges.

Malesia a botanic-geographic region consisting of Malaysia, Indonesia, the Philippines and New Guinea.

mallee 1. shrubby eucalypt with multiple stems arising from an underground rootstock known as a lignotuber; 2. a plant community in semi-arid regions across southern Australia in which malllees are dominant.

margin the edge or boundary line of an organ.

mericarp a one-seeded portion of a dry dehiscent fruit that splits away into an individual fruit, as in some members of the Geraniaceae family.

midrib the main central vein that runs the full length of a leaf.

monocotyledon one of the two major subdivisions of flowering plants; monocotyledons bear only one seed leaf at the seedling stage, e.g. palms, lilies and grasses. Called monocot, for short.

mucronate with short stiff point (mucro).

mulga a plant community in arid parts of inland Australia, in which the mulga, *Acacia aneura*, and other shrubby wattles are dominant.

nectar a sweet, sugary liquid secreted from a gland known as a nectary.

node the point on a stem where one or more leaves arise.

nut a dry one-seeded fruit that does not split open when mature.

obcordate heart-shaped with the broadest part above the middle.

oblanceolate (of leaves) lance-shaped, with the broadest part toward the tip.

obovate (of leaves) egg-shaped with the broadest part toward the tip.

opposite (of leaves) arising in pairs at the same level, but on either side of the stem.

orbicular (of leaves) circular, or almost so.

ovary the hollow basal portion of a pistil that contains one or more ovules and produces the fruit after fertilisation take place; ovaries found above the calyx are called superior, while those found below the calyx are called inferior.

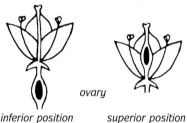

inferior position   *superior position*

ovate egg-shaped.

ovoid egg-shaped, applied to a solid form.

ovule one or more minute roundish structures found within the chamber of the ovary. Each ovule contains an egg cell that develops into a seed after fertilisation.

palmate (of leaves) divided into lobes or leaflets that radiate from the leaf stalk like the fingers on a hand.

panicle a compound inflorescence with many branches, each bear two or more flowers.

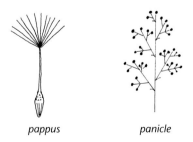

pappus   *panicle*

pappus a tuft of fine hairs or bristles on the fruits of many plants of Asteraceae; they often persist on the fruit and facilitate its dispersal.

pedicle the stalk supporting an individual flower or fruit.

peduncle the common stalk that supports a group of flowers of fruits.

peltate (of leaves) circular, with the stalk attached to the middle of the lower surface instead at the edge of the leaf.

pendent hanging down.

perennial a plant with a lifespan of more than two years.

perianth the calyx and corolla of a flower.

petiole the stalk of a leaf.

phyllode a flattened stalk that functions as a leaf, e.g., the leaves of some species of *Acacia*.

pinna (plural pinnae) one of the primary divisions of a pinnate leaf (leaflet).

pinnate (of leaves) a compound leaf, divided once with leaflets arranged on both sides of a common stalk.

pistil the female seed-bearing organ of a flower, containing the ovules and comprising the ovary, style and stigma.

pod a general term applied to any dry and many-seeded fruit that splits when ripe to release its seeds, e.g. pods of legumes or acacias.

pollinia a group of waxy pollen grains found in orchids.

procumbent having stems trailing or lying flat on the ground, but not taking root.

prostrate lying flat on the ground.

pseudobulb the fleshy, bulb-like thickened stem found on many orchids.

pubescent covered with short, soft downy hairs.

pungent ending in a sharp point.

raceme an inflorescence where a series of lateral flowers is arranged along a single stem. Each flower has a stalk.

ray floret one of the outer strap-like flowers of an Asteraceae flowerhead.

raceme

receptacle the enlarged uppermost part of the flower stalk on which the floral parts are borne.

recurved curved downward or backward.

reduced undeveloped or not properly developed.

reflexed bent downward or backward at a sharp angle.

regular (of flowers) radially symmetrical.

reniform resembling a kidney in shape.

resinous covered with a hardened, sticky substance.

reticulate marked with a network of veins.

revolute margins rolled backwards to the undersurface.

rhizome a creeping horizontal stem usually growing either at ground level or just below.

rosette a group of leaves radiating from the same point on a short stem, usually at ground level.

runner a slender, horizontal-growing stem that takes root at each node where it touches the ground.

saprophyte a (usually leafless) plant that obtains food from dead or decaying organic matter.

scalloped the margin notched with rounded or broad and blunt teeth.

schizocarp a dry fruit that splits longitudinally into mericarps.

sclerophyll a group of plants with hard stiff leaves.

sclerophyll forest a forest dominated by trees with sclerophyll leaves, namely the eucalypts.

sepal one of the separate parts of the calyx, usually green and leaf-like.

serrate (of leaves) margins having sharp forward-pointing teeth, like a saw.

sessile without a stalk.

shrub a perennial woody plant usually with two or more stems arising from or near the ground.

silky a covering of soft, appressed, fine hairs.

simple (of leaves) having a single blade and not divided into leaflets.

solitary (of flowers) occurring singly in each axil.

spathe a large bract enclosing the inflorescence.

spathulate spoon-shaped.

spike an unbranched, elongated inflorescence with stalkless flowers.

spike

spine a hard, pointed structure.

stamen the male portion of a flower, comprised of a pollen-bearing anther and the supporting stalk (filament).

standard the large upper petal of a flower of the family Fabaceae.

stellate star-shaped.

stigma the part of the carpel that receives the pollen, usually at the tip of the style.

stipule a leaf-like appendage at the base of the leaf stalk in some plants; usually paired; sometimes modified as spines.

stolon a horizontal stem that grows just above ground level and takes root at the nodes.

striation a marking with parallel lines or grooves.

style the stalk of the female organ connecting the stigma and ovary.

succulent fleshy or juicy.

sucker a new shoot growing from the roots of the parent plant.

tendril slender, usually coiling part of some climbers that supports the stem.

terete slender and cylindrical in cross-section.

terminal situated at the tip.

terrestrial growing on the ground.

thorn a sharply pointed branch, or curved spine.

throat (of flowers) the inside part of a tubular or funnel-shaped flower.

tomentose covered with short, closely matted hairs.

toothed (of leaves) a generalised term referring to margins that are toothed in various ways, including crenate, dentate and serrate.

tree a perennial woody plant usually with a single main stem (trunk) and a distinct upper crown.

trifoliate having three leaves or leaflets.

umbel a cluster of individual flowers where several flower stalks arise from the same point at the top of the main stem; a compound umbel is when the umbels themselves are arranged in an umbel.

simple umbel

undulate (of leaves) with a wavy margin.

unisexual (of flowers) of one sex only; having functional stamens or pistils, but not both.

united joined together or fused.

valve the segment of a capsule that splits to release seeds.

venation (of leaves) the arrangement or pattern of veins.

villous covered with long, weak hairs.

whorl ring of leaves or floral parts encircling a stem at the same level.

wing (of flowers) the two lateral petals of a Fabaceae flower.

woolly with long, soft, rather matted hairs.

INDEX

Figures in **bold** refer to main entries and figures in *italics* refer to photographs.